MOSSES AND LICHENS

Nature Books With Colour Plates

AMERICAN ANIMALS
Witmer Stone and Wm. Everitt Cram

AMERICAN FOOD AND GAME FISHES
David Starr Jordan and Barton W. Evermann

BIRD HOMES	A. R. Dugmore
BIRD NEIGHBOURS	Neltje Blanchan
GAME BIRDS	Neltje Blanchan
MOSSES AND LICHENS	Nina L. Marshall
NATURE'S GARDEN	Neltje Blanchan
THE BUTTERFLY BOOK	Dr. W. J. Holland
THE FROG BOOK	Mary C. Dickerson
THE INSECT BOOK	Dr. Leland O. Howard
THE MOTH BOOK	Dr. W. J. Holland
THE MUSHROOM BOOK	Nina L. Marshall
THE REPTILE BOOK	Raymond L. Ditmars
THE TREE BOOK	Julia E. Rogers

OLD MAN'S BEARD, *Usnea barbata*, (L.) Fr.
" The murmuring pines and the hemlocks, bearded with moss "

MOSSES AND LICHENS

A POPULAR GUIDE TO THE IDENTIFICATION AND STUDY OF OUR COMMONER MOSSES AND LICHENS, THEIR USES, AND METHODS OF PRESERVING

BY

NINA L. MARSHALL

Author of "The Mushroom Book"

SIXTEEN PLATES IN COLOUR, THIRTY-TWO IN BLACK AND WHITE, FROM PHOTOGRAPHS BY HANNAH C. ANDERSON; AND MANY TEXT ILLUSTRATIONS

NEW YORK
DOUBLEDAY, PAGE & COMPANY
1907

PREFACE

Mosses and Lichens has been written with the hope that it may meet a need often expressed, for a book with pictures which will help to identify some of the many beautiful growths which, winter and summer, in wood and open, excite the admiration and arouse the curiosity of all nature lovers.

It is the result of the author's desire to know something of the dainty plants which are so lavishly employed by nature in beautifying the trails and brooks of the North woods. The more striking mosses and lichens were collected and carried about until by the kindness of one friend and another "learned in mosses," names were secured for them.

No book was found which offered an easy path to the knowledge desired. In truth, no book was found which could be used at all until many months of patient labor in a botanical laboratory gave the necessary foundation.

Then the author, urged on by friends who would have an easy path or none, set to work to make pen-and-ink sketches of bits of moss and details of structure. After a number had been made with some degree of success, a new plan was suggested by experience. An accurate detail was made with the aid of a microscope or was procured from a rare work, *Bryologia Europæ;* and with this detail a tuft or cushion on a large scale was built up and then reduced to natural size with a camera. Later, with the success crowning persistent attempts, Mr. J. A. Anderson and Miss H. C. Anderson succeeded in photographing specimens not too small, direct from nature. The plates in the book are the measure of their success.

Thanks are due to Dr. Lucien M. Underwood, of Columbia University, for his never-failing readiness to give encouragement and valuable assistance; also Mrs. E. G. Britton, who has named most of the mosses collected by the author and has been ever ready to suggest works for reference and to render assistance in other ways. Thanks also are due to Dr. Howe, of the New

v

York Botanical Gardens, and to Dr. Curtis, of Columbia, for assistance with certain subjects; and especially to Mr. Williams, a moss and lichen specialist of the New York Botanical Gardens, who named the lichens pictured in the book and undertook the laborious task of reading the copy before it was submitted to the publishers.

The pen-and-ink drawings were made by the author direct from nature or were redrawn from the works mentioned in the "Authorities consulted."

CONTENTS

PART I

vii

PART II

ix

PART III

PART IV

LEAFY-MOSSES (*Continued*)

xiii

COLOURED ILLUSTRATIONS

Mosses and Lichens

BLACK AND WHITE PLATES

Mosses and Lichens

PART ONE
MOSSES AND LICHENS AT HOME

CHAPTER I

MOSSES AND LICHENS AT HOME

"Children of lowly birth,
    Pitifully weak;
Humblest creatures of the wood
To your peaceful brotherhood
Sweet the promise that was given
Like the dew from heaven:
    'Blessed are the meek,
        They shall inherit the earth';
Thus are the words fulfilled:
Over all the earth
Mosses find a home secure.
On the desolate mountain crest,
Avalanche-ploughed and tempest-tilled,
The sweet mosses rest;
On shadowy banks of streamlets pure,
Kissed by the cataracts shifting spray,
For the bird's small foot a soft highway
For the many and one distressed.

. . . .
Little sermon of peace."
                                        Willis Boyd Allen.

No FREQUENTER of the woods can be unfamiliar with the more conspicuous lichens and mosses. It is with them that nature adorns her bare unsightly children. She drapes the time-worn evergreens with gray fringes (see Frontispiece) and decks the old tree-stumps with red or yellow corals. Soft lichens spread over the ground in the deep shade of the pine trees, while pale green or yellow rosettes creep over the fence-rails and the big rocks in the pasture lot. (See Colour Plate II.)

"Far above among the mountains the silver lichen spots rest, starlike, on the stone; and the gathering orange stain upon the edge of yonder western peak reflects the sunsets of a thousand years."—*Ruskin.*

Lichens and mosses are met with all over the world, in the cold North and in the sunny South, in the East and in the West,

3

by the seashore and on the highest mountain peaks. They are the first growths to appear on the rocks and in the places which give no foothold to other plants. When the side of a mountain is torn away by frosts and floods, and the bared rocks, shorn of their forest trees and shrubs, are left unsightly with nothing to tempt other plants to make a home on their ledges, then the lichens come and cover the bared cliffs with delicate traceries and mantles of exquisite grays and greens. They need no soil, a polished rock will meet their need.

"Meek creatures; the first mercy of the earth, veiling with hushed softness its dustless rocks; creatures full of pity, covering with strange and tender honour the scarred disgrace of time."—*Ruskin.*

The foothold of the lichens is often so insecure that one must exclaim as he sees them, "How do you grow in such unfavourable places? On what do you subsist? No soil! No water! Dry as tinder! Crumbling at any rude touch!" If the plant could answer, no doubt it would say, "There must be pioneers to open up new territory for higher plants, so from the earliest times nature has employed us to do this work. We travel swift as the wind for we travel with the wind. We are fed by the rains and the dews, the hard rocks soften at our touch and give us food."

"The chapel and bridge are of stone alike,
  Blackish-gray and mostly wet;
  Cut hemp-stalks steep in the narrow dyke,
  See here again, how the lichens fret
  And the roots of the ivy strike."
  Browning—By the Fireside.

It is true that these little plants as they lie upon the rocks, secrete an acid which dissolves the hard minerals. It is true that they have the power to condense moisture from the air, however little it may be, for they must have water as an item of food and as a medium by which mineral-salts dissolved from the rocks may enter the interior of the plant and may pass from cell to cell to those parts where they are to be worked up into plant food.

The lichens are often the forerunners of rock-loving mosses as without the scanty soil prepared by their chemical action and, without the slight foothold which their debris afford, many mosses would be unable to get a start upon the forbidding rock.

4

YELLOW WALL-LICHEN, *Thelochistes parietinus,* (L.) Norm.

. . . Yellow rosettes creep over the fence-rails . . .

With the mosses nature first clothes naked sides of ditches and clay banks and spaces between stubble of hay and corn. These otherwise unsightly spots she covers and makes attractive with a bright green carpet. Even the hard soil along the city pavement or in the tiny city yard she covers with a velvety coat of young moss plants, although they rarely develop further than this velvet stage.

> "All green was vanished save of pine and yew,
> That still displayed their melancholy hue;
> Save the green holly with its berries red,
> And the green moss that o'er the gravel spread."
>
> *Crabbe—Tales of the Hall.*

The blackened embers of the picnic fire are hidden with Golden Cord-mosses (Colour Plate III) and the roadsides in the woods and the slopes to the lake are carpeted with sturdy Hairy-caps (Colour Plate X). The crumbling roofs of deserted cottages and the unused well-sweep and old oaken bucket are decorated with soft tufts of green. Indeed the mosses are lodged in the crevices of the stones which line the well itself and late in the winter when all the world is asleep under its blanket of soft white snow, these little mosses grow and flourish unaffected by the cold above.

Nature distributes the mosses lavishly in all humid climates, regardless of altitude, cold or heat. They are found on trees living or dead, on earth or on rock, in streams and on the land.

"The orange stain, which is time's finger mark on the gray wall, and the cups with scarlet edges spread for fairy banquets—the soft green beds into which our feet sink, and all the loveliness which we think of when we think of—mosses."—*Ruskin.*

Who has not loved the mossy banks and the little velvet cushions which cling to the plaster of the old wall (Colour Plate IV) or spring up in the crevices of the pavement, giving restful spots of green to the dreary monotony of brick and stone? Children play with mosses and lichens. Poets sing their charms. Artists endeavour to reproduce their wonderful colours traced on bark and rock.

Aside from their artistic charm, mosses and lichens have other charms for all who will pause awhile to study their habits, and for all who will linger long enough to make out what the plants are doing in their humble way. They have wonderful

5

mechanical contrivances for the physicist, curious processes of interest to the chemist, and many suggestions for the philosopher.

Go into the woods and pastures after a rain. You will find a beauty and loveliness on rocks and trees and fallen logs which were not even suggested on a dry sunshiny day. The wood is in her glory at such times, and everyone who once sees her in her splendour will visit her again.

> " Here are cool mosses deep,
> And thro' the moss the ivies creep."
>
> *Tennyson—The Lotos Eaters: Choric song.*

The habit the mosses and lichens have of changing form and colour is one full of interest. The crisp gray moss cushions, which quickly turn green in the rain, must excite curiosity (Colour Plate IV). Pause awhile by a fresh green bank of Hairy-caps (Colour Plate X) wet with dew, and as the sun comes out and shines upon the little plants, watch them shrink away, changing the fresh bank into one brown and bare. Watch them again in a rain or when the evening dew is falling, to see every apparently dead brown plant revive and become green as before. The cause of the change is easily seen by one looking closely. The plant does not die when the sun shines, it simply folds the edges of its leaves together and turns them up against the stem so that their horny tips, instead of their delicate leaf surfaces, are presented to the sun.

The cause of the upturning of the leaves of the Hairy-caps, the change of colour of many mosses and lichens from gray to green, the methods by which they subsist on bare and barren rocks and soils, and endure extreme and sudden changes in the dryness and humidity of the air, are all interesting questions to be answered by the microscope, together with careful observations in the field.

Gray or crimson Bog-mosses (see Colour Plate III), steadily working their way over swamps and ponds, preparing a foothold for larger plants, illustrate to us how the great peat-bogs of Ireland and of other parts of world were made.

Whether one study the mosses and lichens for their natural beauty, for their habits, or from a botanical standpoint, they are interesting. They are true lovers of fresh air and clear running water, beautiful creatures in beautiful homes. They are

6

beautiful even when dried and pressed for the herbarium, so that one with a taste for collecting may regard the artistic as well as the useful.

The wide distribution of the mosses and lichens and their power of enduring great cold renders them available for study at all times of the year. They are reported to have been found in all parts of the globe.

Dr. Isaac I. Hayes who in 1854 discovered Grinnell Land, tells of finding "moss" as far north as Booth Bay in Greenland, in Latitude 76° 30'. The uses to which the moss was put in their distress were varied. After improvising a hut from a crevice in the rock by filling open places with loose stones pried from the frozen ground, they made a roof of sails and thatched it a foot thick with "moss" dug with their tin dinner plates from under two feet of snow. All cracks were closed with the moss, and tapers of "moss" dipped in oil were depended upon to light their dismal quarters.

The habit of using moss for filling in chinks and cracks is a common one among all pioneers, as one may see by observing the log huts in newly opened districts, for mixed with clay it forms a useful cement. This art is not known alone to man.

> " Within a thick and spreading hawthorn bush
> That overhung a molehill large and round,
> I heard from morn to morn a merry thrush
> Sing hymns of rapture, while I drank the
> Sound with joy—and oft an unintruding guest,
> I watched her secret toils from day to day;
> How true she warped the moss to form her nest,
> And modell'd it within with wood and clay."
> *Claire—The Thrush's Nest.*

CHAPTER II

HOW TO KNOW THE LICHENS AND MOSSES — WHAT THEY ARE DOING ON ROCKS AND TREES

Under the name of moss, in the popular mind, are included all small flowerless plants which grow in cushion-like tufts on stone or wood or bark. The name "moss" is made to do duty for the lichens, the mosses and their near relatives, the Hepatics, plants which differ widely in structure and appearance, as those will see who give more than a passing glance.

LICHENS

If a small plant, rootless, of almost any colour except bright green, grows as a dainty mat—a *thallus*—flat (Colour Plate V) or ruffled (Plate II) on its support, one may suspect that it is a lichen. If in addition to this habit of growth, it bears its fruits in flattened coloured disks (Colour Plate VII) one may know it is a lichen, also if the plants branch like corals (Colour Plate XI), or hang in fringes (Colour Plate I) from the trees, and are without leaves, one may suspect that they are lichens and may be pretty sure of it if the fruits are little coloured disks or cushions on the tips of the branches. The "Florida Moss," which grows in long gray fringes from the trees in the South, is neither a lichen nor a moss, but is a true flowering plant with stamens and pistils, the old seed capsules are often found still clinging to this moss-appearing plant, in the season when it

Aulacomnium Heterostichum.
Moss.

8

Hepatic.   Hepatic.   Hepatic.

is not in flower. It was probably to this plant Gannet referred
when he wrote:

> "A cloister dim, where the gray moss waves,
> And the live-oaks lock their arms at will."

TRUE MOSSES

Spore-case
without lid.   Lid.

Bryum argenteum.

Spore-case   Spore-case
with lid re-   with lid.
moved to
show teeth
wanting.

Hedwigia ciliata

If plants are small and green,
with leafy stems, and have the
habit of living in such close
proximity as to form
velvety cushions, (*Cera-
todon purpureum*) one
may suspect them of be-
ing mosses, but if they
have this habit of growth, or grow in clusters resembling tiny
ferns or miniature trees and bear their spores in little cases
opening by lids, one may feel confident that they are the true
mosses as distinguished from hepatics.

Hepatic. Spore-case split into
four symmetrical valves.

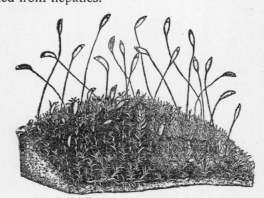

Ceratodon purpureum, Velvety Cushion.

9

HEPATICS

If the plants are green, growing flat and ribbon-like or as prostrate stems with paired, veinless leaves and with fruits umbrella-like or cups which do not open by lids but split irregularly into symmetrical valves in order to permit their spores to escape, one may know them to be hepatics.

The beauty which mosses lend to the surfaces upon which they live is pretty generally conceded. One has but to recall the frequent reference which our poets make to them to feel that they have always appealed to the poetic eye.

Mnium affine. Moss.

" On our other side is the straight-up rock ;
   And a path is kept 'twixt the gorge and it,
By boulder-stones where lichens mock
   The marks on a moth, and small ferns fit
Their teeth to the polished block.

. . . . .

These early November hours,
   That crimson the creeper's leaf across
Like a splash of blood, intense, abrupt,
   O'er a shield else gold from rim to base,
And lay it for show on the fairy-cupped
   Elf-needled mat of moss.''

         Browning—By the Fireside.

Ruskin says: " To them, slow-fingered, constant-hearted, is entrusted the weaving of the dark, eternal tapestries of the hills.''

Whittier in " The Bridal of Pennacook," to the query of "Why turns the bride's fond eye on him, in whose cold look is naught beside the triumph of a sullen pride?" replies:

> " Ask why the graceful grape entwines
> The rough oak with her arm of vines ;
> And why the gray rock's rugged cheek
> The soft lips of the mosses seek :
> Why with wise instinct, Nature seems
> To harmonise her wide extremes,
> Linking the stronger with the weak,
> The haughty with the soft and meek ! "

Shakespeare calls the mosses "idle":

> " It is dross, usurping ivy, brier,
>   or idle moss."
>
> *Comedy of Errors*, Act II, Sc. 2.

Scientists of to-day tell us that the rock-loving mosses and lichens are at work upon the "everlasting hills" to convert them into new soil ; that the saprophytic mosses on dead logs in the forest are at work returning to Mother Earth the materials which her tree-children took from her many years ago. They tell us that bog-mosses are reclaiming the marshes for higher plants, and that the water-loving mosses are receiving from the brooks lime-solutions which were brought up from depths below, and are laying them down in places where they are useful to man. As our knowledge of their practical value increases we shall not lose sight of their beauty, a new wonder will be added to our knowledge and many new interests to our trips "among the nodding ferns and mosses cool."

Their association with aged castles and trees is so familiar to everyone that the poet has but to mention mosses and lichens to picture lonely places and peaceful decay. "Moss-muffled forests dim" and "the rocks where the brown lichen whitens" give to us a feeling of loneliness, while the picture of Oliver—

> " A wretched, ragged man o'ergrown with hair "

is complete when Orlando finds him sleeping on his back

> " under an oak, whose boughs are mossed with age."
>
> *As You Like It.* Act. IV, Sc. 3.

Wordsworth tells us:

> " There is a thorn—it looks so old,
> In truth, you'll find it hard to say

11

> How it could ever have been young,
>
> .   .   .   .   .
>
> It stands erect and like a stone
> With lichens it is overgrown."

Spenser expresses another idea when he says of the ancient oak:

> "But now the gray moss marred his rine ;"

and Shakespeare also when he introduces Tamora, Queen of the Goths, to

> "A barren, detested vale   .   .   .
> The trees, though summer, yet forlorn
> O'ercome with moss, and baleful mistletoe."

Titus Andronicus, Act II, Sc. 3.

Mosses and Lichens are both soil-makers. They work by two methods. The one chemical, the other mechanical. By chemical action they either construct plant tissue of gases taken directly from the air or they first free from rock or wood or earth-mould, the minerals needed and then construct them into plant tissue. By mechanical action they pry off bits of soil from hard rock, arrest dust and debris brought to them by the wind, and constantly add to the mass, such plant tissue as they themselves are continually shedding.

> "Upon this herbless rock a small gray lichen
> Did fix her home.   She came with meek intent,
> To bless her stern and sterile place of rest ;
> And presently her gentle sisters followed,
> Some vestal white, and some in robes of brown,
> And some in yellow vestures, labouring all
> At the same work, with tiny cups held out
> To catch the raindrops, and with mattocks small
> To pierce the rock.   And well did they effect
> Their destined purpose."

One of the most important sources of the nourishment of plants is carbon dioxide (CO_2). It is the gas which bubbles up from "soda water" and it is the gas breathed out by animals. It is formed wherever a candle, lamp, or wood is burning or wherever vegetable or animal matter is decomposing. The gas is itself a compound of an elementary gas, oxygen (O) united with an elementary solid, carbon (C) known by the common names of charcoal and graphite. Stated in a general way, the carbon dioxide passes through the walls of the plant cells into the cell-contents and there by the leaf-green (chlorophyll) the oxygen gas (O) is set free to return to the atmosphere, and the solid carbon (C) is worked up with water into plant foods called carbohydrates, compounds of carbon and water, of which starch, sugar, and plant tissues are examples.

" A small sisterhood of plodding lichens
  Wrought on the rock ; the sun, the wind and rain,
  Helping then gladly, till each fissure filled
  And fit for planting, mosses came in haste
  And strewed small seeds (spores) among them, destined they
  To clothe the stern old rock with softest verdure
  With ferns and flowers, where yet the labouring bee
  May find pasture."

Certain lichens carried by the winds to places unsuitable for other plants, begin their work of dissolving the inhospitable rock to obtain mineral salts which the leaf-green may, together with water, manufacture into plant food; the delicate threads of the lichen work their way in and out among the particles of rock too small to be visible to the naked eye, and as they swell with water absorbed from the atmosphere, they pry off tiny particles of rock, thus slowly but surely preparing soil for higher forms.

The mosses also can take their start in life on bare and rugged rock, although not so generally as the lichens.

If a tuft of *Grimmia apocarpa* is lifted away from the lime-stone upon which it is growing, one may see corroded depressions in the neighbourhood of the place where the stemlets of the moss colony meet, and one may see the rhizoids of the moss imbedded in loose particles of limestone which have been separated from the main rock by a dissolving fluid which the rhizoids secreted upon the rock. In this way the moss obtains mineral salts which are necessary for its growth. The solid rock is crumbled to a dust which may be blown by the wind to other localities, or which may remain on the spot and furnish soil for higher plants. In addition to the chemical action which the moss exerts in dissolving the rock, it, as well as the lichen, exerts a purely mechanical influence, for a growing rhizoid penetrates wherever the merest particle of limestone has been dissolved and by mechanical pressure separates the particles of limestone which remain.

The mosses and lichens are truly efficient agents in rendering rocks available for plant life by retaining minute particles of soil

13

but their work does not stop here, for as the older plants die and crumble and mingle with the disintegrated rock, an incredible amount of earth-mould is formed which is a favourable site for higher forms of mosses, ferns, and other spore-bearing plants.

That the leafy parts above arrest to a remarkable degree the dust which pervades the atmosphere, not only along dusty road-sides and open plains, but also in remote mountain valleys, in Arctic ice fields, and in most of the elevated parts of the earth's crust, will be evident to one who detaches and examines a small tuft of *Barbula*, which everywhere occurs on roadside walls. He will be surprised to learn the extent to which the road dust has been lodged in the older dead parts of the plants, and he will be equally surprised to learn with what tenacity the dust is held. The power the older parts of the plants have of holding the dust is due to certain alterations which take place in the lifeless cell-tissue. To be convinced that fine dust is also carried to the more remote and elevated regions, one must examine the lichens and dark *Grimmias*, *Andræas* and other rock mosses which grow in small cushion-like tufts on weather-beaten mountain crags, when he will find that not much less dust has been arrested by them than by the *Barbula* living near the dusty roadside.

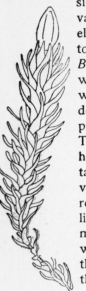

Andræa rupestris
Plant with spore-case.

Old crumbled lichens, together with dust blown thither by the wind, accumulate under the thallus, or leaf-like expansion of the lichen, and soon form a suitable home in which moss spores may grow. The mosses in turn add their share to the accumulation of humus preparatory to the coming of the ferns, and the ferns in turn prepare for the trees with winged seeds, the evergreens and birches, which require no very great depth of soil, sturdy pioneers of mountain forests.

It is true that all green plants do a similar work, but they do not work under such primitive conditions as do the mosses and lichens.

Aquatic mosses possess, perhaps to a greater degree, the power of arresting and retaining mud and fine sand hurried along by a violent rush of water. The plants of *Hypnum rusciforme* and

Amblystegium riparium, which cling to rocks in streams, are so conglomerated by mud and sand that they cannot be freed from it until the plants have become dried and shrivelled. *Limnobium molle*, which grows in the turbid waters from glaciers, has such an abundance of earthly particles adhering to it that only the green tips of the leaf-bearing stems are visible above the gray-coloured cushions imbedded in the mud. It is the dead parts alone which retain in their thick felt of interwoven filaments, the firmly divided mud and sand. That they are able to do this is due to the fact that the cell-membranes swell up and become slightly mucilaginous. This mechanical retention and storage of dust by rock-plants, and of mud by aquatic plants, is of the greatest importance in determining the development of the earth's covering of vegetation. The first settlers are crustaceous lichens, minute mosses, and algæ. Larger lichens and mosses are able to gain a footing on the substratum prepared by them.

> " 'Tis spring-time on the eastern hills!
> Like torrents gush the summer rills,
> Through winter's moss and dry dead leaves
> The bladed grass revives and lives,
> Pushes the mouldering waste away,
> And glimpses to the April day."
>
> *Whittier—Mogg Megone, Pt. III.*

The dead filaments, stems, and leaves of this second generation arrest dust in the air and mud in the water, and thus prepare a soft bed for the germs of a third generation, which on rocks consists of grasses, composites, pinks, and other small herbs, and in the water of pond-weeds, water-crowfoots, hornwort, and related plants. The second generation is produced in greater abundance than the first, and the third develops more luxuriantly than the second. The third may be followed by a fourth, fifth, and sixth, each successive generation crushing out and supplanting the one preceding it.

Another marked and important change results from these small beginnings. Streams on rather flat lands are turned from their courses by the accumulation of debris made possible by the arrested sand and mud, ponds have their outlets choked so that often new outlets must be cut, and small lakes are often cut in two by a natural divide which is due to the accumulation of sand and silt bound together, first by water plants and later by shrubs and trees.

The fact that at the present time the lichens and mosses are the first plants to appear on the soil, leads one to think that in ages gone by these little plants may have been the first to appear on the earth, and that they may have reigned supreme for a time in the plant world. This view is not sustained by positive testimony from the rocks, as there is no fossil evidence that mosses existed in Paleozoic times, nor has any certain trace of a moss been found in the coal-measures. Fossil mosses have been obtained almost entirely from tertiary and quaternary deposits.

Notwithstanding that there is no fossil evidence that mosses did exist, there is no evidence that they did not exist, as their absence from the plant records written in the older formations is probably to be accounted for by reason of their insignificant size and the difficulty of their preservation.

Another use the lichens and mosses subserve in the economy of Nature is illustrated by their habit of retaining great quantities of water in their spongy mass both on lofty mountain heights and in the forests of the valleys.

In many parts of the world it is principally the moss-covered soil of the forests which, by collecting the rainfall, prevents the pouring down from mountains of violent and excessive torrents of water.

Above the tree-line, in slight depressions on the sloping, rocky mountain sides, one may often find extensive patches of Sphagnum-moss and Reindeer-lichens which are crisp and dry on the surface, and yet retain so much water in their matted bases as to render it possible for one to obtain a supply of clear water. From areas of moss more extensive and of greater depth, tiny rills often trickle on their way to join other rills of similar origin. The sources of many a babbling brook or purling spring in the valley may be traced to the supersaturated moss-bed of a mountain forest.

" Desolate ledges, frost-riven and bare,
    A tiny rivulet bore on their breast;
  Cloud-gray mosses and lichens fair
    Mutely besought her to slumber and rest."
                                        Willis Boyd Allen.

" Thou hastenest down between the hills to meet me at the road,
  The secret scarcely lisping of thy beautiful abode
  Among the pines and mosses of yonder shadowy height,
  Where thou dost sparkle into song, and fill the woods with light."
                                        Lucy Larcom.

16

MARSH BUILDING ON MOUNT MARCY

Upon the open summit of Mount Marcy, 5,344 feet above sea level, there are two small marshy areas. One is a decided depression in the northeast slope; the other is on the eastern slope and nearer the summit. The water necessary to maintain the character of these marshes is probably supplied in part by rainfall, and in part by melting of snows which have accumulated in the crevices of the rocks above. The two marshes are cold botanical gardens of natural formation, unique indeed, as there is no evidence that the soil for them could have been brought from other sources, while everything suggests that the mosses and lichens at the present time growing on the bare surfaces of the rocks are active soil-makers. The boulders of the summit are variegated by the different colours of the lichens growing on their hard and almost naked surface. The rock beneath the lichens is more soft and scaly than elsewhere, and the moss tufts have the spaces between their lower stems and leaves filled with dirt and sand. The soil in most places is but a few inches deep, and largely composed of dead vegetable matter. Only plants of the most hardy nature are found here, and these are small and imperfect representations of similar plants growing at lower altitudes. The total number of species found on the summit is 206, of which 103—just half of the total number—are dependent for their existence on the other half, the Lichens, Liverworts, and Mosses.

MOSSES WHICH BUILD UP LIMESTONE

In trickling springs of mountainous regions, and on the limestone rocks of Niagara Falls, and in other localities are found mosses which obtain part of the carbon dioxide (CO_2) they require by the decomposition of the bicarbonate of lime [$H_2 Ca(CO_3)_2$] dissolved in the surrounding water. The monocarbonate of lime ($CaCO_3$), which is insoluble in ordinary water, is then precipitated in the form of incrustations upon the leaves and stems of the plants. *Gymnostomum curvirostre, Trichostomum tophaceum, Hypnum falcatum*, and others which regularly occur in streams arising from springs loaded with bicarbonate of lime [$H_2 Ca(CO_3)_2$] in solution become completely incrusted with lime, but go on growing at the tips as the older and lower parts imbedded in lime die off. In consequence, the bed of the stream itself becomes calcified and elevated, and, in the course of time, banks of calcareous tufa are formed, which may attain to considerable dimensions. Banks raised in this manner are known which are not less than forty-eight feet in height. To construct them, it is estimated that mosses must have been at work on them for more than 2,000 years.

CHAPTER III

LICHENS IN HISTORY

Somewhat authentic reference to lichens is found in the writings of the Greek philosopher Theophrastus (382-287 B. C.), a pupil of Aristotle. He gives us imperfect descriptions of Old Man's Beard *(Usnea barbata)* and *Roccella tinctoria*. Dioscorides, a Greek physician, and the founder of botany, who flourished in the first and second centuries, and also Gaius Plinius, a Roman naturalist (23-79), who perished in the eruption which destroyed Pompeii, both wrote of lichens which may have been those described by Theophrastus. It is not improbable, however, that they were speaking of *Marchantia* or some other liverwort. The fact that lichens had few qualities which rendered them particularly conspicuous, caused them to be largely neglected by the early botanists. They are not as a rule striking in colour, size, or form and they have no marked useful or harmful properties. The incentive which led to the early study of plants was a desire to find properties which would be of use in medicine or in the household, therefore the early herbalists gave their attention to plants with real or imaginary medicinal properties.

The lichens which could yield a dye were among the first to receive attention. *Roccella tinctoria* is supposed to have yielded the blue and purple dye of the Old Testament (Ex. XXV: 4). The dye called oricello, was certainly in use before the first century of our era. The knowledge of the dye was lost after the fall of the Roman Empire, but in 1300, Federigo, a Florentine of German parentage, accidentally rediscovered the method of preparing and using it. He is said to have achieved great success, and to have become the head of a distinguished family, the Oricellari, Roccellari, and Rucellai. From which we have *orseille*, the name of the dye material, and *Roccella*, the name of the genus of which *Roccella tinctoria* is a member. A blue litmus solution is produced by fermenting this lichen. It may be turned red by adding an acid and then turned blue again by adding an alkali as

19

ammonia or limewater. For this reason it serves as a test for acid and alkaline substances.

LICHENS AS DRUGS

Since many lichens had a fancied resemblance to certain parts of the human body, they were supposed to be a cure for the disease of that part of the body which they resembled. Old Man's Beard *(Usnea barbata*, Colour Plate I) was used to promote the growth of hair. Yellow wall lichen (*Xanthoria parietina*, Colour Plate II) was given for jaundice.

Peltigera canina dried and finely powdered and mixed with red pepper formed an anti-hydrophobia powder *(Pulvis antilyssus)* of the London Pharmacopœia. In the history of the Royal Society it is recorded that several mad dogs belonging to the Duke of York were saved by this powder.

A prescription of Dr. Mead reads: "Patient is bled and ordered to take a dose of *peltigera* in warm milk for four consecutive mornings thereafter. He must take a cold bath every morning for a month, and for two weeks subsequent, a bath three times a week."

LICHENS AS FOOD

"Iceland moss" *(Cetraria Islandica*, Colour Plate VII) is even now used as an article of food, as it contains a high per cent. of lichen-starch.

The Spotted Lungwort *(Sticta pulmonaria*, Colour Plate VII) was considered a sure cure for lung trouble and was used in a Siberian monastery for a beer which was noted for its peculiar bitterness.

The manna of the Israelites is supposed to have been a species of Lecanora *(Lecanora esculenta)*. This lichen is plentiful in Algeria and Tartary, as well as in mountainous districts of other countries. It is its habit to grow and spread rapidly and, as it is loosely attached, it is often carried by the wind down the sides of mountains into the valley, where it is spoken of as "Rains of manna." Kirghiz Tartars eat it as "earth bread."

It first forms thick-wrinkled and warted grayish-yellow crusts on the stones. Within, they are as white as parched corn.

As the plant grows older the crust is rent and loosened from the substratum, while the edges curl over until the loosened piece forms an elliptical warted body about the size of a hazel-nut. The Manna Lichen is sometimes brought down in such quantities by the rain that it accumulates to a depth of several inches, and in the Steppe region, and in the high lands of southwest Asia is used as a substitute ıor corn.

From the time of Dioscorides in the first century, A. D., until 1825, advance in exact knowledge of lichens was practically nothing. Between 1825 and 1868 considerable progress was made in the chemical study of lichens, the investigations still being primarily made with a view to improving the dye industry.

France took the lead in improved methods of extracting dye as well as of applying it.

LICHENS

"Little lichen, fondly clinging
In the wild wood to the tree,
Covering all unseemly places,
Hiding all thy tender graces,
Ever dwelling in the shade,
Never seeing sunny glade."

R. M. E., Lichens.

CHAPTER IV

THE ORIGIN AND NATURE OF LICHENS

STRANGE opinions were entertained in regard to the origin of lichens. The belief was general that they were spontaneously generated. In them the philosopher found the origin of plant life. "Spontaneously, inorganic stone became living plant!" Dr. Hornschuch wrote in 1819, "Algæ, lichens, and mosses may develop without seed from decomposing water. The decomposition of water induced by warmth and sunlight gives rise to the common ancestral type of algæ, lichens, and mosses. This ancestral type is a vegetable infusorium known as *monas lens* which, when acted upon by light and air, undergoes an evolutionary transformation into algæ, lichens, and moss."

Nees Von Esenbeck, in 1820, was wont to lead his pupils to an old castle in order to demonstrate *ad oculos*, how the green substance when occurring on rocks will develop into lichens.

De Bary was the first author to hint at the true nature of lichens (1866). His conception of the lichen as a dual organism composed of a fungus and an alga, was upheld by the researches of Schwendener and Bornet in 1868.

Further investigation seems to prove that the lichen is not an individual plant, but that it is the result of an alliance perhaps for mutual benefit between two forms of plant life, an alga and a fungus. The alga gives the green colour to the lichen and is a relative of the simple plants which make damp stone or woodwork green on the shady sides of streets and houses and trees. The fungus is a relative of the toadstools and moulds. If one look at a piece of white mouldy bread, or in the ground at the base of a toadstool, one can see a true fungus plant which is simply a network of fine white treads *(hyphæ)* stealing their food instead of manufacturing it for themselves. They have lost their leaf-green granules, the tools with which plant-food is manufactured from air and water and mineral salts, but they have acquired the power of absorbing great quantities of water and of resisting alternate drying and wetting.

The alga will perish if exposed to dry air, but when kept moist is capable of taking elements from the air and of manufacturing them into plant-food by means of little granules of leaf-green it has in its cells.

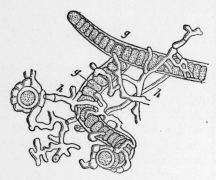

An Alga-fungus company. The cut shows a magnified portion of a lichen, *Stereocaulon ramulosum*, (Sw.), (*h*) colourless hyphæ of a fungus enveloping, (*g*) filaments of a blue-green alga *Scytonema*.

In the alliance the fungus is entirely dependent upon the food manufactured by the green alga and in return keeps the sun's rays from the alga and absorbs water for its work.

The Alga-fungus company, or lichen, is perhaps one of the earliest instances of division of labour, a little community in which one party manufactures and supplies food to the other which serves as protector.

The gray-green of a lichen is then due to the fact that a bright-green plant is covered over by a translucent white plant, and the brighter green of the wet lichen is due to the fact that the wet strands of the fungus are rendered transparent by the absorbed moisture, and permit the colour of the imbedded green to be seen.

A magnified portion of a dissected lichen very much resembles a tangle of fine white threads in which are scattered bits of green.

The white threads of the fungus creep around in search of moisture and as a rule determine the shape the lichen is to be, while the green cells or threads of the alga follow their protecting fungus. However little moisture there may be in the surrounding air, the fungus threads absorb it for their working companion, and so the lichen can live in places too dry and parched for other plants.

"Strong in loveliness, they neither blanch in heat nor pine in frost."

On account of this dual nature it has been difficult to decide where to place the lichens in the plant kingdom; to decide whether they belong with the algæ, with the fungi or have a place as individual plants.

It is claimed that with the microscope one may often determine the species of the associated fungus, as well as that of the associated alga and that this alga freed from the lichen-fungus pursues its normal mode of life and can then be identified.

It is also claimed that lichens have been formed from the spores of a fungus partner allowed to germinate on free-growing algæ, and that a variety of lichens have thus been developed and that the same alga will produce different kinds of lichens if associated with different fungi, and that spores of the fungus-partner have been grown on nutrient solutions and have produced a fungus. One instance is known of a fungus-partner *(Cora pavonia)* which can lead an existence independent of the alga-partner.

HOW A LICHEN IS MADE

According to this theory, if a wandering fungus spore meets a group of algal cells with which it can live in harmony, a lichen-fungus-company may be founded on the spot. This lichen may grow and flourish and may from time to time send forth representatives to found new colonies.

Coccocarpia molybdia. A section of the thallus showing the green cells of the alga covered by the colourless cells of the fungus. When the lichen is damp the colourless cells are more translucent and the green cells show more and the lichen is greener than when dry.

By another method, which is somewhat analogous to the budding of higher plants, the partners for the new colonies arise within the parent lichen company. Certain groups of cells (Soredia) separate from the rest, each group consisting of one or more algal cells enmeshed in a dense weft of fungus hyphæ. At the proper time the surface of the parent lichen ruptures, and the numerous social groups appear, giving to the old lichen that attractive hoary or frosted appearance they so often have. With the aid of the wind these easily travel, to form new companies.

The fungus spores *(ascospores)* which enter into partnership with groups of alga cells are produced in sacs *(asci,* singular

HYPNUM UNCINATUM, Hedw.

GOLDEN-CORD MOSS.
Funaria hygrometrica, Sibth.

GEORGIA PELLUCIDA, Rabenh.

NECKERA PENNATA, Hedw.
. . . A moss creeping around the tree trunk . . .

SPHAGNUM CYMBIFOLIUM, Ehrh.
. . . Crimson bog-mosses . . . illustrate how the peat-bogs . . . were made . . .

ascus) in organs of various shapes, knobs, or flat disks *(apothecia)*, or cup and flask-like cavities *(perithecia)*. In addition to these large spores *(ascospores)* of the knobs and cups there are smaller spores *(conidia)* produced in smaller cavities scattered over the thallus. There is much conjecture as to what may be the function of these spores.

In tropical countries there is found a very beautiful fanlike, greenish - yellow lichen *(Cora pavonia)* having a thallus marked with concentric ridges. This lichen bears its spores on the under surface on tiny clubs *(basidia)* instead of in sacs. The algal partner is one of the unicellular blue-green algæ *(Chroöcoccus)* often found in muciliginous masses in damp places. Another tropical form *(Dictyonema)* grows as delicate blue-green, felt-like plates standing out from the tree-branches to

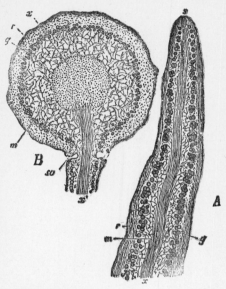

Usnea barbata, **(Fr.)** *(A)* A vertical section through a strand of the lichen.

(B) A cross section of a strand at a point where a radiating strand was cut in vertical section. *(s)* Apex of strand, *(r)* cortex, *(g)* algæ, *(m)* pith layer, *(x)* a central card, *(sa)* section of a radiating branch with its central cord, *(x)*.

to which they are attached. The algal partner in this case is a blue-green, branching, and thread-like species *(Scytonema)* found enveloped in a mucilaginous mass in fresh water. The fungus-partner in both the *Cora pavonia* and the *Dictyonema* is one of the group which forms leathery crusts on twigs and tree trunks.

Another lichen, *Laudatea,* has the same partners as the *Dictyonema*. It is a crustaceous form and in it we find the exception to the rule, that the fungus is the leading member of the lichen firm. In it the alga has the upper hand and determines the direction of the growth.

One lichen *(Emericella variecolour)*, which resembles a tiny puff-ball, is known to be due to the confederacy of a member of the pouch-fungi group *(Gasteromycetes)* with an alga *(Palmella).*

In the majority of lichens the algæ are arranged in definite layers, sometimes—as in the gelatinous lichens—they are distributed through the whole thickness of the thallus. The fungus partner which, with but few exceptions, directs the growth of the lichen, determines whether it shall encrust the surface so that it cannot be removed without injury, or whether it shall form shields and ribbons lightly attached, or corals and fringes fastened at one point.

Although it is impossible without microscopic examination to determine the exact relations of one lichen to another, much pleasure may be derived from an acquaintance with their external form alone. No plants are more readily preserved and none will

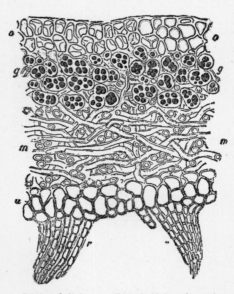

so satisfactorily respond to one's effort to revive them. Even after they have been dry for years they will become as beautiful as ever if placed in a moist atmosphere. One may find them everywhere and at all times of the year. Their power of absorbing moisture is truly wonderful. It is stated that if living lichens which have become dry in the air, are left in a place saturated with moisture, they take up 35 per cent. of water in two days and as much as 56 per cent. in six days. Certain lichens after a long continuance of dry weather will absorb one-half their own weight

Stictima Juliginosa, (Dicks.) Nyl. A section showing (*o*) the upper cortex, (*u*) the under cortex, with (*r*) rhizoids; (*m*) Pith layer showing hyphæ in side and end views; (*g*) gonidial zone, with the blue-green alga *chroococcus.*

of water in ten minutes and will lose it as quickly when exposed to dry air. It is an interesting experiment to put a mass of Reindeer-lichen in a glass of clear water, and note how quickly

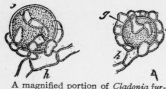

A magnified portion of *Cladonia furcata* (Huds.) *Fr.* (*g.*) The alga *protococcus* enveloped by colourless strands (*h*) of a fungus.

it will expand into a beautiful fresh plant. One may appreciate their wonderful absorbing power by comparing the dry forest trail with a wet one. The old tree stumps are decked, as for a banquet, with branching, coral-like *Cladonia*, a lavish display of fairy candelabra! The red tips of *Cladonia cristatella* and the brown tips of *Cladonia mitrula* are in rich contrast with their frosted green branches. The gray goblets of *Cladonia pyxidata* and *Cladonia*

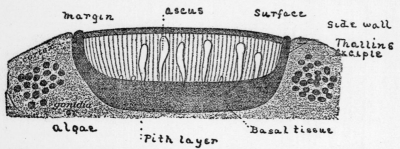

An ideal section through the thallus of a lichen at a point where an *apothecium* is situated.

gracilis are suggestive of many a wood-sprite revel. In cedar woods and on sunny mountain slopes, Reindeer-lichen (*Cladonia rangiferina*), covers the ground with a carpet of loveliest grays, crisp and crumbling when dry but soft as a sponge when moist, and

"O'er yon bare knoll the pointed cedar shadows drowse on the crisp, gray moss." J. R. Lowell—*An Indian Summer Reverie.*

The reindeer in Lapland feed almost entirely

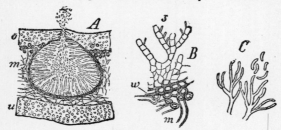

Gyrophora cylindrica, (L) Ach. (*A.*) A magnified section of a lichen thallus at a point where a *perithecium* (*Pycnidium*) is situated: showing (*o*) the upper surface, (*u*) the under surface, (*m*) the pithy layer, (*b*) the interior and (*c*) the opening of the perithecium.

(*B*) A highly magnified bit from the interior of A; (*s*) sterigmata—the tiny stalks upon which the spores are borne, (*w*) Wall of the pycnidium. (*m*) Side and end views of hyphæ from the pitty layer.

(*C*) Sterigmata with spores from the lichen *Cladonia Novæ Angliæ*, (*Delise*).

27

upon this lichen, and in times when food has been scarce, even man has been glad to avail himself of it.

In Sweden at one time the people made their bread from this lowly plant.

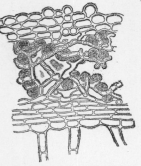

In moist places, velvety green ruffles (*Peltigera*, Colour Plate VII) spread on the ground or on stones and stumps, the edges of the ruffles set with fruit-disks curled in such a way as to resemble brown finger nails, or dogs' teeth. In the days when drugs were selected because of a fancied resemblance to the part of the body in need of cure, *Peltigera canina* was considered a cure for hydrophobia and received its specific name *canina* because of the resemblance of its fruit-disks to a dog's teeth. When dry the surface of the ruffles is a light quaker-drab, which quickly changes to a bright green when the lichen is damp.

Coccocorpia molybdæa. Section of thallus to show algæ and hyphae in definite layers.

It is on the bark of trees that one finds the richest harvest of lichens. They are found in the greatest profusion on the north sides of the trees and for this reason serve the woodman as a guide through the forest. Emerson in "Wood Notes" refers to this, when he says:

"The moss upon the forest bark
Was pole-star when the night was dark."
(Colour Plate IX)

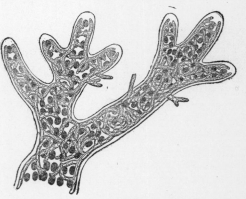

The encrusted lichens, *Parmelia* (Colour Plate V), and *Sticta* (Colour

Ephebe Kerneri. A gelatinous lichen with the alga distributed throughout the thallus.

Plate VII) which grow flat on rocks and trees, cling so closely that they can with difficulty be separated. Their pretty gray or green mats dotted with shining brown fruits grow from the centre outward in an ever-widening circle, covering old fence rails, unpainted cabins, and all other hard unsightly things which Nature wishes to render soft and beautiful.

Collema pulposum (nat. size). A gelatinous lichen with *Nostoc* as alga.

"O'er yon low wall, . . . whose rough, discordant stone
Is massed to one soft gray by lichens fine
The tangled blackberry, crossed and recrossed, weaves
A prickly network of ensanguined leaves."
J. R. Lowell—An Indian Summer Reverie.

The ruby-throated hummingbirds know these lichens and so use them in decorating their nests (Plate I) as to make it difficult to distinguish them from lichen-covered knot holes. The Lungwort *(Sticta pulmonaria,* Colour Plate VII), so called from the resemblance of the pitted surface to the surface of a lung, does not encrust the bark on which it grows, but clings lightly to its support when moist and curls up its under white surface when dry, to protect its green surface. On the same tree with the Lungwort one often finds an hepatic *(Porella platyphylla,* Colour Plate XIV), with braided strands, and a moss *(Neckera pennata,* Colour Plate III) creeping around the tree trunk its strands in parallel rows.

On overhanging cliffs by lake or stream, or on huge rocks in the forest, one finds the oddest lichen of all, the Rock Tripe (Colour Plate XI). When wet, the velvety green shields lie flat, held by a stout cord at their centres. As the air around them becomes dry, the edges begin to curl, bringing the soot-black

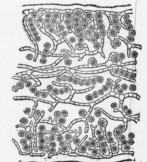

Section of *Collema pulposum* to show uniform distribution of the alga throughout the whole thickness of the thallus.

under surfaces to the light to form black tubes here and there over the rocks. With every change in the moisture of the air the Rock Tripe curls and uncurls, writhes, and twists; at one time presenting its gray or green surface, at another its black. This lichen is also used for food and is said to have saved the life of Sir John Franklin in the Arctic seas, when he was reduced to starvation.

29

CHAPTER V

LEAFY MOSSES

" The tiny moss, whose silken verdure clothes
The time-worn rock, and whose bright capsules rise,
Like fairy urns, on stalks of golden sheen,
Demand our admiration and our praise,
As much as cedar, kissing the blue sky,
Or Krübul's giant flower.   God made them all,
And what He deigns to make should ne'er be deemed
Unworthy of our study and our love."

All true mosses produce their spores in a spore-case of one shape or another which opens, with few exceptions, by a lid.   The spore-case may be situated at the summit of the stem of the moss-plant or on one side of the stem.   It may or may not be supported upon a pedicel (*seta*).

Many species of moss have two rows of teeth about the rim of the spore-case, while some have one row and some have none.   The

Plant with closed spore-case.

Andrea rupestris. An exception to the rule that a moss spore-case opens by a lid.

Spore-case opening without a lid.

Pottia truncata; spore-case opening by a lid.

Spore-case open and spores falling.

Archidium Ohiense. An exception to the rule that a spore-case opens by a lid.

Plant with spore-case immersed by the leaves.

30

Portion of
peristome.

Neckera pennata.

Spore-case
with lid re-
moved to show
single row of
teeth.

*Gymnostomum cal-
careum.* Spore-case
without teeth.

Hypnum uncinatum. Por-
tion of peristome to show
cilia and teeth of the inner
membrane and one tooth
of outer membrane with
annulus at the base.

teeth may vary greatly in shape and number; as a rule, there are four, sixteen, thirty-
two, or sixty-four.

The spore-case when immature is often
covered by a cap or veil *(calyptra)*. The veils vary in shape
and in size, sometimes persisting a long time, sometimes falling
away in the early stages.

All leafy mosses have
leaves which may vary
in size, in shape, in

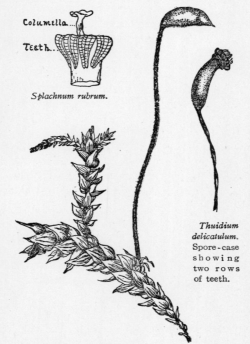

Columella...
Teeth...

Splachnum rubrum.

*Thuidium
delicatulum.*
Spore-case
showing
two rows
of teeth.

Funaria hygrometrica. Spore-
cases borne on pedicels growing at the summit of stem.

Brachythecium rivulare. Spore-case borne on a
pedicel growing from the side of the stem.

31

texture, in colour, and in the nature of the margin, this being sometimes entire, and sometimes toothed, sometimes with a thickened margin or with one made up of cells very different from those within.

The species of mosses are based on the characters of the plant, the spore-case, the pedicel, and the leaves, together with their habit of growth.

Everything about the moss-plants indicates that their purpose in living is to reproduce their kind. Each part is designed and perfected with this end in view. In the struggle for existence they have come to adapt themselves to the most varied conditions, but a certain amount of water is as necessary to them as to all other forms of life. Without water the male cells can never reach the egg-cells and the leaf-green *(chlorophyll)* cannot manufacture plant food. It is true that there are species which have ceased to attempt the formation of spores in localities where the rainy season is never long enough to permit their reaching maturity. In such species the plants become very dry, the leaves

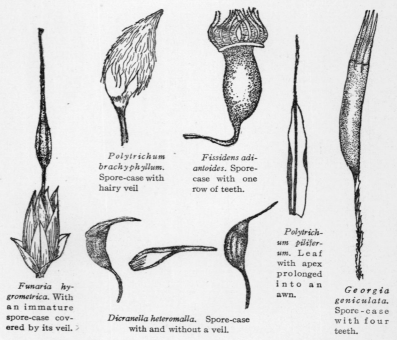

Polytrichum brachyphyllum. Spore-case with hairy veil.

Fissidens adiantoides. Spore-case with one row of teeth.

Funaria hygrometrica. With an immature spore-case covered by its veil.

Dicranella heteromalla. Spore-case with and without a veil.

Polytrichum piliferum. Leaf with apex prolonged into an awn.

Georgia geniculata. Spore-case with four teeth.

and branches break off and are blown hither and thither by the wind, each piece being capable of growing into a new plant, if it has moisture long enough to permit it to get well started. It can then endure long periods of drought and can avail itself of small quantities of moisture which may be condensed from the air.

It must be remembered that normally all plant food is manufactured by the green colouring matter in the leaves and stems of plants, and that these little agents can work only in the light. The light must not be too weak, or the leaf-green becomes yellow and cannot work; again the light must not be too strong or the leaf-green is destroyed and the water in the plant is too rapidly evaporated, with the result that the plant dies.

In order that moss plants may avail themselves of small quantities of water and may

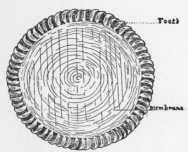

Polytrichum commune. Summit of spore-case showing membrane surrounded with sixty-four teeth.

Catharinea undulata. Tip of spore-case with thirty-two teeth attached by their tips to a membrane.

Octoblepharum albidum. Spore-case with eight teeth.

Apex of leaf to show entire margin.

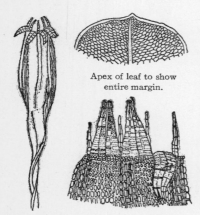

Spore-case.   Part of peristome.
Ulota Hutchinsiæ.

Aulacomnium heterostichum.   Leaf apex to show serrate margin.

33

withstand the fierce heat of the sun, they have various interesting contrivances for folding their leaves so as to retain what moisture they have absorbed, and they have methods of transferring their delicate leaf-green from one part of the plant, too much exposed to the sun, to a part less exposed, or of surrounding the leaf-green-bearing cells

Portion of leaf to show marginal cells different from body cells.
Mnium punctatum.

Stem with leaves.

Mnium cuspidatum.
Stem with leaves.

Pogonatum Alpinum. Apex prolonged into an awn. Margin serrate. Surface covered with delicate cells.

in a wall of large colourless cells. This arrangement accounts for the fact that some mosses, as the peat-mosses *(Sphagnum,* Plate XI), white-mosses *(Leucobryum,* Colour Plate IV), and others appear light gray when dry and green when wet.

The luminous moss has given up the struggle for a place in the outer world and has retreated to caves where but a few rays of light enter. It has adapted itself to the semi-darkness by devising a method whereby it can converge the several feeble rays which fall upon it so that they form one beam

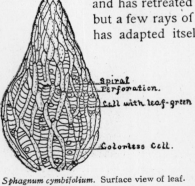

Spiral Perforation.

Cell with leaf-green

Colorless Cell.

Sphagnum cymbifolium. Surface view of leaf.

Bryum argenteum. Leaf with open cell-structure

34

PLATE I

. . . The ruby-throated hummingbirds know these lichens and so use them in decorating their nests as to make it difficult to distinguish them from lichen-covered knot-holes. . . .

sufficiently strong to permit their leaf-green to manufacture plant food.

THE HAIRY-CAP MOSSES

Among the best subjects for a beginner are the Hairy-caps, the most common mosses, which every-one who frequents the woods will find bordering trails and wood-roads, or covering the ground in

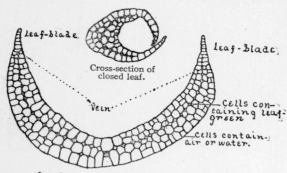

Cross-section of closed leaf.

Leucobryum vulgare. Cross-section of open leaf.

Pogonatum urnigerum. Leaf open to expose the delicate surface.

almost all open places. They are so large that with a hand-glass many of the principal parts may be made out and will thus serve as a foundation for a study of other mosses.

FRUITING PORTION (SPOROPHYTE).

The most striking part of the plant *(Gametophyte)* is the fruiting portion *(sporophyte)* with its parts. The spore-case is a thin-walled cylindrical box with four or six sharp edges running lengthwise. The spore-case is borne on a flexible pedicel (*seta*), the two together resembling a tiny Turkish pipe. In certain stages of this moss the spore-case is entirely covered with a conical light-brown, hairy veil fringed about the

Polytrichum juniperinum. Leaf closed to cover the delicate surface.

Polytrichum juniperinum.

35

base. When this veil falls, the case is tightly shut by a round lid, resembling in some species a tiny Tam-o-Shanter, and in others a tiny dunce-cap.

The lid has a point in the centre and its edges fit closely about the rim of the spore-case.

When the lid is thrown off, sixty-four blunt teeth are seen to border the rim of the case. They are bent inward, and bear at their extremities a thin membranous disk (*epiphragm*) which now closes the case.

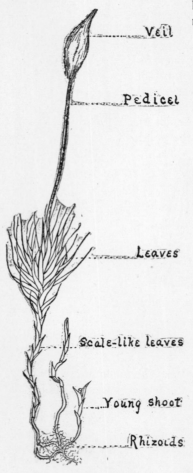

Spore-case without veil and with a short-pointed lid.

Polytrichum juniperinum.

Spore-case with veil.

Polytrichum gracile. Spore-case with long-pointed lid.

Polytrichum commune. Summit of spore-case with sixty-four teeth surrounding a membrane.

Polytrichum piliferum.
Moss Gametophyte.

Within the spore-case are myriads of green, dust-like spores, which, when scattered by the wind, will grow into new plants, if they fall in favourable places.

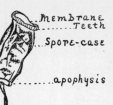

Membrane
.......Teeth
...Spore-case

........apophysis

..............pedicel

Polytrichum juni-perinum. An old sporophyte with lid removed.

HOW THE SPORES ESCAPE FROM
THE SPORE-CASE

When the weather is damp, although the spores are ripe, the teeth of the Polytrichum mosses hold the membranous disk so that the spores cannot escape. When the weather is dry the teeth are so modified as to make a ring of holes between the teeth and the edge of the disk, through which the spores may pass.

There are mosses with their teeth triangular in shape. These have the bases of the triangles fastened at the rim and the points

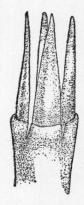

Tetraplodon mnioides. Spore-case with eight pairs of teeth turned back.

Leucobryum vulgare. Portion of single peristome showing four teeth split half way to the base.

Georgia pellucida. Top of spore-case with four teeth.

meeting at the centre. In some species the teeth simply arch up, remaining fastened at the points, and let the pores escape, while in other species they turn back like the ray flowers of a daisy.

Some species have at the base of the teeth a single or double row of short bead-like cells (*annulus*) which swell up at the proper time to push off the spore-case lid.

Spore-case
...annulus
.......Teeth

Funaria hygrometrica. Summit of spore-case.

37

When the spores of the Hairy-cap are mature, the pedicel bends to bring the spore-case into a horizontal position, and the sides of the spore-case wrinkle up, and by so doing oust the spores.

HOW A SPORE BECOMES A LEAFY-MOSS PLANT

The spores which the wind carries from the spore-case to favourable places germinate. The spore first swells and sends forth a delicate tube which divides into a net-work of cells (*protonema*). Some cells (*rhizoids*) of the protonema contain leaf-green (*chlorophyll*) and extend over earth or wood or stone as a fine green web. Upon this green web little bud-like structures appear which develop into leafy

Spores.

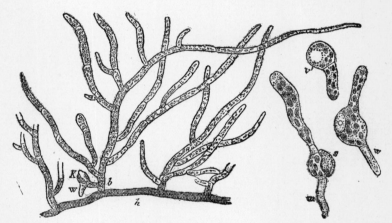

Widely branching protonema.
w. Rhizoid of the moss-plant starting at *K.*
h. A main filament of protonema from which branching protonema *h* has grown.

Funaria hygrometrica

Spore germinating.
w. Rhizoid; *s.* Outside wall of spore; *v.* Vacuole; *p.* Protomena.

moss-shoots. The leafy structure is the part one ordinarily sees and knows as "moss."

As a rule, when the Hairy-caps and other mosses are well grown, the protonema disappears. In a few species, as in the Beard Moss (*Pogonatum brevicaule*), it persists, being visible as a soft green covering on the ground, with small plants on its surface and conspicuous spore-cases erect upon the plants.

HOW A SPORE-CASE IS FORMED

Upon the leafy part which is known as the moss-plant there soon appear little organs which together are to produce **the** sporophyte, spore-case, pedicel and foot.

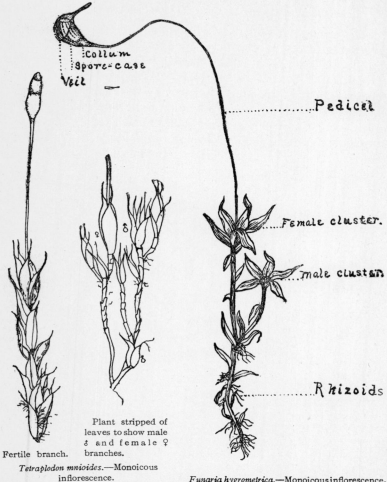

Collum
Spore-case
Veil

Pedicel

Female cluster.

male cluster

Rhizoids

Fertile branch.

Plant stripped of leaves to show male ♂ and female ♀ branches.

Tetraplodon mnioides.—Monoicous inflorescence.

Funaria hygrometrica.—Monoicous inflorescence.

One organ contains an egg-cell and is known as the *archegonium;* the other organ contains the fertilising cells (sperm-cells) and is known as the *antheridium.*

The archegonia and antheridia of the Hairy-caps are on

different plants (*dioicous*, two households). This plan is common to many species of mosses, while other species have the antheridia and archegonia on the same plant (*monoicous*, one household).

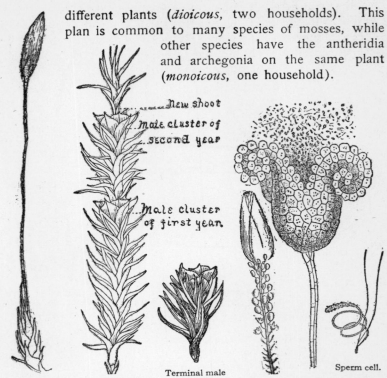

Female plant.   Male plant.   Terminal male flower-cluster.   *Antheridium* bursting and sending forth sperm cells. (See page 46.)

Sperm cell.

Polytrichum.—Dioicous inflorescence.

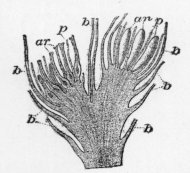

Phascum cuspidatum.—Paroicous inflorescence. Vertical section through stem to show (*an*) male and (*ar*) female flowers side by side on the same plant. (*b*) Leaf blades. (*p*) Paraphyses.

Trematodon ambiguum. Examples of autoicous inflorescence. Two male clusters and one female cluster.

The sperm-cells which develop in the antheridia are tailed and swim in water to an archegonium which contains an egg-cell.

The sperm-cells pass down the necks of the archegonia, unite with the egg-cells, and after

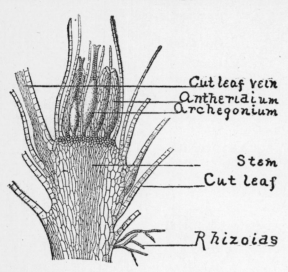

Cut leaf vein
Antheridium
Archegonium

Stem
Cut leaf

Rhizoids

Bryum binum. Stem cut vertically.

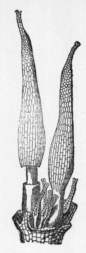

Summit of a stem with two perfect sporogonia and five withered antheridia. One sporogonium is entirely within the archegonium wall; the other is raising the archegonium wall as a calyptra.

the union, each egg-cell begins to divide, forming new cells until a *sporogonium* is completed.

As the sporogonium, still within the archegonium wall, grows upward, the wall of the archegonium is torn away at the base and is carried up as a veil on the

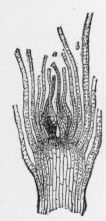

Funaria hygrometrica. Moss stem cut vertically to show (*a*) archegonia alone, (*b*) leaf blades.

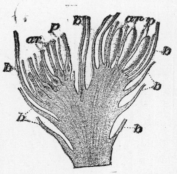

Phascum cuspidatum. Stem cut vertically to show: (*ar*) archegonia on one branch and (*an*) antheridia nearby on another branch; (*p*) paraphyses and (*b*) leaf blades.

41

growing sporogonium, thus the veil of the spore-case is the old archegonium wall.

HOW A HAIRY-CAP PROCURES A MAXIMUM AMOUNT OF LIGHT

The leaves of a *Polytrichum* have many points of interest.

It is a recognised law in nature that the position of the leaves of a tree or plant is such as to admit the greatest amount of light and air possible to the greatest number of leaves. Since it is the habit of these mosses to grow perpendicularly with little or no branching and to have the leaves long and slender, the leaves are so placed on the stem as to form a spiral of leaves, every eighth leaf lying directly above the first one counted. If a line be started at one leaf, and wound about the stem joining all eight leaves, it will be found that it has coiled three times about the stem. The leaves joined form "one story." If a plant with several stories of eight leaves each has straight perpendicular lines drawn joining leaves which lie one directly above another, it will be found that the distance between each line is ⅜ of the circumference of the stem.

Pogonatum Alpinum. Upper view showing transparent base and lamellæ covering the surface excepting along the serrate margin.

Anomodon apiculatus. Leaf with vein extending to the apex.

Ceratodon purpureum. Cross section of leaf showing blade one cell thick, and vein several cells thick.

The fraction which represents the horizontal distance will always have for a numerator the number of spirals in a story and will always have for the denominator the number of leaves in a story. In some *Polytrichum* mosses every thirteenth leaf is directly over the first one counted, so that it would require a spiral of five coils to connect all thirteen and would require the circumference to be divided by thirteen perpendicular lines, each line $\frac{5}{13}$ of the circumference

42

CLIMACIUM DENDROIDES, Web. & Mohr.

. . . Gray cushions which turn green in the rain . . .

POGONATUM BREVICAULE, Beauv.
Remarkable in that it retains the protonema

CERATODON PURPUREUM, Brid.
. . . Velvet cushions which cling to the plaster of the old wall . . .

CATHARINEA ANGUSTATA, Brid.

from the next line. If the two fractions are reduced to the same denominators $\frac{40}{104}$ and $\frac{39}{104}$ and compared, it will be seen that the leaves were but little more crowded. The extra crowding is compensated for by the greater distance between two succeeding leaves in the same line and by the fact that the leaves in the second instance are narrower than the first.

HOW A HAIRY-CAP AVOIDS TOO STRONG LIGHT

The devices for avoiding the extreme heat of the sun are perhaps still more wonderful than those for obtaining a sufficient amount. It is a fact that in the leaves of the Hairy-caps only the upper surface of the leaves is so constructed as to be injured by too dry heat. The cell walls of the lower surfaces are on the contrary thick and impervious to water, so that they cannot give

Bryum argenteum. Leaf with open cell-structure and midvein extending only part way to the apex.

Catharinea undulata. Cross section of leaf to show the leaf-blade one cell thick, and the lamellæ rising from a thickened vein.

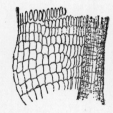

Dicranum flagellare. Part of leaf to show open cell-structure of base. Solid vein on the right of cut.

up moisture to the air when it is dry, a character which insures against loss by evaporation, for when the air is dry the mosses simply turn the awn-pointed leaves upwards with the points and the impervious under-surfaces to the sun and the delicate cells toward the stem.

VEGETATIVE PART
(*Gametophyte*)

The structure of the leafy-mosses is mostly very simple. The leaves are generally but one cell thick from surface to surface, except along a line from apex to base where they form a mid-vein (*costa*).

43

The leaves have no epidermis and no breathing pores as do the leaves of higher plants.

LEAVES OF POLYTRICHUM

The leaves of a *Polytrichum* represent about the highest stage in the development of mosses. The mid-vein is broad, and only at the extreme margins is the leaf-blade one-layered.

The central tissue of the mid-ribs of the leaves continue so as to unite with the central axis of the stem in a manner quite analogous to that found in stems of higher plants. A cross section of a leaf shows that the marginal cells and a line of cells running through the central part are comparatively thin-walled and are

Catharinea angustata. Cross section of leaf to show the thin blade and two lamellæ rising from the vein.

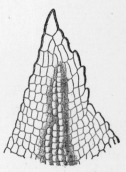

Catharinea undulata. Upper surface of the apex of a leaf showing lamellæ with thin leaf-blade on either side.

Pogonatum Alpinum. Upper face of leaf to show delicate lamellæ.

empty water-conducting cells similar to the wood-ducts (*tracheæ*) of a fibro-vascular bundle in a higher plant. The next layer is composed of similar but smaller cells containing starch. The rest are thick-walled cells (*sclerenchyma*). The outer cells contain more or less leaf-green (*chlorophyll*). When breathing pores occur they are on the spore-case walls.

The cells of the upper surfaces, have their walls exceedingly delicate, so that they can absorb gases and permit gases or water to leave them. The thin blades (*lamellæ*) are undoubtedly the result of an effort on the part of the plant to increase to the highest degree its absorbing surface without widening the leaf-blade itself. By directing the growth of the delicate cells upward in thin blades, this end is accomplished.

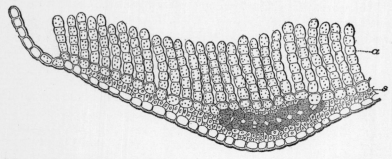

Polytrichum. Cross section of a portion of a leaf to show: (*a*) lamellæ, (*s*) sclerenchyma. Thickened cells of vein. The leaf-blade one cell thick shows on the left.

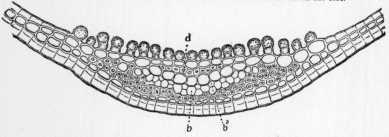

Polytrichum strictum. Cross section of leaf through the midvein to show bead-like lamellæ on the upper surface and thick-walled cells on the under-surface.

THE STEM

The stems of most mosses are simple in structure, they have no vascular bundles for strengthening the stem and for the purpose of carrying liquids from one part to another. The cells of one part differ but little from the cells of another part; those on the exterior may have thicker walls so as to form a firmer rind-layer, and those of the interior may be elongated and serve for the storage and transmission of albumen and hydrocarbons.

The stem of the Hairy-cap is perhaps the most highly developed of all moss stems.

A cross section shows a central portion of thick-walled cells

45

with here and there cells whose walls have remained thin and yellowish. Immediately without the central portion is a zone of several layers of thin-walled narrow cells, bounded

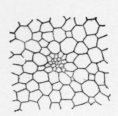

Aulacomnium palustre. Cross section of central part of stem.

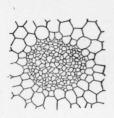

Climacium dendroides. Cross section of central part of stem.

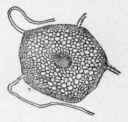

Mnium undulatum. Cross section of stem to show cell structure without fibro-vascular bundles.

on the outside by from one to three layers of cells with thin, mostly dark-brown, walls. These as well as the cells lying immediately within are characterised by the starch contained in them as are the narrow cells of the leaf-traces.

Polytrichum commune. Cross section of stem.

The "roots" are very simple in structure, being either hair-like tubes or simply chains of cells. To distinguish them from the roots of higher plants they are called rhizoids.

ANTHERIDIA

Antheridia, or the male organs of the Bryophytes, are spherical, oval, or club-shaped bodies, with long or short stalks. They consist of an outer wall of a uniform layer of cells, and an interior tissue formed of numerous small cells, in each one of which a sperm-cell has its origin. (See diagram on page 40).

The sperm-cell is a spirally coiled filament, thickened at the rear and pointed at the forward end with two long fine cilia projecting from the point.

When mature, the antheridia walls rupture, and the sperm-cells, in virtue of their coils, spring from the antheridia and by means of their cilia swim in water to the archegonia.

ARCHEGONIA

An archegonium is produced by a multiplication of cells which form a flask-shaped body. The lower or swollen part of the

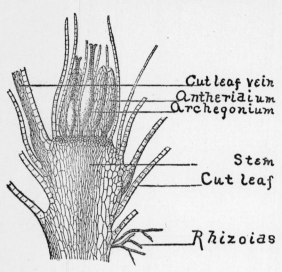

flask contains an egg-cell (*ovum*) and the upper portion is drawn out to form the neck which in the early stages is filled with a layer of cells. Later the chain of cells becomes a mucilaginous jelly, w h swelling with water, bursts open the lid of the neck, and lying on the summit arrests the sperm cells which pass

Bryum binum. Vertical section of stem.

that way in the water, and directs their course down the neck of the flask to the egg-cell (*ovum*) with which they are to blend.

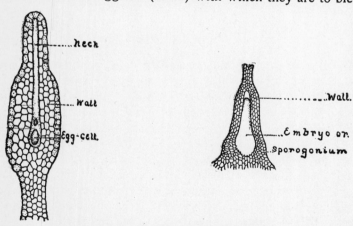

Sections of archegonia, *Sphagnum cuspidatum.*

47

The archegonia and antheridia are developed among the leaves of the moss-plant. As has been stated before, they may be on separate plants (*dioicous,* of two households), or they may

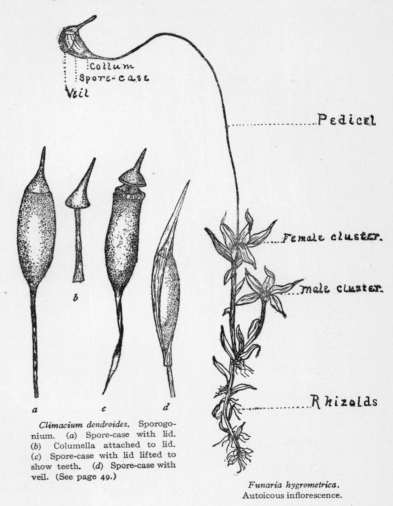

Collum
Spore-case
Veil

Pedicel

Female cluster.

Male cluster.

Rhizoids

Climacium dendroides. Sporogonium. (*a*) Spore-case with lid. (*b*) Columella attached to lid. (*c*) Spore-case with lid lifted to show teeth. (*d*) Spore-case with veil. (See page 49.)

Funaria hygrometrica. Autoicous inflorescence.

both be separated on different parts of one plant (*autoicous*), or side by side on the same plant *(paroicous)* or on the same part of the same plant *(synoicous)*—Monoicous—one household—is a general term including the last three forms.

48

THE DEVELOPMENT OF A SPORE-CASE
(Sporogonium)

After the union of the sperm-cell of the antheridia, with the egg-cell of the archegonium, a division of the egg-cell takes place,

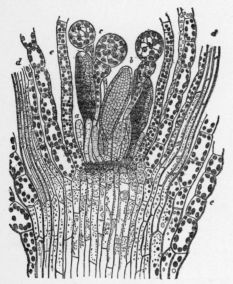

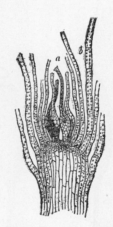

Vertical section through male flower-cluster. (*a*) Young antheridium. (*b*) Mature antheridium. (*c*) Paraphysis. (*d*) Leaf-vein. (*e*) Leaf-blade.

Vertical section through female flower-cluster. (*a*) Archegonium. (*b*) Leaf-blade.

Funaria hygrometrica.—Dioicous inflorescence. (See page 48).

which brings about a multiplication of cells, the ultimate result of which is a mass of tissue called a sporogonium, which is the

Sphærangium muticum. Sporogonium with wall partly removed to show columella with spores attached.

Funaria hygrometrica. Summit of sporogonium to show the annulus rolling back from the teeth.

fruit of the moss made up of the lid, spore-case, teeth, annulus, spores, and columella. (See diagrams on pages 48 and 53.)

CALYPTRA

The calyptra or veil is the dry remains of the outer wall of the archegonium in which first the egg-cell and then the embryo moss-plant were developed, for as the embryo within enlarges, the wall of the archegonium sooner

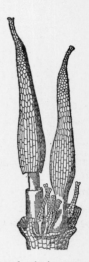

Funaria hygrometrica. Young sporogonium still covered with its veil.

Encalypta ciliata. Old sporogonium with fringed and transparent veil.

Two developing sporogonia with five shrivelled archegonia at their base. The figure on the left shows the archegonium wall severed from its base thus disclosing the pedicel of the spore-case within.

or later ruptures near the base, and is carried up by the growing spore-case. This severed archegonium wall may be thin and smooth and often split up one side, or it may be as in the Hairy-caps rough with hairs, caused by the stretching and ultimate rupturing of the fibres which composed the tissue of the walls.

Pogonatum brachyphyllum. Spore-case with hairy veil.

Tetradontium repandum. Spore-case with conical veil.

50

SPORE-CASE

In the early stages of a developing spore-case the cells may be distinguished as forming two groups, first an outer wall consisting of a number of layers of cells and second an inner mass of cells; the outer wall is separated from the inner mass by a

Spore-case borne on a short
pedicel, lid wanting.

Veil split up one side.　　　　　　　　　　　　　　　　　Spore-case with veil.

Astomum Sullivantii. (See page 50).

space filled with air. The centre portion of the inner mass will become the columella and the enclosing stratum of cells *(arche-sporium*—beginning of spores), will be the "mother-cells" of the spores. Just outside the mother-cells between them and the air-space will be a layer of cells (the *endothecium).*

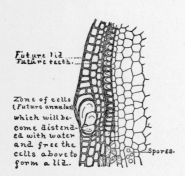 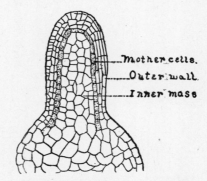

Funaria hygrometrica. Portion of a vertical section through a young sporogonium.

Sphagnum acutifolium. Ehrh. Vertical section through an early stage of a sporogonium.

THE LID OR OPERCULUM

The upper part of the spore-case is in the leaf-bearing mosses usually thrown off as a lid *(operculum).* In order that the upper portion of the spore-case may be separated from the lower, either one of two things happens: The walls of a zone of cells of the spore-case wall, in the exterior layer, separates from the adjoining walls when the spore-case is mature, or a zone of cells consisting of one or more rows has the cell-walls modified so that when they are distended by absorbed moisture, the zone of cells is displaced as a ring or annulus and so frees the outer layer of cells in the upper part of the spore-case to form a lid.

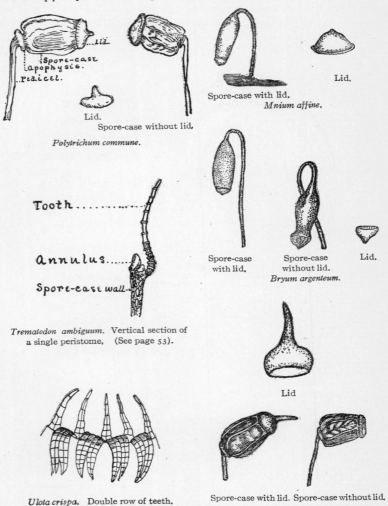

Lid.

Spore-case

apophysis.

Pedicel.

Lid.

Spore-case without lid.

Polytrichum commune.

Spore-case with lid.

Mnium affine.

Lid.

Tooth

Annulus

Spore-case wall

Trematodon ambiguum. Vertical section of a single peristome, (See page 53).

Spore-case with lid.

Spore-case without lid.

Bryum argenteum.

Lid.

Lid

Ulota crispa. Double row of teeth. (See page 53).

Spore-case with lid. Spore-case without lid.

Polytrichum sexangulare.

TEETH OR PERISTOME

When the lid falls, as a rule, one or two rows of teeth are discovered. They are the remains of the cell-walls lying just within the layer which separated as a lid. (See diagrams on page 52.)

If the outer walls of this layer of cells become thickened and split from the summit downward, but one row of teeth will be formed; if the inner walls as well, become thickened, and only

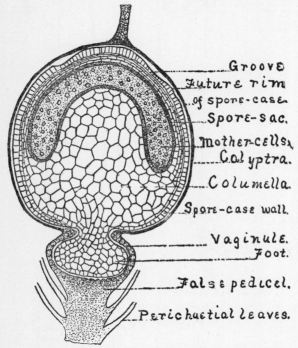

Sphagnum acutifolium. Ehrh. Vertical section from a young sporogonium, (See page 49).

Funaria hygrometrica.
Annulus.

Fissidens adiantoides.
Old spore-case.

Tetraplodon mnioides.
Tip of spore-case.

53

the side walls break down, then an inner row of teeth or cilia will be formed. All the varied forms of teeth are determined by the portions of the cell-walls which remain.

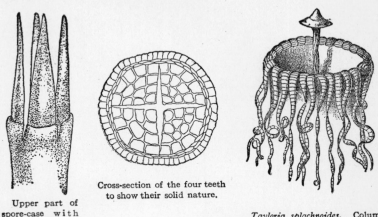

Upper part of spore-case with four teeth.

Cross-section of the four teeth to show their solid nature.

Georgia pellucida.

Tayloria splachnoides. Columella attached to the base of the spore-case.

In the genus *Georgia*, after the outer layer of the upper part of the spore-case has fallen away as a lid, the whole inner layer splits into four triangular valves which form the teeth.

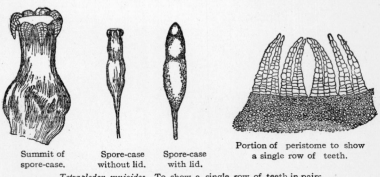

Summit of spore-case.

Spore-case without lid.

Spore-case with lid.

Portion of peristome to show a single row of teeth.

Tetraplodon mnioides. To show a single row of teeth in pairs.

In *Fontinalis antipyretica* the inner peristome forms a lattice work due to the breaking down of the inner cell-wall faces and the retention of the side walls.

The columella of many mosses shrivels up and disappears

54

when the spores are ripe; in some cases it remains attached to
the base of the spore-case when the lid falls; in some cases it is
severed from the base and remains attached to the lid.

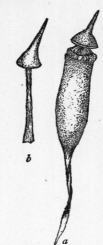

Spore-case with
columella attached
to the base and
summit.
Sphærangium muticum.

Spore-case with
short pedicel and
conical veil.

Veil.

Spore-case
with lid.

Spore-case
with shriv-
elled lid.
Gymnostomum curvirostrum.

Lid with colum-
ella attached.

Climacium dendroides.
(*a*) Spore-case with lid
lifted to show teeth.
(*b*) Columella attached
to the lid.

In *Polytrichum* mosses it remains standing in the spore-case
and retains at its summit a plate of cells (epiphragm) in the form
of a thin membrane to the rim of which are attached the tips of
the teeth.

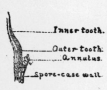

Inner tooth.
Outer tooth.
Annulus.
Spore-case wall.

Thuidium minutulum.
Vertical section of
double peristome.

Columella
Teeth.

Splachnum rubrum.
Columella attached to
the base of the spore-
case; teeth turned
back.

Pogonatum brevicaule. Upper part of spore-case with
thirty-two teeth surrounding the epiphragm.

The structure of the peristome in the *Polytrichum* mosses is
entirely different from that of other mosses. The teeth are composed of bundles of thickened fibrous cells arranged in crescent
form. The ends of the crescent point upward and are united

55

with the adjacent ends of the bundle next to it. On the inner face of each tooth is a growth of cells extending inward as a thin blade; the tip of each tooth is connected with a thin, papery membrane which covers the opening of the spore-case. From the under surface of this membrane, processes like little curtains

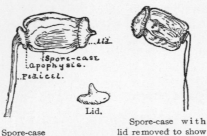

Spore-case
with lid.

Spore-case with
lid removed to show
epiphragm.

Polytrichum commune.

Fontinalis antipyretica. Summit of spore-case with inner teeth forming a cone; outer teeth curled in.

hang down and in the young stages of the spore-case reach the basal membranes, so that the case is completely closed. Later, when the spores are mature, the "curtains" shrink away from the basal membranes and leave little holes between the teeth for the exit of the spores.

In the species of *Catharinea* the epiphragm is not attached to the apices of the teeth, but hangs from them by processes which at first exactly line the inner surfaces of the upper parts of the teeth. As the spores within the spore-case mature they exert a pressure upon the under surface of the epiphragm which causes it to rise and at the same time to peel upward the lining of each tooth. As the linings of the teeth are torn away, they curve upward and inward until they lie against the under surface of the epiphragm, which then appears to rest upon the tips of the teeth. When in this position, the tiny

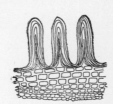

Three teeth showing bundles of fibres.

Summit of spore-case with sixty-four teeth surrounding the epiphragm.

Polytrichum commune.

spaces between the teeth open into the spore-case and through them spores may escape.

THE PEDICEL OR SETA

The seta has undoubtedly been developed for the purpose of raising the spore-case to a height where the spores may be most advantageously scattered. In many mosses the seta becomes

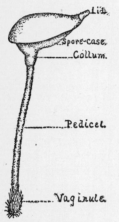

Buxbaumia aphylla.
Sporophyte.

Ulota crispa.

Catharinea undulata. Summit of spore-case with thirty-two teeth attached to the epiphragm.

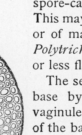

Funaria hygrometrica. Cross-section
of seta.

abruptly larger just below the spore-case to form an apophysis. This may be long and cylindrical, or of many other forms. In the *Polytrichum* mosses it is a more or less flattened disk.

The seta is surrounded at the base by a sheath which is the vaginule and may be the remains of the base of the archegonium.

The pedicels (*setæ*) have various methods of twisting or turning while growing so as to bring the developing spore-case into positions most favourable with reference to light and moisture.

57

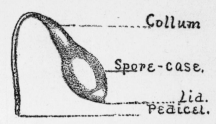

Leucobryum vulgare.
(*a*) Young plant. (*b*) Terminal leaves with root-hairs, each capable of growing into a new plant.

Leptobryum pyriforme.

Collum

Spore-case.

Lid.

Pedicel.

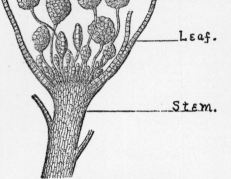

Gemma.

Leaf.

Stem.

Georgia pellucida. Vertical section of gemmæ cluster.

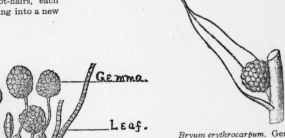

Bryum erythrocarpum. Gemmæ in the axis formed by leaf and stem.

Ulota phyllantha. Portion of a leaf with gemmæ on the apex.

Gemmæ cluster enlarged.

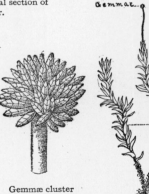

Spore-case

Pedicel

Gemmæ

Fertile branch.

Sterile branch.

Rhizoids

Aulacomnium androgynum.

58

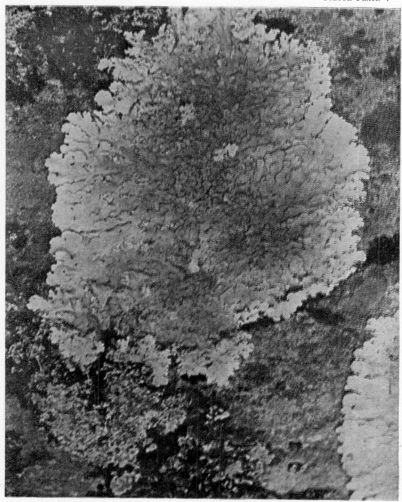

PARMELIA CONSPERSA, (Ehrh.) Ach.

" . . . Where lichens mock the marks of a moth . . . Elf-needled mat of moss "

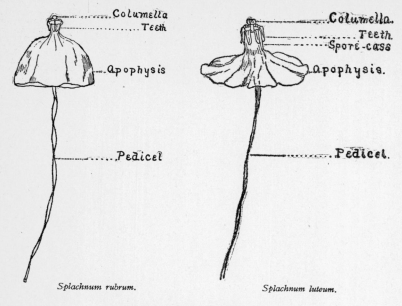

Splachnum rubrum.   *Splachnum luteum.*

ASEXUAL REPRODUCTION

The ultimate aim of the plant in developing all these complex parts is to produce tiny dust-like spores which are found in a ripened spore-case, to insure their safe keeping until all conditions are favourable for their dispersal, and then to disperse them in the most effectual way. Why it has been favourable for the perpetuation of the mosses to evolve these complicated methods, is a marvel and past the mind of man to reveal, for the plants have other and simpler methods of reproducing their kind which are, as far as man can see, just as effectual as the complicated method.

Phascum cuspidatum. Spore-case with veil and short pedicel.

Almost any part of the moss plant is able to develop protonema cells from which new plants may grow.

Every one of the hair-like roots (*rhizoids*) from any part of the plant has the power of developing protonema.

The protonema of *Phascum* and *Ephemerum* lives on from year to year, reproducing new plants which live but one year.

In the species *Barbula*, little cellular bodies covered with a dark

59

membrane and with their cells filled with food material appear in abundance on the protonema. Each one of these is capable of growing directly into a moss-plant or of producing protonema upon which moss-plants may grow.

Portions of a growing sporogonium, or of leaves, or of stems, may produce protonema.

Special buds or gemmæ are also formed on many species. *Georgia pellucidà* produces cellular bodies with stalks in clusters at the extremities of special stems, the clusters surrounded with a rosette of leaves. That all gemmæ are modified leaves is an accepted theory.

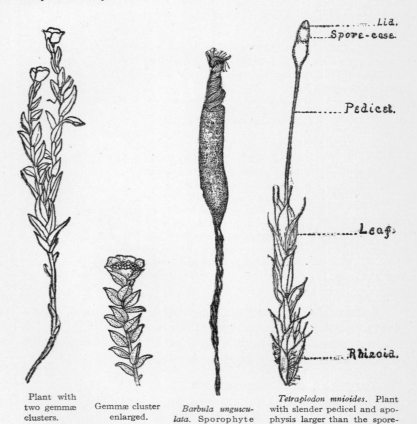

Plant with two gemmæ clusters.

Gemmæ cluster enlarged.

Georgia pellucida.

Barbula unguicu-lata. Sporophyte with twisted seta.

Tetraplodon mnioides. Plant with slender pedicel and apophysis larger than the spore-case.

CHAPTER VI

THE POSITION OF HEPATICS AND MOSSES IN THE PLANT KINGDOM AS SHOWN BY A COMPARISON OF HOMOLOGOUS PARTS

" Quorsum, inquient multi, tantum laboris in rebus adeo tenuibus insumtum ?—cui bono hæc omnia ?   Primo ; ut cognoscamus sapientiam creatoris, quæ in minimis non minus elucet, quam in magnis plantis."
                    Dillenius in præfatione ad Hist. Musc.

" Wherefore, many ask, is so much labour spent on such small things? —for what good are all these things ?   Primarily; that we may know the wisdom of the Creator, which shows itself not less in the smallest plants than in the great ones.
          Dillenius, in the preface to The History of Mosses.

> " If by the microscopic glass
>   Survey'd, you'll see how far surpass
> The works of nature, in design,
> And texture delicately fine,
> And perfectness of every part,
> Each effort of mimetic art ;
> And as the gardener's watchful care,
> The ground, of native clothing bare,
> Indues with vegetable soil ;
> And with the waste's collected spoil
> The tender plants exposed defends ;
> So the Great Gardener, mindful, sends
> The mossy tribes wherewith to shun
> The pinching frost, the scorching sun."

AFTER one has become familiar with the conspicuous parts of a thalloid and leafy hepatic, and a leafy moss, it is interesting to study the homologies or origin of the parts, and to determine the position of the plants in the plant kingdom.

To quote Dr. L. M. Underwood : *

" The group known since the time of Adanson as the *Hepaticæ* stands in a unique position on the boundary line of

---

*L. M. Underwood, Bot. Gazette Vol. xix, 1894, p. 347.

thallose plants, and its position is not only intermediate from a structural standpoint, but in its relation to the evolution of the higher plants it stands as a key or link between the lower or simpler, and the higher or more complex.

"The hepatics possess almost no utilitarian aspect. Beyond the doubtful use of one or two for medicine, and the occasional occurrence of one or more tropical species as weeds, they are, so far as the physical condition of the human race is concerned, an entirely useless group of plants . . . and yet from the higher standpoint of genetic relationship, there is probably no single group of plants that occupies such a unique position in the plant world. What the group 'Vermes' is to the animal kingdom, the *Hepaticæ* are to plants, with this difference, that we have here a much less complicated group of organisms with which to deal."

MINUTE STRUCTURE

To understand the relation of this plant group it is necessary to have some knowledge of the microscopic structure of a developing moss plant, both liverwort and leafy-moss, and a knowledge of plants less and more complicated in structure than the mosses. This knowledge can to a certain degree be acquired by a study of somewhat diagrammatic drawings of magnified sections of algæ, mosses and ferns. If after this preliminary knowledge has been acquired, an opportunity occurs to see the sections themselves under a compound microscope, the interest will be intensified.

PROTONEMA

As was stated, a germinating moss or hepatic spore results in a single cell or a group of cells (*protonema*.) A part of the cells

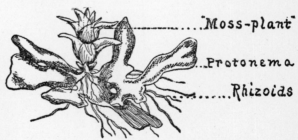

Sphagnum cymbifolium. First or sexual generation.

of the more elaborate protonema are without leaf-green *(chlorophyll)* and seek the darkness afforded by the structure of the substratum in which they serve to anchor the protonema, while they assist in procuring food-materials. Another part of the

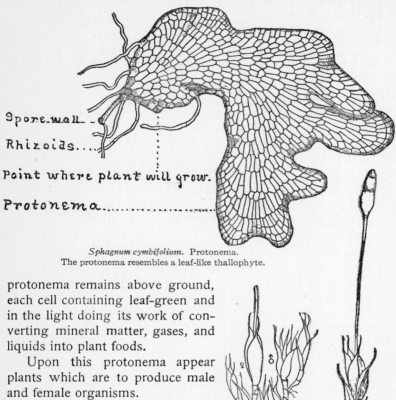

Spore-wall
Rhizoids
Point where plant will grow.
Protonema

Sphagnum cymbifolium. Protonema.
The protonema resembles a leaf-like thallophyte.

protonema remains above ground, each cell containing leaf-green and in the light doing its work of converting mineral matter, gases, and liquids into plant foods.

Upon this protonema appear plants which are to produce male and female organisms.

These plants, together with the protonema are known as the first or sexual generation in the life-history of mosses and hepatics, in distinction from the spore-cases which, in connection with their pedicels and "foot" constitute the second generation.

The protonema resembles some of the Thallophytes, examples of which are bacteria, algæ, and fungi. The Thallophytes are so called

Branch stripped of leaves to show ♂ male and ♀ female clusters.

Female Branch

Tetraplodon mnioides.

63

because their vegetative body is a "thallus," that is to say, is not divided into stem and leaf, like that of higher plants, but grows in water or over a substratum in the form of single cells,

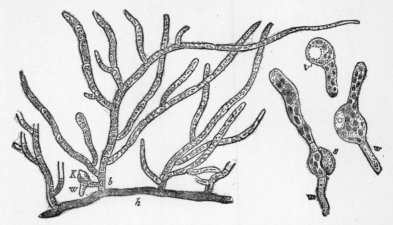

(b) Protonema branching from (h) a primary filament of protonema.
(k) A bud from which a new plant will grow.
(w) A Rhizoid.

Funaria hygrometrica.

Germinating spore
(s) Spore wall.
(w) Rhizoid.
(v) Vacuole in protonema cell.

chains of cells, or ribbon-like patterns of varying designs. The *Bryophytes* or moss-plants agree in many of their stages of development with the *Thallophytes*. Many of the liverworts (*Hepaticæ*), one division of the *Bryophytes*, have never developed

Stipule.

Under side showing stipules.

Upper side.

Ptilidium ciliare. A leafy-hepatic. The magnified stipule shows the simple cell-structure.

further in form than the ribbon-stage or thallus, while others show transitional stages from this ribbon-like form to a leafy stem such as all leafy-mosses possess.

64

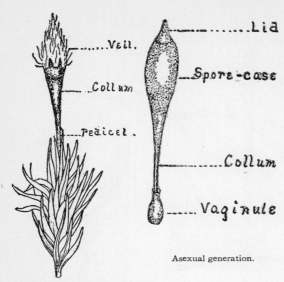

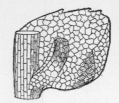

Porella platyphylla. The
leaf and stipule show
the simple cell structure.

Asexual generation.

Asexual generation on the
sexual generation.

Ulota crispa.

A bit of the lichen
Cladonia furcata, showing
an alga of one cell (*Protococcus*) living with a fungus consisting of chains
of cells.

HEPATIC	LEAFY-MOSS	FERN
A germinating spore produces an insignificant *protonema*.	*A germinating spore* produces a well-defined *protonema*.	*A germinating spore* produces a plate of cells (*prothallium*).
Protonema produces ordinarily, an hepatic plant (*gametophyte*).	*Protonema* produces a moss plant (*gametophyte*).	
Gametophyte bears antheridia and archegonia.	*Gametophyte* bears antheridia and archegonia.	*Prothallium* bears antheridia and archegonia. Therefore, prothallium is gametophyte.

All ferns develop from spores, the spores germinate to form—
generally a flat plate of cells (*prothallium*) large enough to be
seen well with the naked eye. The prothallia are heart-shaped

65

and green. They are common around the bases of ferns in the woods and may be found in green-houses where ferns are propagated. The prothallium is the sexual or first generation in the

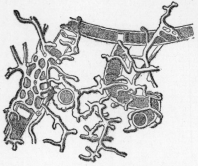

life-history of a fern, for on it are produced the antheridia and archegonia necessary for the production of the embryo which shall grow into a fern plant.

It is not an easy matter to keep clearly in mind the relation of the fern parts and the leafy-moss parts. It will help to do this, if one remember that the criterion by which the decision is to be made is one of origin of parts rather than of function and appear-

The alga *scytonema* growing with a fungus to form the lichen *Stereocaulon ramulosum.* Both alga and fungus consist of chains of cells and belong to the group of *Thallophytes.*

ance. A glance at the parallel columns will show that if one

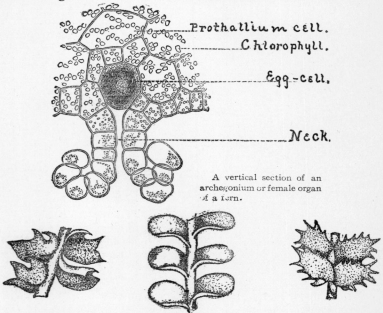

Prothallium cell.

Chlorophyll.

Egg-cell.

Neck.

A vertical section of an archegonium or female organ of a fern.

Hepatics with leafy stems. The leaves have no veins and are but one cell thick.

66

employ the origin and position of antheridia and archegonia as a criterion, then the vegetative part of hepatic plants and moss plants is an homologous stage with a fern prothallium.

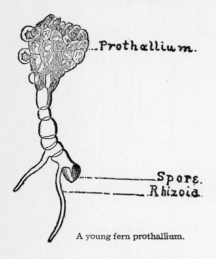

A young fern prothallium.

The sexual or first generation. Under side of a mature fern-pro-thallium on which are borne an-theridia—male organs, and arche-gonia—female organs.

Again, if one employ as a criterion that which originates from a fertilised archegonium, then the spore-case, foot, and pedicel (*sporophyte*) of an hepatic and moss are homologous

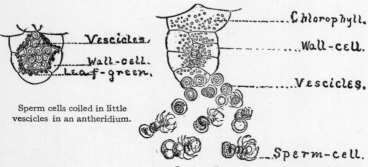

Sperm cells coiled in little vescicles in an antheridium.

Sperm-cells escaping from an antheridium.
Vertical sections of Antheridia.

with the spore-cases, fronds, stems, and roots of a "fern-plant" (*sporophyte*). The sporophyte is known as the asexual generation.

67

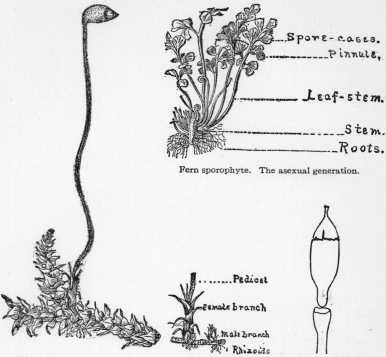

Fern sporophyte.   The asexual generation.

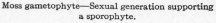

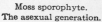

Moss gametophyte—Sexual generation supporting
a sporophyte.

Moss sporophyte.
The asexual generation.

Fern gametophyte—The sexual generation
supporting a sporophyte.

Hepatic gametophyte
supporting a sporo-
phyte.

68

HEPATIC	MOSS	FERN
Archegonia produce foot, and pedicel, and spore-cases containing spores (*sporophyte*).	Archegonia produce foot, and pedicel, and spore-cases containing spores (*sporophyte*).	Archegonia produce fern-"plants,"—roots, stems, fronds, and spore-cases containing spores (*sporophyte*).

One pinnule from a leaf of Ruta-muraria.

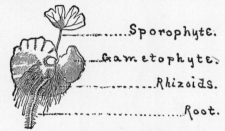

Fern-prothallium—(sexual generation) with young sporophyte (asexual generation).

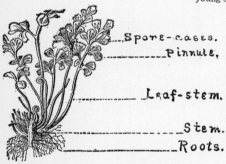

Complete sporophyte—*Asplenium Ruta-muraria.*

In comparing hepatics, mosses, and ferns with a view to determining their relative positions in the plant kingdom one must be careful to compare homologous parts, gametophyte with gametophyte, sporophyte with sporophyte.

A study of the asexual generation, the sporophyte, (spore-case, foot, and pedicel) of leafy-mosses, will show that they have suggestions of the more complex structure found in the asexual stage, (*sporophyte*), of the pteridophytes, a group including ferns (*filices*), horse-tails (*equisetums*), and Christmas-greens (*lycopodiums*), which possess tissue composed of tubular cells (vascular bundles), set apart for the purpose of strengthening the plant and of carrying liquids from one part to another. The Pteridophytes have also true roots or underground organs with a vascular tissue.

69

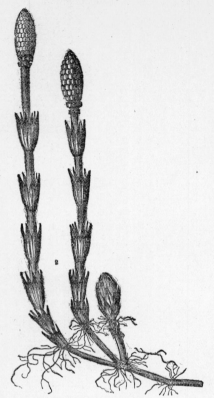

Equisetum arvense. Nat.
size Vernal spore-bearing
shoot with whorls of scale-
like leaves. Asexual gen-
eration.

Equisetum arvense. Natural size Summer sterile
shoot with whorls of branches bearing scale-like
leaves.

Single spore-
bearing scale,
from 3.

Spore with ela-
ters coiled.

Fertile cone
from 2.

Spore with elaters
expanded.

A FOREST BOULDER

A huge boulder showing all stages in Nature's preparations for plant growth. The lower sides are now covered with lichens alone, while the parts above are covered with leafy-mosses which made their start in lichen debris. Ferns nestle in the mosses and a spruce tree sits astride the rock . . .

The hepatics and mosses are therefore classified between the lowest group of plant life (*Thallophytes*), bacteria, algæ, fungi, etc., without stem, leaves, and roots, and the spore-bearing plants which have well-developed stems, leaves and roots, such as ferns, horse-tails, and lycopodiums, (*Pteridophytes*).

The genus *Riccia* has no foot and no pedicel, simply a spore case.

Hepatic sporophyte. The asexual generation.

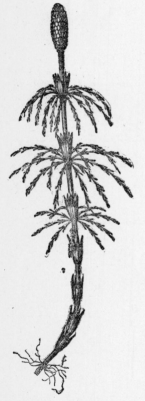

Equisetum sylvaticum with fertile cone and whorls of branches.

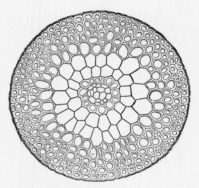

Funaria hygrometrica. A cross-section from the pedicel of the sporophyte. The cells through the centre of the pedicel are modified to form rudimentary fibro-vascular bundles, which one may interpret as foreshadowing the true fibro-vascular bundles found in the sporophyte of ferns, etc.

Male prothallium of a horse-tail with antheridia. Sexual generation.

71

Pores (stomata) for the inlet and outlet of gases which serve for food and respiration are found on certain parts of the sporophyte of leafy mosses and not on the gametophyte ; they are found on the sporophyte of ferns and not on the gametophyte (*prothallium*). They are on the gametophyte and not on the sporophyte of hepatics, (except in the *Anthocerotaceæ*).

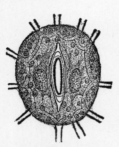

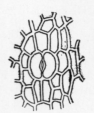

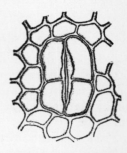

Hypnum Boscii. Surface view of pore from the sporophyte.

Funaria hygrometrica. A pore from the spore-case of the sporophyte.

Polytrichum juniperinum. Surface view of a pore from the spore-case of the sporophyte.

Polytrichum piliferum. Vertical section through a pore.

M. polymorpha. Surface view of pore.

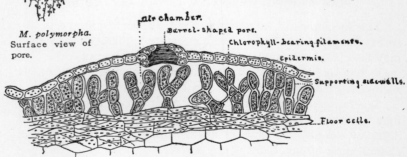

Marchantia polymorpha. Vertical section of a "plant" (gametophyte) through a pore which leads into an air chamber.

72

CHAPTER VII

THE HERBARIUM

HOW TO COLLECT HEPATICS, MOSSES AND LICHENS

Search for them in damp places at all times of the year. They are so much more beautiful when in a moist atmosphere that you will feel inspired to learn as much as possible about them. Collect the finest specimens you find, selecting some in fruit, if possible.

Place your specimens in a convenient receptacle, box, bag or basket; in such a way as to keep them separate, each specimen with a few notes in pencil telling its habitat and the date and place of finding.

Clasp-envelopes, such as are used by dry-goods merchants for samples, will be found particularly desirable as the mosses may be dried in them and may be kept indefinitely before being permanently mounted.

HOW TO PRESERVE HEPATICS, MOSSES AND LICHENS

The specimens to be preserved should be laid between absorbent paper, under a moderate pressure until dry, then they may be placed in envelopes which come for the purpose and these may be glued to regular herbarium sheets or the specimens themselves may be mounted directly upon sheets of paper.

Several specimens of the same species from different localities may be mounted on one sheet; but it is undesirable to put different species on a sheet as this interferes with a proper classification of material.

HOW TO STUDY HEPATICS, MOSSES AND LICHENS WITH THE NAKED EYE AND WITH A LENS

Have both fresh and dry material before you for comparison. If you have only dry material to start with, freshen part of it by

73

soaking in clean hot water and learn what you can with the unaided eye about the colour, texture, manner of branching, and character of pedicel and spore-case. Many of these pretty plants can be easily recognised with the naked eye. If necessary, use a hand lens to determine the shape of the leaves and the character of the spore-case rim.

To study the specimens more in detail have a lens so mounted that it will be possible to dissect the parts with needles while watching the process through the lens.

HOW TO DISSECT HEPATICS, MOSSES, AND LICHENS

To remove leaves from stems, grasp them near their bases with a pair of forceps and strip them downward.

To obtain cross sections of leaves, grasp a bunch between the thumb and forefinger and slice it across from apex to base with a sharp knife. Among the sections there should be found some which will show the structure.

To study the spore-case, cut off the upper portion with a pair of scissors and then holding this on a slide with a needle, split it lengthwise and lay the two parts flat on the glass so that a view is given of the inner and outer surfaces.

Cross sections of stems and rhizoids may be made while holding them between two pieces of pith or candle-wax.

HOW TO STUDY THE HEPATICS, MOSSES, AND LICHENS WITH A COMPOUND MICROSCOPE

To study any part still more in detail, place it in a drop of water or dilute glycerine between two pieces of mica or glass and view it through a compound microscope.

If it seems desirable to preserve the detail, let the glycerine mica-mount remain without· a cover-glass in a place free from dust until the water has entirely evaporated, then slightly warm the slide and place a drop of warm glycerine-jelly on a mica cover and invert this over the mount.

Glycerine jelly and mica may be procured of any dealer in microscope supplies. Small bits of mica may also be procured at slight cost from wall-paper factories or from factories where mica is used in the manufacture of electrical supplies.

NOMENCLATURE

When anyone for the first time refers a newly discovered species to a genus, he gives the species a specific name and appends his own name or an abbreviation of it as the authority, thus, *Bryum argenteum*, L. means that Linnæus referred a species to Bryum and gave it the specific name argenteum and that his classification has not been changed.

If a plant has been referred by one man to a certain genus that later is proved by another man to belong to a different genus, the name or abbreviation of the first author is placed in parenthesis and followed by that of the second author thus:—*Ramalina ceruchis* (Ach.) De Not., means that De Notaris placed the species ceruchis in its proper genus Ramalina after Acharius had placed it in another genus (Borrera).

ABBREVIATIONS OF AUTHORITIES CITED

Ach.—Acharius, Erik, 1757-1819.

Beauv.—Beauvois, Palisot de, A. M. F. J., 1752-1820.

Bosc, Louis Augustin Guillaume, 1759-1828.

Brid.—Bridel, Samuel Elisée, 1761-1828.

Bruch, Philipp, 1781-1847.

Bruch. ms.—A name in manuscript never *printed* by Bruch.

Bruch & Schimper.

Delise, Dominic François, 1780-1841.

De Not.—De Notaris, Giuseppe, 1805-1877.

Dicks.—Dickson, James, 1738-1822.

Dill.—Dillenius, Johan Jacob, 1687-1747.

Ehrh.—Ehrhart, Friedrich, 1742-1795.

emend.—emended, corrected.

Fée, Antoine Laurent Apollinaire, 1789-1874.

f.—fils, son.

Fr.—Fries, Elias Magnus, 1794-1878.

Fuern.—Dr. August Emanuel Fürnrohr.

Girgens.—Girgensohn, Gustav Karl.

Gottsche, Carl Moritz, 1808-1892.

Gr. & Benn or B. Gr.—Gray, Samuel Frederick.   B. or Benn. —Bennett, either Edward or John; two London surgeons who devoted their leisure time to botany in the first part of XIX century.

Hall.—Haller, Albrecht von, 1708-1777.

Hampe, Ernst.
Hampe, l.c., *locus citatus*.
Hedw.—Hedwig, Joannis G., 1730-1799.
Hoffm.—Hoffman, Georg Franz.
Hook.—Hooker, William Jackson, 1785-1865.
Hornsch.—Hornschuch, Christian Friedrich, 1793-1850.
Huds.—Hudson, William, 1730-1793.
Hueben.—Huebener, J. W. P.,   -1847.
Jæger & Sauer.—Jæger and Sauerbach.
Lindb.—Lindberg, Sextus Otto, 1835-
Lindle.—Lindley, John, 1799-1865.
Linn. or L.—Linnæus, Carolus, 1707-1778, or Linné, Carl von.
Linn. l. c.—l. c., *locus citatus*, previously cited.
Marchant, Nicholas,   -1678.
Michx.—Michaux, André, 1746-1802.
Michx., f.—Michaux, François André, 1770-1855.
Mohr, Dr. Charles, 1824-1901.
Muell. ined.—Karl Müller (Halle), 1818-1899.
   Note:—ined. means unedited manuscript.
Muell.—Mueller, Jean (of Aargau), 1849-1851.
Neck.—Necker, Noel Joseph de, 1729-1793.
Nees von Esenbeck, Christian Gottfried, 1776-1858.
Norm.—Norman, Johannes Musæus.
Nyl.—Nylander, William, 1822-1899.
Pers.—Persoon, Christian Henrik, 1755-1837.
Rabenh.—Rabenhorst, Ludwig Christian Gottloeb, 1806-1881.
Raddi, Giuseppe, 1770-1829.
Roehl.—Roehling, Johann Christoph., 1757-1813.
Schimp.—Shimper, Wilhelm Philipp, 1808-1880.
Schreb.—Schreber, Johann C. D.
Schwaegr.—Schwaegrichen, Christian Friedrich, 1775-1853.
Scop.—Scopoli, Giovanni Antonio, 1723-1788.
Sw.—Swartz, Olaf, 1760-1818.
Tayl.—Taylor, Thomas.
Timm, C. T.
Tuckerm.—Tuckerman, Edward, 1817-1886.
Turner, Dawson, 1775-1853.
Web.—Weber, Friedrich, 1781-1823.
Weis.—Weiss, Frederigo Wilhelm, 1744-   .
Willd.—Willdenow, Carl Ludwig, 1765-1812.

PART TWO
LICHENS, GENERA AND SPECIES

LICHENS, GENERA AND SPECIES

The Genus CETRARIA, (Ach.) Fries

The Spanish-shield Lichens.—The members of this genus are generally found on trees, although sometimes they are found on rocks or even earth. The colour on the upper surface is bright yellow, greenish-yellow, straw, olive, or brown.

The *thallus* is expanded and leaf-like or shrubby (*fruticulose* or *fruticose*) with branches compressed or channelled; the lobes are flattened and broad; root-like growths on the under surface (*rhizoids*) are few or wanting.

Fine hairs (*cilia*) are frequently present and sometimes are numerous.

Soredia are rare.

The fruiting disks (*apothecia*) are medium in size or large; they are attached on or near the margin of the lobes; the disk itself is shield-shaped, light chestnut to dark reddish-brown. The shape of the disk suggested the name *Cetraria*, from *cetra*, a Spanish shield.

The Pitted Cetraria, *Cetraria lacunosa*, Ach.—See Plate II.

Habitat.—On trees and old fence-rails, easily detached.

Vegetative organ (thallus).—Leaf-like (*foliaceous*) the lobes rounded, the surface pitted (*lacunose*); pearl to slate colour above, white to darker below, margins scalloped.

Fruiting disks (apothecia).—Abundant on the lobes, somewhat elevated, the disk light chestnut, growing darker, the margin entire.

Name.—The specific name *lacunosa* is from the Latin *lacus*, a saucer, referring to the pitted surface of the thallus.

Iceland Moss, *Cetraria Islandica*, (L.) Ach.—See Colour Plate VII.

Habit and habitat.—On earth.

Vegetative organ (thallus).—Cartilaginous and shrubby (*fruticulose*); usually brown above, lighter toward the base where there is sometimes a red stain.

79

Fruiting disks (apothecia).—Not numerous, shield-like and dark chestnut.

Branches.—Flattened, not hollow, rolled in on the margin which is beset with a fringe of dark-coloured hairs 0.3 to 0.5 mm. long.

Name.—The specific name *(Islandica)* refers to the fact that this lichen is very abundant in Iceland.

Genus USNEA (Dill.) Ach.

Thallus shrub-like *(fruticulose)* or pendulous, in cross-section round or angular, grayish-green, to greenish-white, sometimes straw-coloured; the interior consisting of a central tough cord surrounded by a cottony layer.

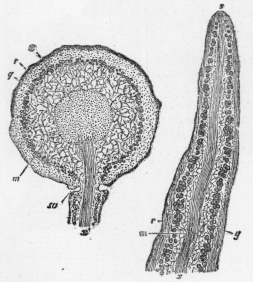

The fruits *(apothecia)* shield-shaped *(scutellæform)*, pale, with a fibrillous margin, spores more or less ellipsoid, undivided, colourless.

The name is derived from *achneh,* the Arabic for lichen.

The Bearded Lichen, *Usnea barbata,* (L.) Fr.—See Colour Plate I, frontispiece, also Plate III.

Cross section through
the thallus.

Vertical section through
the thallus.

Usnea barbata. Fr. (*x*) central tough cord; (*x*) central tough cord of radiating fibre; (*m*) cottony layer; (*g*) algæ; (*sa*) radiating fibre; (*r*) cortical layer; (*s*) apex of thallus.

Habitat.—On trees, both living, and dead.

Vegetative organs (thallus).—Shrubby *(fruticulose)* often pendulous, greenish, covered with numerous radiating fibrils of the same colour; the interior tissue *(medulla)* consisting of a central cord surrounded by a cottony layer. The branches are circular *(terete)* in cross-section and are rough with papillæ.

Plate II

THE PITTED CETRARIA, *Cetraria lacunosa*, Ach.
. . . ruffled upon its host

Fruiting organ (apothecia)—Shield-like *(scutellæform)* with a pale disk.

Name.—The specific name *barbata* is the Latin for "bearded."

The Hair-like Usnea, *Usnea trichodea,* Ach.

Habit and habitat.—On trees in long waving tufts.

Vegetative organ (thallus).—Pendulous, greatly elongated. The few secondary branches are smooth, bearing numerous lax fibrils of variable length, cross-section circular *(terete).*

Fruiting organ (apothecia).—Small, disk pale flesh-colour with margin bearing very few fibrils.

Name.—The specific name *trichodea* is derived from the Greek τρῖχοειδὴς, resembling hair, and refers to the thallus.

Genus THELOCHISTES, Norm., emend.

The thallus is leaf-like *(foliaceous)* or scale-like; usually yellow, appressed or sometimes ascending and scrub-like; the fruits *(apothecia)* are yellow and shield-like *(scutellæform).* The spores are colourless, ellipsoid, simple, or with the ends divided off by partitions *(polar-bilocular)* the end spaces sometimes united by a tube running through the middle space.

The Yellow Wall-lichen, *Thelochistes parietinus* (L.) Norm. *(Xanthoria parietina)*—See Colour Plate II.

Habit and habitat.—On trees and rocks usually near bodies of water.

Vegetative organs (thallus).—Leaf-like, pale yellow to orange above, white below; loosely appressed to the surface on which it grows, the margins sometimes ascendant, not gelatinous when moist.

Fruiting organs (apothecia).—The disk orange, the margin *(thalline exciple)* entire.

Spores.—Colourless, ellipsoid, polar-bilocular.

Name.—The specific name *parietina,* is from the Latin *parie (t-) s,* a wall, referring to its habit of growing on stone walls.

Genus PARMELIA, (Ach.) De. Not.

Parmelias usually grow as horizontal mats, gray, blue-green, dark brown, or brown tinged with green. They are closely attached by black rhizoids to rocks and trees and are distinctly branched and lobed. If the thallus is torn across and viewed with a hand lens, the torn edge shows that the thallus is composed of a layer of long, loose, white fibres (the medullary layer) between thin but more substantial surface tissues (cortical layers). Over the surface of the mat are scattered flat or saucer-shaped disks (*apothecia*) generally brown with a thin margin. These are numerous toward the centre. The apothecia have suggested the generic name *Parmelia* from *parma*, a small round shield. Many species have also a powdery appearance due to the bursting of the surface to emit little bodies (*soredia*) which may grow into lichens.

Parmelia conspersa, (Ehrh.) Ach.—See Colour Plate V.

Habit and habitat.—On rocks and stones; degenerate on dead wood.

Vegetative organs (*thallus*).—Leaf-like, not gelatinous when moist. Pale green or straw-coloured above, blackening below, appressed, the margin sometimes ascendant; cartilaginous, membranaceous, the lobes mostly rather narrow sub-linear and much divided, smooth, not wrinkled, the centre often bearing little stalked bodies with knobs (*isidiophorous*).

Fruiting organs (*apothecia*).—Disks chestnut; margin (*thalline exciple*) entire.

Spores.—Ellipsoid, simple, colourless.

Name.—The specific name *conspersa*, besprinkled, refers to its surface which looks as if sprinkled with little grains.

Parmelia physodes, (L.) Ach.—See Plate V.

Habit and habitat.—Common on dead limbs of pines and hemlocks, lightly attached to its support. When it completely encircles the smaller twigs the tree has a particularly attractive appearance.

Vegetative organs (*thallus*).—Gray-green above with finely cut, inflated lobes, usually overlapping; black beneath except at the margins where it is smooth and brown.

Fruiting organs (*apothecia*).—Large shallow cups; reddish-brown with entire margins.

Name.—The specific name *physodes* is from the Greek φῦσα, bellows, and οἰδ, like, and refers to the inflated character of the lobes.

NOTE: The illustration shows a variety (*vittata*) with the thallus more narrowly dissected than in the species.

82

OLD MAN'S BEARD, *Usnea barbata*, variety *Florida*

Parmelia saxatilis, (L.) Fr.—See Plate XV.

Habit and habitat.—On rocks.

Vegetative organs (thallus).—Greenish or ashen-gray above (sometimes reddish) somewhat ornamented with a fine network and with shallow depressions; black beneath with dense hairs (*rhizoids*) reaching the margin, much cleft with narrow lobes, with margins wavy and bordered with a fine white beading (*soredia*).

Fruiting organs (apothecia).—Chestnut border (*thalline exciple*), rather thick, somewhat evenly notched.

Spores.—Simple, ellipsoid, colourless.

Name.—The specific name *saxatilis*, the Latin for "rock," refers to the habitat.

Parmelia perlata, (L.) Ach.—See Plate VI.

Habit and habitat.—The lichen is found on both rocks and trees.

Vegetative organs (thallus).—Greenish-yellow, gray green, slate colour and even light brown above; black beneath with a reddish-brown border which rolls up so as to bring the brown lobes in rich contrast to the surface colours. The lobes have no fine hairs on their margins and are frequently covered with a white powder (*soredia*).

Fruiting organs (apothecia).—Large, greenish-brown, entire margins which split down to the centre when the disk is mature.

Name.—The specific name *perlata* is the Latin for "widely spread."

The Wrinkled Parmelia, *Parmelia caperata,* (L.) Ach.

Habit and habitat.—Grows on trees and rocks to form light pea-green, wrinkled and wavy mats.

Vegetative organs (thallus). — Leaf-like, appressed, horizontal, cartilaginous; lobes usually broad and rounded with entire margins; the upper surface usually covered with a very light green powder (*soredia*); the under surface, black with a reddish-brown margin and scattered thread-like bodies (*fibrils*).

Fruiting organs (apothecia). — Cup-shaped, with wavy margins often grainy (*sorediferous*).

Spores.—Ellipsoid.

Name.—The specific name *caperata*, the Latin for "wrinkled," describes the habit of growth.

Genus PHYSCIA, Fries.

The vegetative portion (*thallus*) of the **Genus Physcia** is leaf like, star-like, or sometimes with narrowly linear divisions, beneath it has usual fibres of varying length; the generic name is from the Greek φύσκη, a blister, evidently referring to the inflated appearance of the thallus in some species.

The fruiting portion (*apothecia*) are shield-shaped, with the surface often covered with a whitish powder:

The spores are elliptical, brown, two-celled in our species.

Physcia leucomela, (L.) Michx.—See Colour Plate VIII.

Habit and habitat.—On trees, most common southward.

Vegetative organs (*thallus*). — Ascendant and elongated, mostly smooth, often narrowly linear, the densely entangled lobes irregularly divided; beneath white, the margins beset with strong, branched blackish fibrils.

Fruiting organs (*apothecia*).—Medium-sized, on short pedicels, the disk white, powdery, the border lobed; the spores are bilocular.

Name.—From the Greek λευκός, white, and μέλας, black, referring to the strong contrast between fibrils and surface.

Genus UMBILICARIA, Hoffm.

Thallus horizontal, leaf-like (*foliaceous*), scarcely divided, leathery; either smooth or fibrillose beneath, attached to its support by a single point.

Fruits (*apothecia*) black, round, convex or sometimes irregular in outline.

Spores somewhat coloured, ellipsoid, either without cross-walls or with both horizontal and vertical walls.

The generic name is from the Latin *umbilicus*, a navel, referring to the single point at which the thallus is attached to its support.

The Blistered Umbilicaria, *Umbilicaria pustulata*, (L.) Hoffm.

Habit and habitat.—On rocks in dry localities.

Vegetative organs (*thallus*).—Horizontal and leaf-like, cartilaginous; ash-coloured above, whitish toward the centre, pale brownish or ash-coloured below; smooth on both surfaces,

OLD MAN'S BEARD, *Usnea longissima*

. . . Used to promote the growth of hair. A member of the genus *Ramalina* is seen on the lower end of the twig, and a member of the genus *Parmelia* is seen on the upper end

often covered with a white powder (*pruinose*), with numerous pustular protusions above and corresponding indentations below.

Fruiting organs (*apothecia*).—Somewhat shield-like.

Name.—The specific name *pustulata* is the Latin for "blistered" and refers to the protusions on the thallus.

Rock Tripe, *Umbilicaria vellea*, (L.) Nyl.—See Colour Plate XI.

Habit and habitat.—On rocks in high mountains.

Vegetative organs (*thallus*).—Large, one-leaved, leathery and somewhat smooth, ash-coloured with a bloom above; brownish to black, and hairy, below.

Fruiting organs (*apothecia*)—Small, appressed, orbicular and plaited, becoming convex.

Name.—From the Latin *vellus*, fleece, referring to the hairy nature of the under surface.

Umbilicaria Dillenii, Tuckerm.

Habit and habitat.—On rocks.

Vegetative organs (*thallus*).—Leaf-like, leathery, the largest species known; brownish-green above, smooth and even; intensely black below with crowded, short fibrils, attached only at one point.

Fruiting organs (*apothecia*).—Orbicular, convex, attached only at the centre, the disk ridged concentrically.

Name.—Named in honour of the great botanist Dillenius.

Umbilicaria Muhlenbergii, (Ach.) Tuckerm.—See Colour Plate XI.

Habit and habitat.—On rocks.

Vegetative organs (*thallus*).—Large, leathery to rigid, irregularly pitted; olive-brown above, darker below.

Fruiting organs (*apothecia*).—Oblong and appressed, passing into irregular, often star-like plaited clusters without a common margin.

Name.—The specific name was given in honour of a Henry H. Muhlenberg.

Genus PELTIGERA, (Willd.) Fée.

The Crescent-shield Lichen. The vegetative portion (*thallus*) of the **Genus Peltigera** is leafy and often large; it is veiny and rough, hairy beneath; the algal layer is blue-green, excepting in two species (*venosa* and *aphthosa*).

85

The generic name *Peltigera* from the Latin *pelta*, a shield, and *gerere*, to carry, refers to the fruits which are shield-shaped with a more or less scalloped border; they are borne close to the upper surface of the thallus, usually some distance back from the margin but occasionally on the margin.

The spores are long and narrow, four- to many-celled, at length colourless. It is a small genus of mostly cooler regions.

The Dog Peltigera, *Peltigera canina*, (L.) Hoffm.—See Colour Plate VII.

Habit and habitat. This lichen grows in extensive patches on logs or on the ground.

Vegetative organ (*thallus*).—Large greenish-gray, ashy, or brownish: membranaceous, round-lobed; furrowed and downy on the upper surface: whitish beneath with light-coloured veins and hairs, sometimes becoming dark.

Fruiting disks (*apothecia*).—Reddish-brown; of large size; rounded, becoming semi-revolute and vertical. Supposed to resemble dogs' teeth and for this reason, on the supposition that "Like cures like," used as a remedy for hydrophobia.

Name.—The specific name *canina* from the Latin *canis*, a dog.

Spores.—Somewhat needle-shaped; four- to eight-celled.

Peltigera aphthosa, (L.) Hoffm. and **P. polydactyla,** (Neck.) Hoffm., are quite similar in general appearance to *P. canina*, (L.) Hoffm. *P. aphthosa* however, has the thallus smooth above, more or less sprinkled over with brown warts, and contains green algæ, not blue-green as in the two following species. *P. polydactyla* differs from *canina* in being smooth above and nearly naked beneath and conspicuously reticulated with brown veins.

Genus STICTA (Schreb.) Fr.

The thallus is leaf-like, variously lobed but with the lobes usually wide, rounded, or elongated. The under surface is sometimes smooth but is commonly covered with short, soft hairs (*villous*), and dotted with little cups or rounded heaps (*cyphels*). A cross-section of this lichen shows that the irregular, coloured zone (*gonimous layer*) is composed of either green cells (*gonidia*) or bluish-green cells (*gonimia*).

The fruiting organs (*apothecia*) are shield-like (*scutellæform*), elevated, and near the margin of the thallus.

86

PARMELIA PHYSODES, (L.) Ach., variety *vittata*

. . Lightly attached to its host—reddish-brown fruiting disks, large and shield-shaped with entire margins

The generic name *Sticta* from the Greek στικτὸς, dappled, refers to the strikingly spotted appearance of some species.

The spores are spindle or needle-shaped with 2 to 4 cross-walls; they are reddish or colourless; they vary but slightly in the different species.

Sticta pulmonaria (L.), Ach.—See Colour Plate VII; also Plate VII.

Habit and habitat.—On rocks and trees.

Vegetative organs (thallus). — Leaf-like, leathery; tawny or olive, loosely attached to the surface on which it grows, lobes large, entire, with rounded sinuses; upper surface netted and deeply pitted; under surface pale to white with rounded prominences outlined with slender hairs. Often bordered with little white grains (*soredia*).

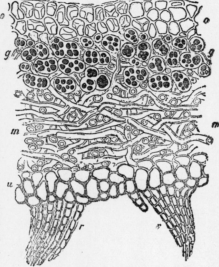

Stictina fuliginosa. (*o*) Upper cortex; (*u*) lower cortex; (*r*) rhizoids; (*m*) pith layer; (*g*) gonidial layer.

Fruiting organs (apothecia).—Not very common sessile on the margin of the lobes.

Name.—The specific name *pulmonaria*, lung, refers to the resemblance the under surface has to the surface of a lung.

Sticta amplissima, (Scop.) Mass.—See Colour Plate VII.

Habit and habitat.—On fallen trunks and trees.

Vegetative organs (thallus). Extending over quite large areas, in an ever-widening circle appressed to the surface on which it grows; leathery, smooth, becoming wrinkled with age; ashen-green above; tawny, and covered with short, soft hairs (*villous*) beneath; the lobes elongated, wide, usually compacted, or narrow and repeatedly lobed.

Fruiting organs (apothecia). — Scattered, sometimes quite large, the disk chestnut; the margin entire and inflexed.

Name.—The specific name *amplissima*, the Latin for "very extensive," refers to its habit of growth.

87

Genus STEREOCAULON, Schreb.

The vegetative organ or thallus is two-fold, consisting oᴜ a scale-like (*squamulose*) or granulose, horizontal growth which usually disappears, and a vertical growth which becomes shrub-like, with fruit-bearing branches (*podetia*). The podetia are solid and clothed more or less with a white powder (*soredia*) and with granules (*phyllocladia*) which become scale-like or pass into coral-like branchlets.

The fruiting organs (*apothecia*) are at first little disks soon becoming convex; solid, terminal, or lateral; dark-brown, or black.

The generic name *Stereocaulon* is compounded of the Greek στερεὸς, solid, and καυλὸς, a stalk.

When dry these lichens are very brittle, but when moist they may be handled freely.

Stereocaulon paschale, (L.)—See Plate VIII.

Habitat.—On rocks.

Vegetative organs (*thallus*).—Primary, usually wanting. Secondary, growing in round thick mats; podetia long and slender, much branched and covered with scale-like (*squamulose*), crenate, dark-gray granules and inconspicuous cottony fibres.

Fruiting organs (*apothecia*).—At or near the apicus of the podetia, small, with disk convex dark-brown.

Name.—The specific name *paschale* is the Latin for *"Passover."* Its significance is not evident.

NOTE:—*S. paschale* is closely related to *S. tomentosum* which is as its name implies conspicuously covered with cottony fibres.

Genus CLADONIA, Hoffm.

The horizontal thallus of the **Genus Cladonia** is scale-like, rarely granulose; and may or may not persist.

The fruiting branches (*podetia*) are hollow, sometimes opening to the exterior; leathery, cup-shaped, or funnel-shaped; sometimes shrub-like, and very much branched; rarely club-shaped.

The fruiting organs (*apothecia*) are usually little heads (*cephaloid*) hollow within, they are variously coloured, but never black. The spores are ovoid-oblong; simple; colourless.

The generic name *Cladonia* from the Greek, κλάδος, a branch,

88

was given by Georg Franz Hoffman to describe the characteristic habit of growth.

Brown-fruited Cup Cladonia, *Cladonia pyxidata* (L.) Fr.— See Colour Plate XII.

Habit and habitat.—On stumps and on the earth.

Vegetative organs (*thallus*).—Primary, thallus scale-like and variously lobed. Fruit-bearing branches (*podetia*) hollow, 5 to 25 mm. tall, top-shaped, short-stalked, granulose, warty or scurfy; margin spreading, bearing sessile or stalked apothecia.

Fruiting organs (*apothecia*).—Brown.

Name.—The specific name *pyxidata*, suggested by the podetia, is derived from the Greek πυξίς, a small box.

The Fringed Cladonia, *Cladonia fimbriata*, (L.) Fr.—See Plate IX.

Habitat.—Earth, stumps, etc.

Vegetative organs (*thallus*).—The primary commonly persistent as little scales variously incised on the margin, sea-green above, olive to white or dusky below; often powdery (*sorediate*).

Fruiting organs (*apothecia*).—Brown, sometimes on tooth-like projections of the goblet-shaped podetia.

Fruit-bearing branches (*podetia*).—Hollow, 1 to 3 cm. tall, goblet-shaped, rather long-stalked and slender; the margin erect, often with tooth-like projections sometimes bearing fruits (*apothecia*); surface (*cortex*) disintegrating into a fine white powder.

Name.—The specific name *fimbriata*, the Latin for "fringed," refers to the margin of the goblet-shaped branches. The forms of *Cladonia fimbriata* are extremely varied and difficult to determine. Dr. Wainio recognises sixteen varieties and a large number of sub-varieties, twelve varieties are well known in North America.

The Scarlet-crested Cladonia, *Cladonia cristatella,* Tuckerm.—See Colour Plate XII.

Habit and habitat.—Dead wood, etc.

Vegetative organs (*thallus*).—Coral-like (*cladoniæform*); fruiting branches (podetia) hollow, cylindrical, sometimes branched, 2 to 4 mm. tall; smooth or with the surface wrinkled.

Fruiting organs (*apothecia*).—Scarlet knobs at the tips of the fruiting branches.

Name.—The specific name *cristatella*, suggested by the bright fruits, is derived from the Latin *crista*, a crest.

Reindeer Lichen, *Cladonia rangiferina*, (L.) Hoffm.—See Colour Plate VIII.

Habit and habitat.—On earth often covering extensive areas.

Vegetative organs (thallus).—Shrubby (*fruticulose*). Fruiting branches (*podetia*) 4 to 10 cm. tall, branches cylindrical and hollow, 5 to 1.5 mm. thick, the divisions mostly wide-spreading; the sterile tips curved and drooping; without a distinct outer layer (*ecorticate*), the surface fibrous sometimes mealy or warty; ashy-white or tinged with greenish straw-colour.

Fruiting organs (apothecia).—Tiny brown knobs on the tips of the fruiting branches.

Name.—"Reindeer lichen" because reindeer feed upon it in winter.

The Cornucopia Cladonia, Red-fruited Cup Cladonia, *Cladonia cornucopioides*, (L.) Fr.

Habit and habitat.—On the earth.

Vegetative organs (thallus).—Branching like coral *cladoniæ-form*); fruiting branches (*podetia*) hollow, elongated-top-shaped, about 15 to 35 mm. tall; smooth, becoming warty.

Fruiting organs (apothecia).—Scarlet knobs on the tips of the fruiting branches.

Name.—The specific name *cornucopioides*, suggested by the podetia, is compounded of three Latin words: *cornu*, a horn, *copia*, plenty, and *oid*, like.

PARMELIA PERLATA, (L.) Ach

PART THREE
HEPATICS

LIVERWORTS OR HEPATICS

HEPATICÆ

Liverworts are as a rule found only in damp shady places, and it is not their habit to occupy very large areas of ground. With but few exceptions the plant lies close to the object upon which it grows holding to it by short hair-like cells *(rhizoids)*.

Excepting the fruiting portion, the liverwort plant (the vegetative body) is either ribbon-like *(thalloid)*, or a stem with scale-like leaves *(foliose)*; the greater number of liverworts are therefore distinguished as thalloid and foliose.

RIBBON-LIKE OR THALLOID HEPATICS

Genus MARCHANTIA, (L.)

Marchantia polymorpha (See Colour Plate XIII) is a good example of a thalloid form, and from it one may learn, without a microscope, the principal parts.

Vertical section through
a pore.

Gemma.

Surface view
showing pore.

Marchantia polymorpha

The plant itself lies flat upon the earth and has **a** distinct upper and lower tissue.

The lower tissue develops short root-like hairs which serve to anchor the plant.

The upper tissue appears as if marked off into small rhomboidal spaces in the centre of each of which a pore may be seen.

93

Little cups are often present on the upper surface, with green disks (gemmæ) in them.

Upright umbrella-like growths on which are borne the male and female organs are found also on the upper surface.

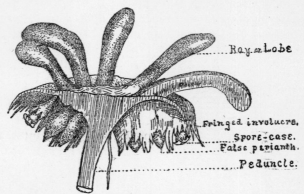

Marchantia polymorpha.   Vertical section of female receptacle.

The male peduncle is capped with a flat, slightly lobed receptacle.   The female peduncle is capped with a receptacle bordered with deep finger-like lobes.

The male organs (*antheridia*) are developed in the upper surface of the scalloped receptacle.

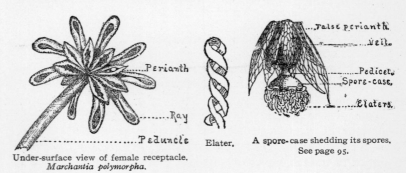

Under-surface view of female receptacle.
Marchantia polymorpha.

Elater.

A spore-case shedding its spores.
See page 95.

The female organs (*archegonia*) are developed on **the under** surface of the receptacle bearing the finger-like lobes.

Spore-cases filled with spores and spirally twisted threads (*elaters*) later occupy the place of the archegonia between the long lobes.

94

A veil (*calyptra*) surrounds the spore-case.

A false perianth surrounds the veil.

A fringed covering (*involucre*) encloses all the spore-cases between two lobes. When the spore-case is mature, it bursts irregularly for the scattering of the spores.

The spore germinates to form one cell or a small group of cells (*protonema*) from which later will be developed the plant already described.

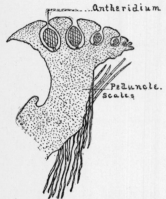

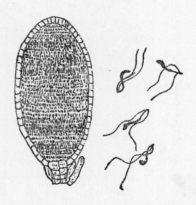

Marchantia polymorpha. Vertical section of male receptacle. See page 94.

Marchantia polymorpha. Vertical section of Antheridium from male receptacle. Sperm cells at the right.

Marchantia polymorpha, (L.)

Habit and habitat.—Along wet banks, in bogs, beside streams, about green-houses, and on damp ashes on the shady side of houses.

Name.—The generic name *Marchantia* was given by the son in honour of his father, Nicholas Marchant, a French botanist who died in 1678. The specific name *polymorpha* is compounded of the Greek, πολὺς, many, and μορφή, form.

Plant (gametophyte).—Peculiar dull-green, with broad ribbon-shaped thallus generally once or twice forked. Costa or mid-vein broad. Upper surface divided off into rhomboidal spaces *(areolæ).* One stoma or pore in the centre of each rhomboidal space. Gemmæ cups, saucer-shaped with toothed margins, are often present.

95

Section of plant.—(1) Shows well-marked epidermis.

(2) Shows that each pore leads into an air-chamber.

(3) That the side walls of each air-chamber support the epidermis as a roof.

(4) That cells containing chlorophyll spring up from the floor of each chamber. These cells assimilate gases which enter the air-chamber through the pores, they also take in oxygen gas and give out carbon-dioxide gas. The floor-cells transmit or store up food.

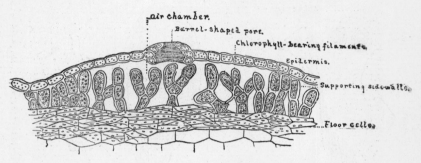

Marchantia polymorpha. Vertical section through the thallus at a point where a pore occurs.

Habit of flowering.—Antheridia or male organs are imbedded in the upper surface of a shield-shaped, radially lobed disk supported by a peduncle and bearing scales on the under surface. This male receptacle (*androecium*) grows from the upper surface of the thallus. Archegonia or female organs are borne on the under side of a radially lobed disk supported upon a peduncle on the upper surface of the thallus. The lobes are finger-like, 8 to 11, usually curved downward.

Marchantia polymorpha. In ascending order the cuts show stages in the development of an antheridium.

Section of male disk.—Shows antheridia concealed in depressions in the surface of the disk.

Male flowers (antheridia).—Oval upon a pedicel (*seta*). Section shows a wall and numerous cells containing spermatozoids, each with two fine cilia.

Section of female disk.—Shows archegonia on the under side of the disk.

96

SPOTTED LUNGWORT, *Slicta pulmonaria*, (L.) Ach.
. . "a sure cure for lung trouble"

Female flowers (archegonia).—Flask-shaped. Cuts 1, 2, 3, 4, 5, 6, 7, 8, show stages in development. *Section in early stage,* 3, shows a wall of cells; an egg-cell and canal-cell in the

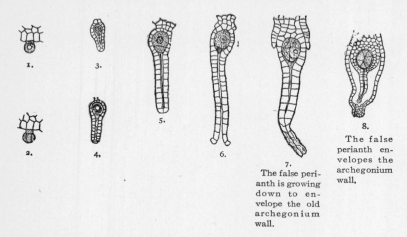

1.

2.

3.

4.

5.

6.

7.
The false peri-
anth is growing
down to en-
velope the old
archegonium
wall.

8.
The false
perianth en-
velopes the
archegonium
wall.

enlarged base of the flask ; **a** canal in the neck of the flask and the summit of the neck closed. *Section in a later stage,* 6, shows a wall of cells: the egg-cell rounded up; the canal-cell shrivelled; the canal open at the summit of the neck.

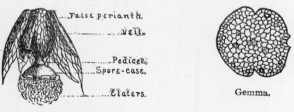

False perianth.
Veil.
Pedicel.
Spore-case.
Elaters.

Spore-case discharging spores.

Gemma.

Marchantia polymorpha.

Development of sporophyte.—A section, 7, of the archegonium after the spermatozoids have entered and fertilised the egg-cell shows the wall of the enlarged portion of the flask surrounded by an involucre, made up of segments, awl-pointed and finely cut, into an irregular fringe often reddish in colour; the egg-cell is divided into eight cells; the summit of the neck is shrivelled. Section later, 8, shows the eight cells multiplied to form an upper portion, the future spore-case and a lower portion, the future foot and pedicel.

Spore-case.—At maturity is exserted, when it bursts somewhat irregularly to discharge its spores.

Spores.—Yellow, nearly smooth, mingled with twice-spiral elaters.

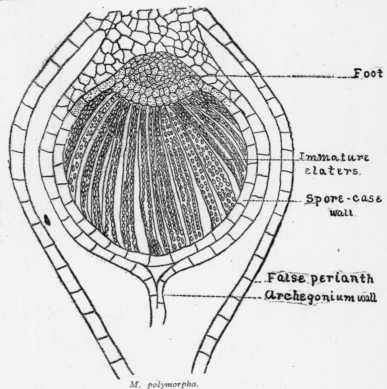

M. polymorpha.

Gemmæ.—Receptacles bowl-shaped, on the upper-surface of the thallus, and open at the top. Gemmæ flat, upright cellular bodies with two indentations at the sides, the growing points. When gemmæ germinate, the side toward the light develops pores (stomata) for the admission of gases and for the egress of gases and water vapour. If germination takes place on land, the stomata are on the upper surface, but if in water lighted from below, then they are on the under surface. Gemmæ are a means of reproducing plants.

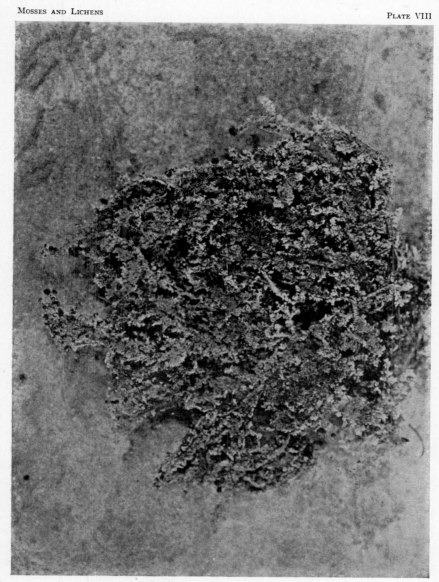

STEREOCAULON PASCHALE, L.
A gray lichen with black fruits

LEAFY HEPATICS, SCALE MOSSES, OR FOLIOSE HEPATICS

Porella platyphylla (See Colour Plate XIV), is a good example of the foliose or leafy hepatics and from a study of it one may become familiar with the conspicuous parts of this class of mosses.

Margins irregular.

Margin inrolled.
Leafy hepatics.

Margin toothed.

The plants grow flat upon the bark of living trees. Each plant consists of a creeping stem, with side branches which may in turn bear branches.

The principal leaves are set at right angles to the stem and their sides overlap so as to conceal the stems.

They are two-lobed with one lobe above the stem and one below.

A third row of leaves grows on the underside of the stem.

Two leaves showing lobe
and lobule.

Creeping stem and branch.

Under view of stem showing
third row of leaves.
Porella platyphylla.

In some leafy hepatics, the tips of the leaves overlap the base of the leaf in front; in others the tips of the leaves are underneath the bases of the leaves in front.

The margins of the leaves of different species vary, they are recurved, toothed, fringed, inrolled, or entire.

The apex may be blunt or pointed or of many other designs.

99

The male organs (*antheridia*) are borne in the axils of the leaves of modified branches.

The female organs (*archegonia*) are on the terminal branches.

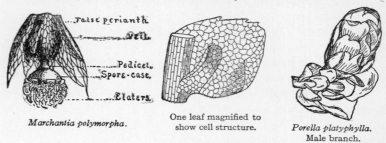

Marchantia polymorpha.

One leaf magnified to show cell structure.

Porella platyphylla.
Male branch.

The spore-cases with their enveloping parts are terminal on the branches; although they appear often to be on the sides because a side branch has grown in the same direction and beyond the main stem.

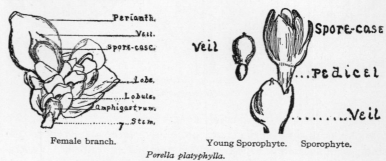

Female branch.

Young Sporophyte.   Sporophyte.

Porella platyphylla.

Beginning with the spore-case as a centre, and observing the parts in order outward, a veil (*calyptra*) may be found, and then a perianth, and outside of all, several slightly modified leaves.

Genus PORELLA, (L.)

The **Genus Porella** is composed of large plants, dark-green to yellowish-brown, usually 2 to 3 times feather-branched.

The lobes of the leaves are very deeply two-parted; the dorsal large, and roundish egg-shaped, usually entire, the ventral lobes smaller, sometimes nearly separate from the dorsal, varying in different species from ovate to lanceolate; underleaves large, entire or toothed.

100

The antheridia are spherical, in the axils of overlapping leaves which form short rigid branches.

The perianth is oval to obovate, flattened at the mouth, which is fringed, toothed or entire. The spore-case is spherical to ovoid-oblong on a short stalk (*seta*) splitting nearly to the base into four parts. The spores are covered with spines. The elaters are once to thrice spiral.

The generic name is a diminutive of the Latin *porus*, a pore. Its significance is not evident.

Porella platyphylla, (L.) Lindle. *Plant (gametophyte).*—Stems 2 or 3 inches long, prostrate, rigid with the tips bent upward; 1 to 3 times regularly or irregularly pinnate; root-hairs in tufts at the base of the under-leaves.

View of upper surface of stem with two leaves.

Under view of stem.
Porella platyphylla.

Two leaves showing lobe and lobule

Leaves.—Deeply two-parted, dorsal lobes overlapping in two rows so as to conceal the stem, obliquely placed relatively to the stem, oval to oblong, apex obtuse, toothed or entire. Ventral lobes oval to oblong obtuse, diagonally pressed to the surface of the upper lobes; margins recurved and entire or with a single tooth at the base; under leaves tongue-shaped, parallel with the stem, margins recurved, decurrent, entire, or sparingly toothed at the base.

Name.—The specific name *platyphylla* from the Greek πλάτυς, flat, and φύλλον, a leaf, describes the prostrate habit of the plant.

Perianth.—Ovate, inflated, narrowed above, margin toothed with a notch on one side.

Veil (calyptra).—Persistent, globose, splitting above.

Spore-case.—Pale yellow-brown on a short pedicel, splitting into four, often irregular valves; elaters bi-spiral.

Spores.—More or less spiny.

101

Habit of flowering.—Male flowers (*antheridia*) and female flowers (*archegonia*) on separate plants (*dioicous*).

Antheridia.—Spherical, short-stalked, single in the axils of two-lobed, pouch-shaped leaves which lie opposite on the stem. These antheridial leaves are united by their margins to the under leaves, and with them form short oval branchlets on the sides of the main branches.

Archegonia. — Numerous, terminal on very short lateral branches.

Genus FRULLANIA, Raddi

The plants are usually in shades of red or brown or even black, although sometimes green. They grow in delicate traceries over the bark of trees or rocks.

 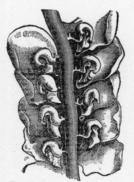

F. ecklonii. A lobule separated from its lobe. A tiny stylus is present at the point where the lobule is attached to the main stem.

F. ecklonii. Under view of a portion of the stem; with eight inflated lobules, each on its lobe, the amphigastra have been removed.

F. complanata. Under view of stem showing 3 cup-like lobules each lying on its lobe: two notched amphigastra are on the stem.

The stems are opaque and branched, each branch arising from the axil of a stem-leaf from which it is always free.

The upper leaves are alternate and are inserted somewhat obliquely. They are two-lobed, one lobe folded to lie over the other. The upper and larger is known as the *lobe* and the lower and smaller as the *lobule*.

The lobule, is an inflated water-sac, in shape resembling a helmet or hood or cylinder and often has at the base a tiny process (*stylus*).

102

PLATE IX

THE FRINGED CLADONIA, *Cladonia fimbriata*, (L.) *Fr.*

The under leaves or stipules (*amphigastra*) are strongly two-cleft and have often tufts of rootlets at their bases.

The male flowers (*antheridia*) are found on short branches either on the same plant with the female flowers (*archegonia*) or on separate plants.

The envelope of the flower (*perianth*) is free and exserted from the leaves. It is 3- to 4-angled and tipped with a short tubular beak (*mucronate*). The veil (*calyptra*) is free and included

Perianth with beak.

Cross-section
of perianth.

The involucre opened
out.

Amphigastra with
rootlets.

F. ecklonii.

in the perianth. The spore-case is somewhat spherical on a stout pedicel 2 to 3 times longer than the perianth. It opens by four valves to eject its spores. There are about 150 species in all, which are well represented in both temperate and tropical zones; about twenty are found in North America.

The generic name *Frullania* was given in honour of Signor Leonardo Frullani, an Italian minister of state.

Frullania Eboracensis, Gottsche.— See Colour Plate XIV.

Transverse
section of the
perianth.

Upper view of
stem with two
leaves.

F. eboracencis.

This dainty hepatic is usually found in some shade of green or red, forming delicate traceries on the bark of trees. It is particularly beautiful on the smooth bark of the yellow birches in the North woods.

The leaves lap as shingles (*imbricate*). The lobule is hood-like (*galeate*), bluntly terminating at the base. The perianth is somewhat compressed with a short, broad beak.

Genus PTILIDIUM, Nees

The species of the **Genus Ptilidium** grow usually in dense and brownish mats, the stems prostrate or ascending, 1 to 2 pinnate or irregularly and sparingly branched, without whip-like branches, the branches are lateral; root-hairs are few and short.

The leaves are obliquely inserted, variously cut or fringed, a character which suggested the name *Ptilidium*, derived from the Greek πτίλον, down, the dorsal segment larger and with its tip lying over the base of the leaf next above it (*incubus*), under-leaves (*amphigastra*) similar but much smaller.

Male flowers (*antheridia*) short-stalked in the axils of more closely imbricate leaves.

Female flowers (*archegonia*) terminal, sometimes apparently lateral because a side branch has grown on beyond the stem which bears it. Bracts commonly two pairs, similar to the leaves.

Perianth free, several times longer than the bracts, cylindrical egg-shaped with constricted mouth.

Veil (*calyptra*) free.

Spore-case egg-shaped on a moderately long stalk (*seta*) dehiscing to the base by four rather rigid valves; spores dotted.

Elaters two to three spiral.

There are about eight species.

Ptilidium ciliare, Nees.—See Colour Plate XIV.

Habit and Habitat.—On fallen logs growing in loosely entangled purple, brown, or dark-green tufts.

Upper view of stem.

Under view of stem to show lobule.

Lobule enlarged to show cell-structure.

P. Ciliare.

Name.—The specific name *ciliare*, from the Latin *cilia*, lash, refers to the fine hairs on the margins of the leaves.

Plants (*gametopythe*).—The plants have stems 1 to $1\frac{1}{2}$ inches long, mostly erect; root hairs few at the base. Branches short, once or twice pinnate.

Leaves.—Crowded, hiding the stem, roundish; lobes lance-shaped, folded toward each other, the front lobe convex and parted half-way down, the back lobe similar, but much smaller; the margins all divided into numerous long hair-like teeth. Under leaves (*amphigastra*) pressed to the stem, rectangular, nearly as large as the upper, four- to five-lobed with marginal teeth. Leaf-cells small, roundish, with thick walls.

Habit of flowering.—Male and female flowers on separate plants, dioicous.

Perianth.—Pear-shaped, pale, dull yellow, mouth narrow, and margined with small short teeth. The bracts at the base un-equally four-lobed with teeth like the leaves.

Spore-case.—Nearly spherical.

Genus BAZZANIA, Gr. and Benn.

The vegetative part of these plants grows in large mats, bright or dark green; the branching stems are 2 to 4 inches long, mostly creeping and bearing many long whip-like shoots with minute leaves and few whitish root-hairs.

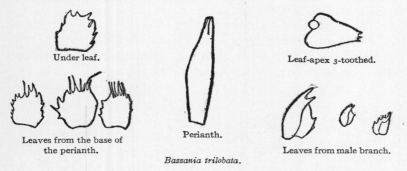

Under leaf.

Leaf-apex 3-toothed.

Leaves from the base of the perianth.

Perianth.

Leaves from male branch.

Bazzania trilobata.

The leaves are egg-shaped, over-lapping and embracing the stem half-way around, they are narrowed to the apex which is bluntly three-to five-toothed. The leaf-cells are six-sided and opaque. The male and female flowers are on separate plants (*dioicous*). The perianth is white and tubular with slight folds in the wall and splits open at one side, the leaves at the base (*bracts*) are very small, scale-like and slightly toothed.

The genus *Bazzania* may be easily distinguished from all other genera by the leaves which are dark green, three-toothed and have the anterior margin of each leaf lapping the posterior margin of the leaf in front.

The genus was named for M. Bazzani, an Italian professor of anatomy.

Bazzania trilobata, L.—See Plate X.

Habit and habitat.—On damp shady banks, forming extensive cushions.

Name.—The specific name *trilobata* is compounded of *tres* (*tri-*), three, and *lobatus*, lobed, referring to the apex of the leaf.

Plants (*gametophyte*).—Shining olive-green; stems simple or once- or twice-forked, 3 to 5 inches long; procumbent or creeping, rootlets few, beset on the under side with minute leafy scales; and numerous thread-like whips (*flagellæ*) about an inch long.

| Stem with sporophyte, the long slender pedicel rising from the perianth. | View of under side of stem to show the third row of leaves. | Stem with leaf enlarged to show cell-structure. | Under leaf. | The tip of the perianth. |

Bazzania trilobata

Leaves.—Olive-green, the upper about $1\frac{1}{2}$ times longer than broad and placed at right angles to the stem in two rows, the sides of the leaves overlapping like shingles, the anterior margin of one leaf overlapping the posterior margin of the leaf in front, apex with three acute teeth, texture firm; the under leaves (*amphigastra*) broad, four-sided, apex three- to five-toothed.

Habit of flowering.—Female flowers on short branches on separate plants. Male flower-clusters minute aments, with folded and toothed bracts, antheridia solitary.

Perianth.—Highly exserted, nearly white, oblong, narrower upwards; mouth slit on one side and with a few teeth. Bracts at the base oval, fringed at the apex and delicate in texture.

Spore-case.—Dark shining-brown, ovate, on a long, slender, white pedicel, the valves slit to the base to form a Roman cross; elaters twice spiral.

Plate X

BAZZANIA TRILOBATA, L.

PART FOUR

MOSSES

MOSSES

PEAT-MOSSES

Genus SPHAGNUM, Dill.

THE peat- or bog-mosses are usually of large size, green or gray, dark-red, yellow, or purple, growing over extensive areas in the wet places of lowlands or mountain summits. They are attractive both to travellers and to botanists and are always a source of wonder on account of their habit of changing colour with every change in the humidity of the air. The individual plants are so perfectly preserved when carefully pressed that they are attractive to the collector, whether artist or botanist. Nature employs these mosses to redeem shallow waters for the use of higher plants. The geologist solves many problems by reading their life-history. The economist uses them for fuel in localities where other vegetation is scanty, and finds them useful packing for plants on account of their ability to hold moisture.

The great Linnæus calls them "flowers of Lapland" and tells us that the Lapland mothers use them for their children's cradles.

THE METHOD BY WHICH PEAT-MOSSES ENCROACH UPON WATER TO FORM LAND

The bog-moss plays an important part in the formation of peat. In a peat-moor the plants on the surface are the tips and branches of the very same plants whose under parts long ago died away.

When a peat-moss spore germinates in water, a meshwork of fine thread-like strands is formed, called the protonema; upon this protonema bud-like growths occur which in later stages are known as the peat-moss plants. These plants very soon lose any root-like growth which they may have possessed, and continue to grow, year after year, from the apex of the stem or from lateral branches just below the apex of the stem.

109

As the floating plants multiply along the borders of a body of water, extending outward over the water as an anchored raft, the immersed dead parts of the moss are continually dropping disintegrated plant-tissue and so build soil from the bottom upward. The accumulation of vegetable matter attached to the living and floating plants on the under side causes the raft to sink gradually ; so gradually that the new growth always rests just at the surface of the water until the depth of the moss-raft is sufficient to permit it to reach the bottom. In time, the weight of the superimposed mass, together with chemical changes which take place in the dead plant-tissue, convert the moss plants into more or less compact peat.

Ideal section of pond showing bog-moss growing outward from the shore.

Ideal section of old pond showing bog-moss growing on the surface of the water and forming a "quaking-bog."

Thus a border of peat-moss soil is built around the shore; and as new plants are continually growing on the water-line, forming new rafts which in turn sink and make new moss-soil, the body of water becomes gradually less until finally it disappears altogether. During this process of marsh building a "quaking bog" occurs, when the moss covers the whole surface of the water but has not yet filled up the underlying water. Both men and animals, while endeavouring to cross a "quaking bog," have sunk through the overlying moss to be entombed in the underlying peat; and, owing to the antiseptic quality of the peat, the bodies have been kept in a state of preservation for hundreds of years.

ICELAND MOSS, *Cetraria Islandica*, (L.) Ach.

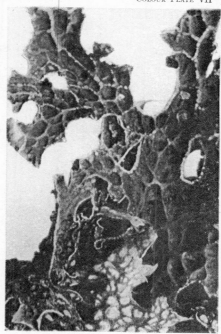

STICTA PULMONARIA, Ach.
"A cure for lung trouble"

STICTA AMPLISSIMA, (Scop.) Mass.
Fruits in flattened coloured disks

THE DOG PELTIGERA.
Peltigera canina, (L.) Hoffm.
"A cure for hydrophobia"

The building of bog-mosses is not confined to depressions filled with water. Strange as it may seem, it is true, that they can climb the slopes of the surrounding shore and extend the marsh up a hill. The hill-climbing character of the moss is due to its habit of absorbing water like a sponge. If one recall the moss habit of making the new growth upon the dead and water-soaked remains of the old plants, he will readily understand that it is as simple for the moss plants to grow up a slope, if it is not too steep, as it is for them to grow on a level.

The value of the bog-mosses as peat producers in the belt over which the great continental glacier swept is greater than that of any water-loving plant. It will be remembered that the great glacier of the Ice Age moved in North America from the northwest in a southeasterly direction as far down as the northern part of New Jersey, and as the climate changed and the great ice sheet receded by melting backwards to its source, it left in its wake numerous small lakes, ranging from a few feet to several miles in diameter. It is in these lakes, when not over a mile in width, that the peat-mosses have found most favourable quarters for their work, for the smaller sheets of water are less liable to be lashed into waves by the wind.

Examples of this method of marsh building are found all over the world. Professor H. W. Brewer reports finding peat-mosses building marshes on Lassen's Peak, California, at an altitude of 5,000 feet. He found *Sphagnum fimbriatum* on the Sierra Nevada Chain, California, at an altitude of 11,000 feet; and *Sphagnum mendocinum* forming swamps near King River, California, at an altitude of from 800 to 900 feet. Examples may be found on the Palisades of the Hudson and on the summits of Mount Marcy and the Shawangunk Mountains in New York, or on the Pocono Mountains, Pennsylvania.

In the pass between Mount Marcy and the highest point in New York State, and Mount Skylight, near the camp and about half a mile from the summits of the mountains, lies "Lake Tear of the Clouds." To-day it is a mere bog-hole, neither large nor deep, but when named by Verplanck Colvin not very many years ago, its clear waters nestling in a rocky basin suggested to him the pretty name. At that time a fringe of peat-moss wreathed its shores and was reflected from it as from a mirror. To-day it is surrounded by boggy shores and is dotted with little islands of similar character; its bottom is soft mud made of decayed vegetable matter. There is no visible inlet that could bring in sediment; it is fed only by the slight drainage of rain and melting ice under the rocks on the adjacent mountain sides, and yet it is never dry.

There are many places all through the Adirondacks which illustrate the same thing in different stages of completion—Connery Pond, Mud Pond, Calamity Pond, Hidden Swamp and Averyville Swamp are examples, all within walking distance of Lake Placid, New York.

Mr. Charles H. Peck tells of an example within fifteen miles of Albany. He says:

"A marsh covered with *Sphagnum*, in my boyhood days, was so soft and yielding that it seemed dangerous to go over some places. It was then productive of cranberries in nearly all parts. Now it is firm in nearly all parts. The cranberry vines have almost disappeared and shrubs and young trees have come up. It is greatly changed. The same sluggish stream flows through the centre; nothing has been done toward draining it, but the mosses, growing at their summits and decaying at their base, have gradually made more dense the soft ooze beneath, till now there is sufficient soil to support sedges, marsh-shrubs and even young trees of tamarack, balsam, and spruce."

The climbing bogs may be found on the east shores of Maine, near the Bay of Fundy, in New Hampshire, Michigan, and Minnesota. They are rare in the United States on account of the short hot summers, and for the same reason, when they do occur, they do not climb declivities of more than 2°. In northern Europe, on the other hand, they climb declivities of 5° and a bog often rises a score of feet above the water in which it stands.

Peat bogs represent the accumulated remains of thousands of generations of plants, among which were the *Sphagnum* mosses. There is conclusive evidence that the *Sphagnum* mosses are an important constituent of peat-bogs now forming; and there is every reason to believe that in ages gone by they served as soil-makers for more complex peat-producing plants. Extensive peat-bogs occur in the northern parts of the world, New England, Ireland, India, and northern Europe, where the peat is used as fuel to a limited extent.

Owing to a peculiar odour given off from burning peat, as well as to other contingencies, it is not popular as a fuel. Its great value lies in the fact that, when bogs are properly drained, they afford the most desirable land for farming purposes. One-fifth of the most fertile fields in Great Britain and Ireland have been won from bog districts by draining. During the time of the Saxon kingdoms, England was to a great extent occupied by morasses which have since been cleared away. Sites of ancient bogs in northern Germany and in the valley of the River Po, Italy, are indicated by the great and persistent fertility of the soil. Probably not far from one-twentieth of the tillable land in Europe was inundated and unfit for agriculture in the eighth century.

Cross section of stem.

Sphagnum acutifolium, var. *rubellum*.
A bit of stem with three stem-leaves and a fascicle of three branches, one appressed and two spreading.

A bit of stem with one stem-leaf and a fascicle of five branches, two appressed and three spreading.
Sphagnum cymbifolium.

(Genus SPHAGNUM)

Peat-mosses are common, growing in more or less compact green or purple patches on the surface of bogs, or along mountain springs and rivulets, or even floating on water. The genus is an easy one to recognise and the plants form an attractive feature of one's walk through woods or over fen-land.

The name *Sphagnum* (Greek σφάγνος) was used by the ancient botanists Theophrastus, Dioscorides, and Pliny to indicate certain non-flowering plants. The name was restricted to a more limited use in 1719 by Johann Dillenius, a German, who was the first professor of botany at Oxford.

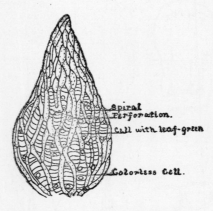

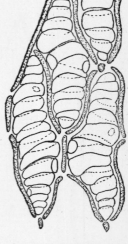

Spiral Perforation.

Cell with leaf-green

Colorless Cell.

Leaf magnified to show large cells with perforations and spiral thickenings and small cells with leaf-green grains.
Sphagnum cymbifolium.

Surface view of leaf cells.

The plants are soft and weak-stemmed mosses, generally of large size, white or yellow, light green or sometimes red. The stems appear almost simple with clusters of branches at the summit and on the sides; the branches at the summit are grouped to form a dense rosette (*capitulum*), while each side cluster (*fascicle*) consists of from 2 to 7 or more branches, some spreading and some appressed to the stem. A cross section of the stem shows three zones of cells—the outer (*cortex*) of large loose cells, the central of pithy cells and the intermediate of woody cells.

The leaves are translucent, without veins, and consist of a single layer of two kinds of cells: (1) Large colourless and transparent cells (*utricles*), generally perforated and lined with

114

spiral or circular thickenings (fibrils) to secure them against collapse. They have lost the cell-contents which were present in a younger stage and are, when dry, filled with air. (2) Smaller cells (*ducts*), containing active cell-contents and leaf-green. They are narrowly linear and form a net of rhomboidal or hexagonal meshes around the large cells. The *stem-leaves* are distant, obliquely inserted, erect or bent downward, flat or concave, tongue-shaped, oval, inserted at the small

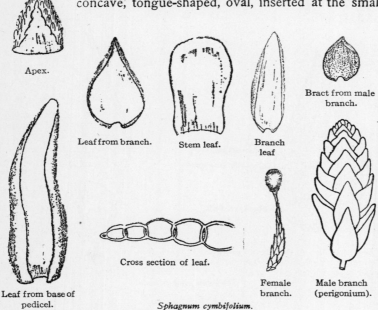

Apex.

Leaf from branch.

Stem leaf.

Branch leaf

Bract from male branch.

Cross section of leaf.

Leaf from base of pedicel.

Sphagnum cymbifolium.

Female branch.

Male branch (perigonium).

or large end generally obtuse. The *branch-leaves* are smaller, round, oval or lance-like, concave or rolled-up lengthwise. Each leaf apex overlaps the base of the next leaf above and every fifth leaf lies in a perpendicular line on the stem, directly over the first leaf counted, that is they are five ranked.

S. acutifolium, var. rubellum. Cross-section of leaf showing cells with cell contents and empty cells with perforations.

The veil (*calyptra*) is a ragged membrane left at the base of the spore-case as the latter grows.

The spore-cases are chestnut brown, globular, without teeth.

Normally they are in the crown (*capitulum*) of the plant, but by an elongation of an erect branch near the apex of the stem they are often left behind so as to appear to have grown from the side.

The pedicels are thick and stocky. [The *Sphagnum* pedicel (*pseudopodium*) does not have the same origin as the pedicel of other mosses].

The lids (*opercula*) are flattened in the form of an inverted saucer. These are normally cast off by the contraction of the spore-case wall. Sometimes a lid remains attached at one point and opens to permit spores to escape or closes to protect them. Sometimes, if wet, a lid does not fall, then the spores germinate within the spore-case and the growing embryos burst the spore-case and escape.

Sphagnum squarrosum. A plant with a sporophyte rising from the perichætial leaves at its summit; the slender pedicel bears a globular spore-case closed with a saucer-like lid and having a ragged veil at its base.

The spores are of two kinds—large four-angled spores (tetrahedral macrospores) and small many-angled spores (polyhedral microspores). The small spores are supposed to be the spores of a parasitic fungus which lives upon the developing spores of the moss. Two hundred and fifty-eight species in all are known, seventy-four being found in North America.

THE PALE TINT OF PEAT-MOSSES

The pale tint of peat-mosses is due to the structure of the leaves. When the moss is wet, the large cells are rendered more transparent and the colour of the small cells can be seen through them. When the moss is dry and the green cells are less evident, then it is paler green or even white.

THE METHOD BY WHICH PEAT-MOSSES ABSORB WATER

The tiny openings of the large cells communicate with similar openings in adjoining cells. When the atmosphere is dry, as has already been said, the large cells are filled with air; but as soon as the atmosphere is moist, the surrounding water rushes through the holes on one side of the large cells and the air is forced out through the holes on the opposite sides. When all the large cells are filled with water, the contents of the small cells can absorb through their thin walls the water from the adjoining large cells.

It may help one to comprehend the structure to imagine a number of thin, transparent-glass capsules of irregular shape, with spiral or circular thickenings of glass in their walls and tiny openings here and there. Imagine the capsules piled up with the openings of each capsule contiguous to the openings of adjoining capsules and all the spaces between filled with very small capsules containing a colourless jelly and green granules.

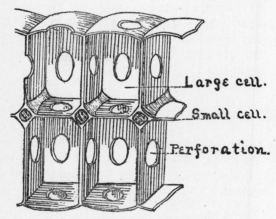

Diagram to show plan of cell-structure.

If the base of this imaginary pile be immersed in water, immediately the water will creep up through the whole system. This is in accordance with nature's law that water rises in fine hair-like tubes or crevices. To understand the process by which the water passes from a large cell to a small cell one must recall another of nature's laws, that whenever a non-crystallisable substance, as the cell-contents of the small cells, is separated by a membranous partition from a crystallisable liquid, as the water in the large cells, the crystallisable liquid will pass through the membranous wall into the non-crystallisable substance.

It is evident that one function of the large cells is to procure water for the small cells to work with; but since this same function would be performed as well if all the cells were filled

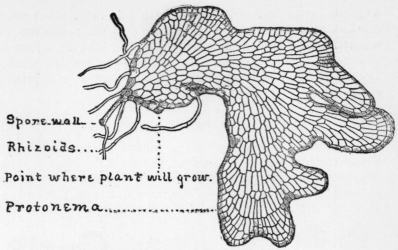

Spore wall
Rhizoids....
Point where plant will grow.
Protonema.

Protonema of *Sphagnum cymbifolium.* (See page 119.)

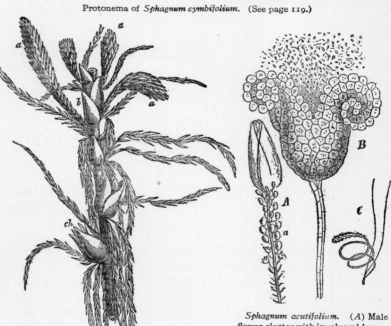

Sphagnum acutifolium. Stem of moss-plant with leafy branches ; (*ch*) involucral leaves of the female flower ; (*a*) involucral leaves of the male flowers; (*b*) stem leaves. (See pages 120 and 121.)

Sphagnum acutifolium. (*A*) Male flower-cluster with involucral leaves stripped off to show male flowers (*a*) antheridia. (*B*) Antheridium bursting and emitting antherozoids. (*C*) Coiled antherozoid with two lashes. (See pages 120 and 121.)

with non-crystallisable cell-contents as in other mosses, one must conclude that the large cells serve other purposes beside that of water carriers. Perhaps they are, when filled with air, a protection to the cells containing leaf-green, serving both as shields against excessive heat and light and as a barrier to excessive evaporation.

THE DEVELOPMENT OF ORGANS

Protonema.—The large spores germinate in water to form a thread-like protonema ; or, on land, to form a flat plate of cells, from which the moss-plant develops. Several stages from spore to adult plant are shown in diagrams 1, 2, 3, 4, 5, 6 and 7. (See also diagrams on pages 118 and 120.)

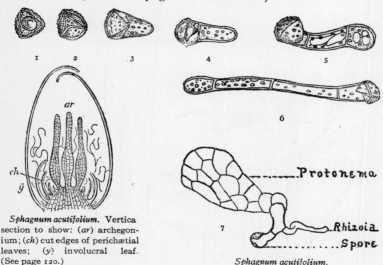

Sphagnum acutifolium. Vertical section to show: (*ar*) archegonium; (*ch*) cut edges of perichætial leaves; (*y*) involucral leaf. (See page 120.)

Sphagnum acutifolium.

Plant (*gametophyte*).—The cells of the protonema by division at one point form the plant—stem, leaves and rhizoids—then the protonema disappears. Upon the moss plant are developed the male flowers (*antheridia*) and the female flowers (*archegonia*). In *Sphagnum acutifolium* the male and female flowers mature in late autumn and in winter and may often be found by digging under the snow.

Antheridium.—An antheridium has its origin in a cell of the outer wall of a branch. This cell divides to make two, one of which divides to form a stem or pedicel, while the second divides to form the globular part of the antheridium. The mature antheridium bursts at the apex, the margins roll back and a cloud

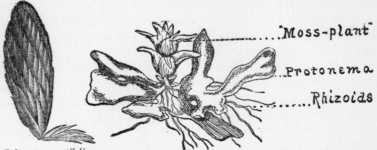

Sphagnum acutifolium. Male flower-cluster with sterile branch at base.

Moss plant on protonema of *Sphagnum acutifolium.*

of flattened membranous sacs (*vesicles*), each containing one spirally coiled antherosoid, are thrown out. The antherosoids are soon set free by the breaking down of the vesicle wall. Each antherosoid is a spirally coiled cell, club-shaped, with two vibratile lashes at the attenuated end.

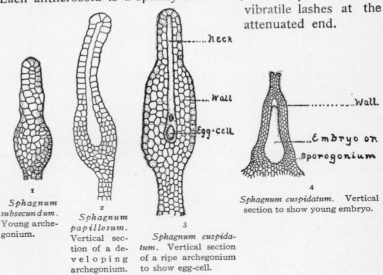

I
Sphagnum subsecundum. Young archegonium.

2
Sphagnum papillosum. Vertical section of a developing archegonium.

3
Sphagnum cuspidatum. Vertical section of a ripe archegonium to show egg-cell.

4
Sphagnum cuspidatum. Vertical section to show young embryo.

Archegonium.—The archegonium is developed by cell-division; it is similar to a tiny flask, at the base of which is an egg-cell (*ovum*) which, after fertilisation, is to become a spore-case (1, 2, 3).

120

Fertilisation occurs early in the spring, that is, sperm-cells (*antherosoids*) from antheridia, swim over in water to a mature egg-cell of an archegonium, coalesce with it and make possible the development of an embryo spore-case (4).

The Spore-case.—The first embryos may be found late in February. A study of their development shows that the fertilised egg-cell divides into four cells and then by repeated division of cells takes the form of the several diagrams in order, A, B, C, and D. The embryo which has been formed as a result of fertilisation is divided into two regions, the three upper segments with the

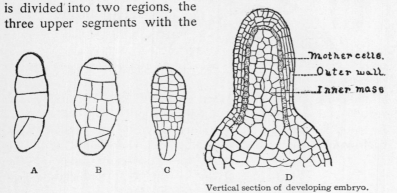

Vertical section of developing embryo.

Sphagnum acutifolium.

apical cell give rise to spores, while the lower segments with the basal cell form a "foot." The rudimentary spore-case is at first sessile, but later is raised by the lengthening of the apex of the branch upon which it is borne.

Veil (*calyptra*).—The veil is the fragmentary remains of the old archegonium wall which was burst by the enlarging spore-case within and left at the base, or carried up on the lid.

Pedicel (*seta*).—The "foot" of the *Sphagnums* is homologous with the pedicel of other mosses, as it is due to a development of the base of the archegonium. The so-called pedicel (*pseudopodium*) is the result of a lengthening upward of the apex of the branch which bears the archegonium. This branch so enlarges just below the developing spore-case as to completely envelop the "foot."

Lid (*operculum*).—When the spore-case is mature enough to open, the upper portion separates from the lower by the breaking down of the walls of a zone of cells. This zone of weak cells is first noticeable in a young spore-case as a groove. This groove is due to one zone of cells growing less rapidly than the zones of cells on either side. The breaking along the groove is due to the thinner walls of the groove cells. One zone of thicker-walled cells forms a rim to the spore-case and the other zone of thicker-walled cells forms the rim of the lid.

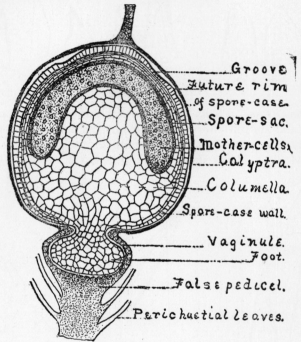

Groove
Future rim of spore-case.
Spore-sac.
Mother-cells.
Calyptra.
Columella.
Spore-case wall.
Vaginule.
Foot.
False pedicel.
Perichaetial leaves.

Vertical section of a young sporogonium.

The character of the leaves and the manner of branching, both of which are visible to the naked eye, enable one to separate the species with some accuracy into eight groups, which are helpful to a beginner, in that they gave him some definite points of difference to look for in a genus of which to the novice all species appear alike.

SYNOPSIS OF GENUS SPHAGNUM

1. *Acuta.*—With branch-leaves erect and *stem leaves* large. Examples: *Sphagnum acutifolium* and *Sphagnum rubellum*. (See diagram on page 123.)

2. *Cuspidata*.—With branch-leaves longer and narrower than the Acuta group, erect, spreading and wavy on the margins when dry; stem-leaves small. Example: *Sphagnum cuspidatum.*

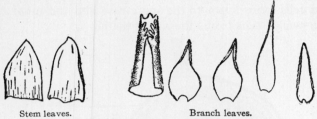

Stem leaves.   Branch leaves.

Sphagnum acutifolium.

3. *Squarrosa*.—Plants stout, branch-leaves spreading open widely and abruptly from the middle of the branch. Example: *Sphagnum squarrosum.* (See diagram below.)

4. *Mollia*.—Plants short, densely crowded, very soft when

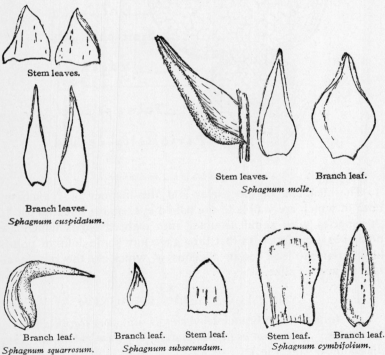

Stem leaves.

Stem leaves.   Branch leaf.

Sphagnum molle.

Branch leaves.

Sphagnum cuspidatum.

Branch leaf.   Branch leaf.   Stem leaf.   Stem leaf.   Branch leaf.

Sphagnum squarrosum.   *Sphagnum subsecundum.*   *Sphagnum cymbifolium.*

123

wet, brittle when dry, branch leaves short. Example: *Sphagnum molle*. (See diagram, page 123.)

 5. *Subsecunda*.—Branch-leaves more or less turned to one side or strongly curved and more or less folded. Example: *Sphagnum subsecundum*. (See diagram, page 123.)

 6. *Cymbiformia*.—Plants robust; stem-leaves large, tongue or boat-shaped, branch-leaves very concave. Example: *Sphagnum cymbifolium*. (See diagram, page 123.)

 7. *Cyclophylla*.—Plants not crowded, stems short, usually without short hanging branches; leaves loosely overlapping, roundish or oval, with a broad blunt apex.

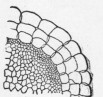

Branch.   Leaf.

Sphagnum cyclophylla.

 Acute-leaved Peat-moss (*Sphagnum acutifolium*), Ehrh.— See Colour Plate XI.

Habit and habitat.—Green or purple or red, common in open, shaded bogs, in valleys or on mountains; many varieties are noted; the variations due to their special habitat.

Name.—The specific name *acutifolium* is compounded of two Latin words *acutus*, sharp, and *folium*, a leaf, referring to the apex of the leaf.

Plants (*gametophyte*).—Stem without pores in the triple layer of cells which form the outer covering; *cluster branches* spreading, 3 to 5, one to two pendent.

Transverse section of leaf.

Part of cross section of stem showing triple layer of cells.

Sphagnum acutifolium.

Leaves.—Stem-leaves large, erect, oval or tongue-shaped; apex irregularly notched; with the large cells lined with a few or no

Plate XI

ACUTE-LEAVED PEAT MOSS, *Sphagnum acutifolium,* (Ehrh.)

spiral thickenings; branch-leaves deeply concave, erect, oval lance-shaped and awl-shaped, apex toothed; margin in-rolled.

Habit of flowering.—Male and female flowers on the same plant (*monoicous*) or on separate plants (*dioicous*); male branches usually red.

Leaves at the base of the spore-case (perichætial leaves).—Oblong, gradually narrowed to a point, apex sinuous, toothed, recurved.

Female branch. Perichætial leaf.

Perigonial leaf with antheridium.

Male branch, perigonium.

Sphagnum acutifolium. Stem of moss plant with leafy branches; (*d*) involucral leaves of the female flower; (*a*) involucral leaves of the male flowers.

Sphagnum acutifolium.

Spore-case.—Numerous, on long false pedicels.

Spores.—Rust-colour, mature in July.

Distribution.—Universal.

The Reddish Peat-moss (*Sphagnum rubellum*), Weis.

Habit and habitat.—Common in the Adirondack Mountains. The plants cover sunny bogs with a deep red carpet.

Name.—The specific name is the Latin *rubellum*, somewhat red.

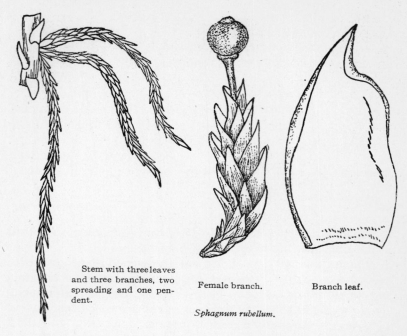

Stem with three leaves
and three branches, two
spreading and one pen-
dent.

Female branch.

Branch leaf.

Sphagnum rubellum.

Plant (gametophyte). — Resembling *Sphagnum acutifolium,* stems softer and more slender.

Leaves.—Stem-leaves broad, obtuse, sometimes with fibrils in the cells; branch-leaves shorter, oval oblong, *apex* obtuse, three-toothed.

Habit of flowering.—Male and female flowers on separate plants (*dioicous*).

The Pointed Peat-moss (*Sphagnum cuspidatum*), Ehrh.

Habit and habitat.—Green or brown, floating in loose tufts in ponds and on the borders of streams flowing from bogs.

Apex.

Leaves of divergent
branch.

Stem leaves.

Sphagnum rubellum.

126

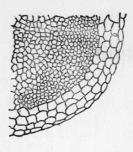
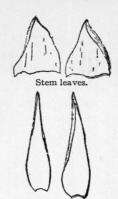

Male branch   Perigonial   *Sphagnum rubellum.* Portion
perigonium.   leaf.   of cross section of stem.

Sphagnum rubellum.

Stem leaves.

Branch leaves.
Sphagnum cuspidatum.

Name.—The specific name is the Latin *cuspidatum,* sharpened at the end, referring to the cluster-branches.

Plants (*gametophyte*).—Long and slender, 6 to 18 inches or even several feet; cluster-branches (*fascicles*), spreading or hanging, not closely appressed to the stem, 3 to 5, tapering to a stout point owing to the fact that the terminal leaves are rolled lengthwise.

Leaves.—Stem-leaves *small,* triangular, apex 2- to 3-toothed; *branch-leaves* loose, *erect spreading, wavy on the margins when dry,* lance-like and taper-pointed, deeply concave, *apex* with several small teeth; awl-shaped at the ends of the branches.

Leaves at the base of the spore-case.—Distant, broadly ovate, *apex* cut square or obtuse; large cells lined with fibrils.

Habit of flowering.—Male and female flowers on separate plants (*dioicous*).

Spore-case.—Scattered down the stem, small, the false pedicel often half an inch long.

Spores.—Light brown, mature in July.

Distribution.—Universal.

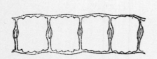

Sphagnum squarrosum. Transverse
section of leaf.

Apex.

Leaves from divergent branch.
Sphagnum squarrosum.

127

The Spread-leaved Sphagnum (*Sphagnum squarrosum*), Pers.—See Plate XII.

Habit and habitat.—Bluish-green, stout, loosely crowded, the summits appearing like edelweiss, almost white when dry; common in boggy places.

Name.—The specific name is the Latin *squarrosum*, scurfy, applied to describe the scale-like leaves of the stem.

Plant (*gametophyte*).—Stems solid, simple or forking, red; cluster-branches 4 to 5, 2 to 3 divergent, the others pendent and appressed.

Stem leaves:

Leaf at base of pedicel.

Female branch.

Sphagnum squarrosum.

Leaves.—Stem leaves soft, spreading or turned backward from the stem, tongue-shaped; *apex* rounded and ragged; branch-leaves spreading widely and abruptly from the middle of the branch, oblong lance-shaped, apex four-toothed.

Leaves at the base of the spore-case (*perichœtial leaves*).—Very broad, thin *apex* rounded and notched.

Habit of flowering.—Male and female flowers generally on the same plants (*monoicous*).

Spore-case.—Large, nearly spherical, shining dark brown, numerous at and near the summit of the plant.

Spores.—Yellow, mature in August and September.

Distribution.—North America, Europe, Asia, Africa.

The Boat-leaved Moss (*Sphagnum cymbifolium*), Ehrh.—See Plate III.

Habit and habitat.—Common in bogs, robust, yellow-green or red, densely crowded when growing out of water, rarely floating, male plants slender with thick flower-clusters.

PLATE XII

THE SPREAD-LEAVED PEAT-MOSS, *Sphagnum squarrosum*, Pers.

Name.—The specific name *cymbifolium* is compounded of two Latin words, *cymba*, a small boat, and *folium*, a leaf, referring to the branch-leaves. Stem solid, simple or two-parted; cortical cells in 3 to 4 layers; cluster-branches (*fascicles*), swollen, 4 to 5, 2 to 3 hanging, the rest curved.

Leaves.—Stem leaves large, tongue-shaped or spatulate, generally turned back from the stem; *apex* rounded and irregularly notched; *branch-leaves* broadly oval and boat-shaped, *apex* finely serrate and rough, densely overlapping; translucent

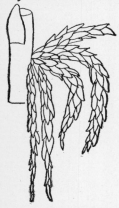

Bit of stem with one leaf and fascicle of four branches, two appressed and three spreading.

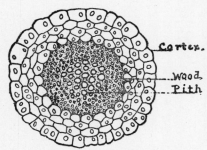

Cross section of stem

Perichætial leaf.

Apex of leaf.

Female branch.

Bract of male branch.

Male flower-cluster.

Sphagnum cymbifolium.

cells (*utricles*) large, with spiral thickenings (*fibrillose*) and few pores, green cells (ducts) narrowly oval.

Leaves at the base of the spore-case (perichœtial leaves).—Small, oval.

Habit of flowering.—Male and female flowers on separate plants (*dioicous*), male branches rather thick, yellow-brown, red, or olive-green.

Veil (calyptra).—As in genus.

Spore-case.—Large, almost spherical, dark brown.

Stem leaf.   Branch leaves.   Antheridium.

Sphagnum cymbifolium.

Pedicel.—As in genus.

Lid (operculum).—Saucer-like.

Teeth (peristome).—None.

Spores.—Rust-colour, mature in July.

Distribution.—Universal.

Genus ANDREÆA, Ehrh.

The species of the **Genus Andreæa** are found in small, brown or black, fragile tufts on granite or slate rocks in high altitudes. They are among the first mosses to grow on rock and are

Andreœa Hartmanii. Leaves.

Andreœa rupestris. Spore-case opening by four valves.

efficient agents in preparing soil for higher forms of plant life. The plants are small with forked branches which start from just below the flower-bearing apex. The leaves are thick, open or

REINDEER LICHEN—A VARIETY.

REINDEER LICHEN, VARIETY ALPESTRIS.

REINDEER LICHEN.
Cladonia rangiferina, (L.) Hoffm.
. . . Reindeer feed upon it . . .

PHYSCIA LEUCOMELA, (L.) Michx.

spreading, ovate to lance-shaped and usually have their surface covered with projecting points.

The terminal oval spore-cases are immersed among the leaves before maturity, but later are protruded by the elongation of the cellular sheath (*vaginule*) surrounding the base of the spore-case. This is known as a false pedicel (*pseudo-podium*). There is no lid, as the case opens by splitting perpendicularly into four or rarely six equal segments which cohere at the apex. There are,

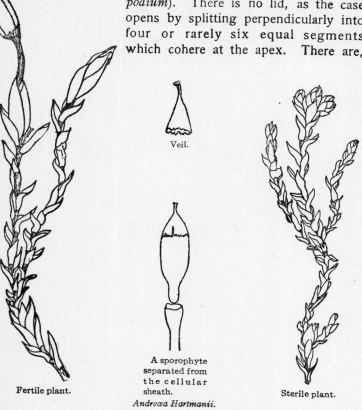

Veil.

A sporophyte separated from the cellular sheath.

Andreæa Hartmanii.

Fertile plant.

Sterile plant.

of course, no teeth when there is no lid. The small spores are at first coherent in fours, later, when the case splits into valves, they are disseminated by the wind, if the weather is dry; if it is damp, the valves draw together to protect the spores.

There are about one hundred species known at present, six or more of them occurring in North America. The specific characters are drawn mainly from the leaves.

By the early writers these mosses were classed with the leafy hepatics (*Jungermania*) on account of their manner of opening the spore-case by valves instead of by a lid. They agree in structure with the true mosses. Their proper place seems to lie between the peat-mosses and leafy-mosses. They agree with the peat-mosses because the spore-case is first enclosed in a sac-like vail and then elongated on a false pedicel. They agree with the genus *Grimmia* in habitat, manner of growth and in structure of their leaves, differing chiefly in the opening of the spore-case.

The name was given by Fredrich Ehrhart, in honour of his friend J. G. R. Andreæ, a Hanoverian naturalist.

The Stone-loving Andreæa (*Andreæa petrophila*), Ehrh.

Habit and habitat.—Found in small olive or dark brown tufts on wet rocks of high mountains.

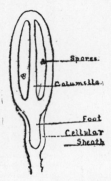

Name.—From πέτρα, a rock, and φιλεῖν, to love, referring to its choice of habitat.

Plants (*gametophyte*).—Stems slender, ⅓ to 1 inch long, leafless below.

A. *petrophila.* Vertical section of spore-case.

A. *petrophila.* Leaves.

Leaves.—Spreading or turned to one side, lance-shaped, rough on the back with projecting points; *apex* sometimes oblique, transparent; *vein* none, *margin* incurved, entire.

Habit of flowering.—Male and female flowers on one plant (*monoicous*).

Veil (*calyptra*).—Thin, closely fitting the spore-case.

Spore-case.—Egg-shaped, immersed in the leaves at its base until maturity and then protruded by the elongation of the cellular sheath (*vaginule*) surrounding its base.

Pedicel (*seta*).—None.

Lid (*operculum*).—None.

Teeth (*peristome*).—None.

Spores.—Small, mature in June-August.

Distribution.—Widely distributed in cooler regions.

The Rock Andreæa (*Andreæa rupestris*), Turner.

Andreæa rupestris has lance-shaped leaves, smooth and with a vein extending beyond the apex.

This moss is common in the mountains of Georgia and North Carolina, descending to the plains northward.

The specific name from the Latin *rupes*, a rock, refers to its habitat.

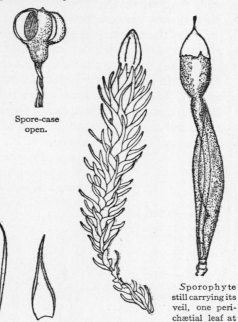

Spore-case open.

Leaves.

Fertile plant, spore-case immersed.

Sporophyte still carrying its veil, one perichætial leaf at the base of the pedicel.

A. rupestris.

Genus SPHÆRANGIUM, Schimp.

The Species of the **Genus Sphærangium** are minute bud-like plants with spore-case immersed, without stems, growing on the ground in clusters, but with no protonema at the base. The lower leaves are small, while the upper are large, somewhat twisted and overlapping as shingles. They are concave or keeled and covered with minute protuberances on the back or on both surfaces. The spore-cases are spherical and for this reason Wilhelm Philipp Schimper gave them their generic name *Sphærangium*, from the Greek σφαῖρα, a ball, and ἀγγεῖον, a vessel. The cases with their

133

tiny erect veils are borne on pedicels and are enclosed in the leaves at their base; when mature they split irregularly and transversely for the emission of the spores, which are small, somewhat globular, minutely granulous and brown.

There are fourteen species known in all, four of them in North America.

Spore-case.

Spore.

Spore-case split open to show columella of spores.

Veil.

S. muticum.

Sphærangium muticum, Schimp. Individual plants are more or less separated.

Habit and habitat.—On bare clay or sandy soil.

Spore-case splitting irregularly and emitting spores.

Leaf-cells.

Sphærangium Schimperanum.

Name.—The specific name *muticum*, blunt, refers to the apex of the spore-case.

Plants (gametophyte).—Like yellow-brown buds ⅛ of an inch high.

Leaves.—The *lower* and *middle* oval and long taper-pointed; *apex* recurved, with a short sharp point; *vein* passing beyond the apex; the *upper* two or three, twice as large as the lower; apex irregularly toothed.

Habit of flowering.—Male and female flowers on the same plant (*monoicous*).

Veil (calyptra).—Very small, erect, conical, with a long beak.

Spore-case.—Orange, spherical, immersed.

Pedicel.—Very short.

Lid (operculum).—None.

Teeth (peristome).—None.

Spores.—Mature in winter and early spring.

Distribution.—Europe, Africa, and North America.

Male and female
branches at the left
and (*a*) rhizoids.

Lower leaf.

Upper leaves.

Plant.

Sphærangium muticum

Genus PHASCUM, Linn.

The plants of the **Genus Phascum** are very small with simple distinct stems. They grow in loose clusters on bare ground under old willows and along brooks and garden paths. The protonema is not persistent.

The leaves are crowded, forming small heads and are lance-shaped with taper-pointed apex and a broad base with a vein extending as an awn beyond the apex. The cells are distinct and pale below, smaller and green above, sometimes with minute projecting points on one or both faces.

The spore-cases are spherical or egg-shaped with a short point or a blunt beak. They are raised on a short, erect or curved

Leaf.

Sporophyte.
Spore-case
with veil.
Pedicel short,
with the vag-
inule at the
base.

Spore-case
split open to
show colu-
mella.

Phascum cuspidatum.

pedicel and break irregularly and transversely for the emission of the large, rough spores, which are borne on a thick, central column (*columella*).

There are ten species known in all, three of them in North America. By some they are believed to be mosses in a primitive condition; by others they are believed to be degenerate forms of higher mosses.

The generic name *Phascum* is derived from the Greek φάσκον, an ancient name for a moss. It was originally applied by Theophrastus to a lichen, *Usnea barbata*, and first used as a generic name for these mosses by Linnæus in 1753. He enumerated three species, all founded on figures made by Dillenius and published in 1741. Schreber limited the name more closely to its modern sense. In a quaint little pamphlet printed in 1770, he praises the invention of lenses which make it possible to see the tiny mosses as if they were of greater stature, and says that the ancients spoke well and wisely when they said "Nature is never more perfect than in small things."

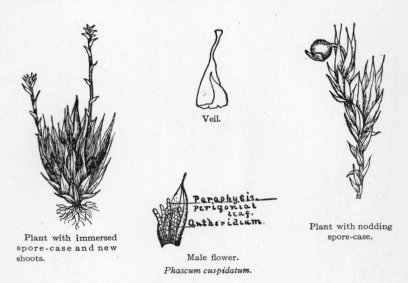

Veil.

Plant with immersed spore-case and new shoots.

Paraphysis. Perigonial leaf. Antheridium.

Male flower.
Phascum cuspidatum.

Plant with nodding spore-case.

Phascum cuspidatum, Schreb.

Habit and habitat.—In loose yellow-green tufts in old fields.

Name.—The specific name *cuspidatum*, pointed, refers to the apex of the leaves.

Plants (*gametophyte*).—Stems simple or branched, $\frac{1}{10}$ to $\frac{5}{10}$ of an inch high, often bushy with numerous fertile stems, dividing from the base or branching above, occasionally whip-like.

Leaves.—Small and few below, much larger and crowded above, broadly lance-like, twisted when dry: *apex* awl-like; *margins* recurved, entire; *vein* thick and extending beyond the

136

apex; *basal cells* large, clear; *upper cells* small, green, with tiny projecting points.

Habit of flowering.—Male and female flowers on the same plant (*monoicous*); male flowers sessile in the axils of the upper leaves.

Veil (*calyptra*).—Split on one side.

Spore-case.—One or several on a plant, erect or nodding, spherical with a sharp point at the top, $\frac{1}{20}$ of an inch in diameter.

Pedicel.—Short and curved, immersed or slightly emergent.

Spores.—Brown, rough, mature in March and April.

Distribution.—North and South America, Europe, Asia, Africa.

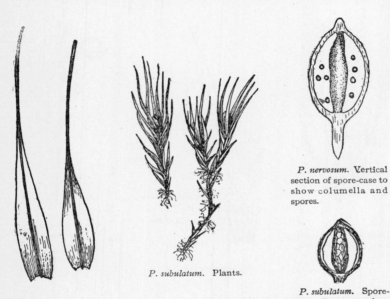

P. subulatum. Plants.

P. nervosum. Vertical section of spore-case to show columella and spores.

P. subulatum. Leaves.

P. subulatum. Spore-case split open to show columella.

Genus PLEURIDIUM, Brid.

The plants of the **Genus Pleuridium** are minute and erect with simple or branching stems clustered to form dense cushions on the ground.

The leaves are small and few below, but longer and crowded above; they are oval at the base, tapering to a long awl-like point with a broad vein forming most of the apex.

The spore-cases are solitary and terminal, immersed on a short pedicel. They are almost spherical with a point on the summit and a persistent columella.

There are thirty-six species known in all, five in the United States.

The generic name *Pleuridium* is derived from the Greek πλευρίδιον, at the side. The name is suggestive of the position of the spore-cases, which in some species appear to be on the sides of the stems instead of on the summits, because a side branch has grown from near the base of the spore-case—but in the same direction as the main stem—leaving the spore-case behind.

Pleuridium subulatum, (Huds.), Rabenh.

Habit and habitat.—In loose bright-green and silky tufts on earth and clay, along woods, banks and heaths.

Name.—The specific name *subulatum*, from the Latin *subula*, an awl, refers to the shape of the upper leaves.

Leaves.

Spore-case with veil.

Spores.

Veil.

P. subulatum.

Plants (gametophyte).—Minute, $\frac{1}{10}$ to $\frac{2}{10}$ of an inch high, simple or branching.

Leaves.—The lower distant, short, oval and taper-pointed; the upper longer, more crowded, spreading; *apex* an awn minutely toothed and rough on the back; *vein* broad, forming most of the awn.

Habit of flowering.—Male and female flowers close together on the same plant (*paroicous*); male flowers naked in the axils of the leaves at the base of the spore-case.

Veil (calyptra).—Split on one side.

Spore-case.—Immersed in the leaves at the base, egg-shaped with a tiny point at the apex (*apiculate*).

Pedicel (seta).—Short, immersed.

Lid (operculum).—None.

138

Teeth (peristome).—None.

Spores.—Rough, mature from March to June.

Distribution.—Quite universal.

Genus BRUCHIA, Schwaegr.

The species of the **Genus Bruchia** are minute, with simple or two-forked stems. They are found growing in loose clusters on the ground.

The stem-leaves are small and distant, those toward the apex being longer and crowded to form a rosette. The vein of all leaves is distinct to the apex.

The spore-cases are emergent, oval and beaked, with a base which tapers into a long solid neck (*collum*). They open irregularly for the emission of the spores as they have no lid.

There are eighteen species in all, two in Europe and eleven in North America.

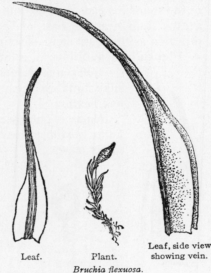

Leaf.   Plant.   Leaf, side view showing vein.

Bruchia flexuosa.

The generic name **Bruchia** was applied by D. Fridericus Schwaegrichen in 1824, in honour of the distinguished bryologist Ph. Bruch, one of the authors of "The Bryologia Europæa."

Bruchia flexuosa, Muell.

Habit and habitat.—Found on clay or on base soil in fields or under old willows and along brooks.

Name.—The specific name *flexuosa*, the Latin for "crooked," refers to the curving of the stems near the bases.

Plant (gametophyte).—In loose tufts, stems comparatively long, curved downward at the base.

Leaves.—Stem-leaves distant, very small, nearly smooth, narrowly lance-shaped and prolonged into an awn; *apex* obscurely serrate.

Habit of flowering.—Male and female flowers close together on the same plant (*paroicous*) or in separate buds on the same plant.

Veil (*calyptra*).—Resembling a bishop's mitre, thin, lobed, or torn at the base.

Spore-case.—Not immersed in the leaves at the base, egg-shaped with a neck (*collum*) shorter or equal to the spore-sac, long-beaked.

Pedicel.—One-tenth to two-tenths of an inch long.

Lid (*operculum*).—None.

Teeth (*peristome*).—None.

Spores.—Mature in the fall.

Bruchia flex-uosa.
Sporophyte.

Distribution.—Found in the central part of North America.

THE PRIMITIVE MOSSES

Genus ARCHIDIUM, Brid.

The species of the **Genus Archidium** are minute terrestrial plants having stems with branches short and erect or long and prostrate.

The leaves are narrowly or broadly lance-shaped; with a vein; the cells are loose and contain but little leaf-green.

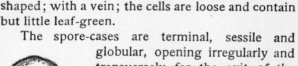

The spore-cases are terminal, sessile and globular, opening irregularly and transversely for the exit of the spores, which are few, smooth and larger than those of any other moss.

Archidium Ohi-ense. Vertical section through sporophyte to show large spores, foot immersed in the upper part (vaginule) of the spore-pedicel.

There are thirty-five species in all, five of them in North America. Their structure is more simple than that of most mosses; and

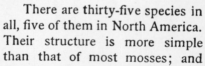

Archidium Ohiense.
Exit of spores.

for this reason Bridel gave it the generic name *Archidium* from the Greek ἀρχίδιον, a beginning.

Archidium Ohiense, Schimp.

Habit and habitat.—Moist meadows and waste fields.

Name.—The specific name *Ohiense* refers to the fact that this moss was first found in Ohio.

Plant (*gametophyte*).—Minute; *stems* slender.

Leaves.—Narrowly lance-shaped, spreading; *apex* awl-like, finely toothed; *vein* extending into the apex of the leaf-blade.

Leaves at the base of the spore-case (perichætical leaves).—Broader and longer.

Habit of flowering.—Male and female flowers in separate clusters on the same plant (*autoicous*).

Veil (calyptra).—Very thin, irregularly torn below.

Spore-case.—Spherical, on short side branch.

Pedicel.—Very short.

Lid (operculum).—Wanting.

Teeth (peristome).—Wanting.

Spores.—Sixteen to twenty, angular, smooth, mature in fall and winter.

Distribution.—North America, Ohio and southward.

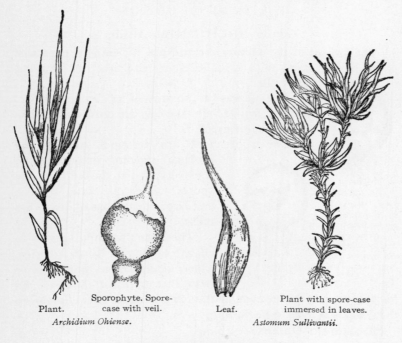

| Plant. | Sporophyte. Spore-case with veil. | Leaf. | Plant with spore-case immersed in leaves. |

Archidium Ohiense.   *Astomum Sullivantii.*

Genus ASTOMUM, Hampe

The species of the **Genus Astomum** are minute, simple or branching plants, living in matted tufts on the ground.

The leaves are lance-shaped, tufted and curling toward the **apex of** the stems.

The spore-cases are erect and symmetrical on a short pedicel and are immersed in the leaves. They have distinctly formed, beaked lids, which are not easily detached. There are no teeth.

The generic name *Astomum*, from *à*, privative, without, and στόμα, a mouth, was given because when first known this moss was supposed to have no lid.

There are seventeen species in all.

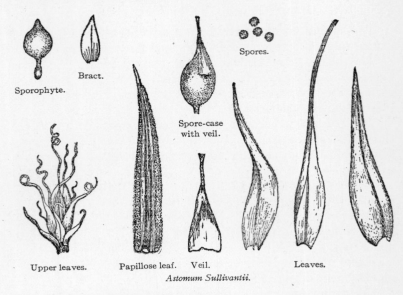

Sporophyte.

Bract.

Spores.

Spore-case with veil.

Upper leaves.

Papillose leaf. Veil.

Leaves.

Astomum Sullivantii.

Astomum Sullivantii, Schimp.

Habit and habitat.—In fields and gardens, living from year to year.

Name.—The specific name *Sullivantii* was applied to this moss by Wilhelm Philipp Schimper, in honour of William S. Sullivant, a noted bryologist.

Plant (*gametophyte*).—Minute, simple, or branched.

Leaves.—The *lower* leaves small, narrowly oval; the *upper* narrowly lance-shaped, densely tufted, covered on the back with tiny projections *papillosa;* curled in various directions when dry; *apex* pointed; *margins* rolled in; *vein* round, extending beyond the apex of the leaf-blade (*percurrent*).

Habit of flowering.—Male and female flowers on the same plant (*monoicous*).

142

Veil (calyptra).—Split up one side.
Spore-case.—Bright orange, symmetrical.
Pedicel (seta).—Shorter than the spore-case.
Lid (operculum).—Short, conical.
Teeth (peristome).—None.
Spores.—Bright, rusty brown, mature in autumn.
Distribution.—North America.

Genus GYMNOSTOMUM, Hedw.

The species of the **Genus Gymnostomum** are found in matted tufts on the ground and on limestone walls and rocks.

The plants have slender stems branching twice or many times to form clusters, with terminal erect spore-cases, cylindrical or globose, exserted on erect pedicels.

The leaves are small, generally larger upwards and tufted at the apex of the stem ; they are lance-shaped with a solid vein prominent on the back.

The lid is long-beaked and falls to permit the escape of the spores. There are no teeth, a character which suggests the generic name, from the Greek γυμνὸς, naked, and στόμα, a mouth.

There are fifty-five species in all, eight of them known in North America.

Gymnostomum calcareum, Nees & Hornsch.

Habit and habitat.—Densely tufted, bright-green above, rusty below ; on shaded limestone rocks.

Name.—From *calcarius*, pertaining to lime, a name suggested by the plant's habit of depositing lime.

Plants (gametophyte).—Stems $\frac{1}{4}$ to $\frac{3}{4}$ of an inch long, covered with rootlets.

Leaves.—The lower very small, gradually or abruptly larger upward ; slender lance-shaped ; *apex* blunt ;

Leaf and cross-section to show prominent vein.

Gymnostomum calcareum.

143

vein extending to near the apex ; *margin* minutely blunt-toothed.

Habit of flowering.—Male and female flowers on separate plants (*dioicous*).

Veil (*calyptra*).—Split up one side.

Spore-case.—Exserted, oblong, yellow-brown, slightly constricted under the mouth when dry.

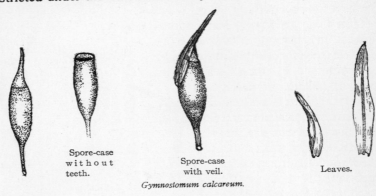

Spore-case
w i t h o u t
teeth.

Spore-case
with veil.

Leaves.

Gymnostomum calcareum.

Pedicel.—$\frac{1}{6}$ to $\frac{2}{6}$ of an inch long.

Lid (*operculum*).—Base conical ; beak awl-like.

Teeth (*peristome*).—None.

Annulus.—Short and persistent.

Spores.—Rare, mature in summer.

Distribution.—Universal.

Gymnostomum curvirostrum, Hedw.

Habit and habitat.—This moss is found on limestone rocks and on deposits of carbonate of lime about springs and streams. The plants obtain the carbonic acid gas (CO_2) which they need, from bicarbonate of lime which is dissolved in the surrounding water. By decomposition of the bicarbonate of lime [H_2 $Ca (CO_3)_2$], which is soluble in water, the monocarbonate of lime ($Ca CO_3$), which is insoluble in water is precipitated in the form of incrustations upon the leaves and stems of the moss, so that in time a very appreciable deposit of limestone is made.*

G. curvirostrum.
with long beak.

Name.—From the Latin *curvus*, curved, and *rostrum*, a beak.

*See page 17.

Plants (gametophyte).—Dark red or brown, matted, *stems* $\frac{1}{2}$ to 5 inches long ; *branches* of equal height, in close clusters, covered with a felt of red radicles.

Leaves.—Spreading, slightly incurved when dry, pointed, lance-shaped, keeled, smooth, or with tiny projections ; *base* transparent ; *margin* entire or slightly serrate and recurved above the base ; *vein* vanishing below the apex.

Habit of flowering.—Male and female flowers on separate plants (*dioicous*).

Veil (calyptra).—Split up one side.

Spore-case. — Egg-shaped, oblong, or nearly spherical, thick-walled, chestnut colour, shining, top-shaped when dry and empty.

Pedicel.—$\frac{1}{6}$ to $\frac{2}{6}$ of an inch long.

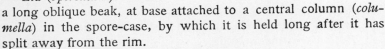

Lid with columella.

Spore-case with lid.

Spore-case with lid lifted.

G. curvirostrum.

Lid (operculum).—With a long oblique beak, at base attached to a central column (*columella*) in the spore-case, by which it is held long after it has split away from the rim.

Annulus.—Two rows of persistent cells.

Spores.—Mature in late summer.

Distribution.—Common in North America, Europe, and Asia. Very abundant in Niagara Falls.

Genus WEISIA, Hedw.

The species of this genus are small and slender, growing in tufts or cushions on the ground. The leaves are lance-shaped and twisted when dry, the apex is awl-like and the vein single.

Peristome.

Portion of peristome.
Weisia viridula.

Leaves.

The spore-case is erect, oval-oblong, symmetrical or rarely incurved on an erect exserted pedicel. There is but one row of sixteen teeth, often imperfect or wanting, granular and transversely barred.

The generic name *Weisia* was given in honour of Frederigo Wilhelm Weiss, a German professor of botany.

About twenty-four species are known in all.

Weisia viridula, Brid.

Habit and habitat.—Common, forming more or less compact cushions on the ground in meadows, broken fields, borders of ditches and grassy roadsides, where it is conspicuous for its bright green colour. Very variable.

Name.—The specific name *viridula* is the Latin diminutive of *viridis*, green.

Plants (gametophyte).—Stems about ¼ of an inch long, simple or branched.

Lid in veil.

Spore-case with veil.

Weisia viridula.

Leaves.—The *lower* minute ; the *upper* much larger, narrowly lance-shaped and curled when dry; *base* enlarged, pale, concave; *vein (costa)* stout and extending beyond the apex into a short sharp point ; *margin* inrolled in the upper part to form a tube, flat toward the base ; *cells* opaque, dot-like, with tiny projecting points.

Habit of flowering.—Male and female flowers on the same plant (*monoicous*).

Veil (*calyptra*).—Smooth, split on one side and reaching to the middle of the spore-case.

Spore-case. — Light-brown, oval, oblong, of thick texture, slightly constricted under the mouth, wrinkled lengthwise when dry.

Dry spore-case.   Top of spore-case with peristome.   Portion of peristome.   Young spore-case.

Weisia viridula.

Pedicel (*seta*).—$\frac{1}{6}$ to $\frac{2}{6}$ of an inch long and twisted to the right.

Lid (*operculum*).—Beak, long, straight or bent obliquely.

Teeth (*peristome*).—Orange-red, variable, slender or broad, often ending abruptly (*truncate*) or split into two parts with 2 to 5 cross bars, sometimes rudimentary.

Annulus.—Narrow, persistent.

Spores.—Mature from March to May.

Distribution.—Universal.

Genus **TREMATODON**, Michx.

The species of the **Genus Tremato-don** are short plants, sparingly branched and forming pale-green or dusky-brown tufts on the ground. The leaves are lance-shaped, tapering toward the apex; a vein is present, and the cells are large and long-hexagonal. The spore-cases are oblong, slightly arched with a long neck (*collum*) once or twice as long as the spore-case. They have long-beaked lids with conical bases and are raised on slender pedicels $\frac{1}{2}$ to $1\frac{1}{2}$ inches long. A

T. ambiguum. Portion of peristome.

simple or compound annulus is present and a single row of sixteen red-brown narrowly lance-shaped teeth cleft to near the base into two unequal forks.

147

The generic name, compounded of two Greek words: τρῆμα, a perforation, and ὀδὼν, a tooth, was suggested by the character of the teeth of one species, *Trematodon ambiguum*, which often have a cleft or perforation running lengthwise of each tooth.

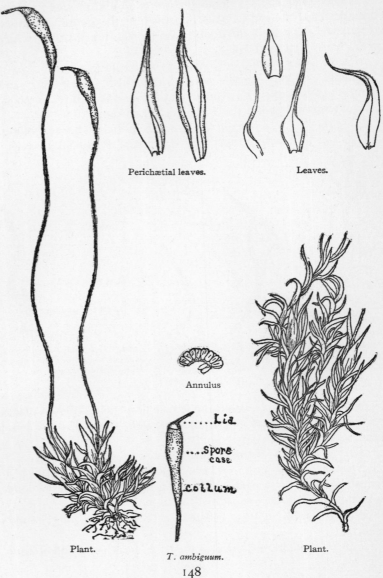

Perichætial leaves.

Leaves.

Annulus

Lid

Spore case

collum

Plant.

T. ambiguum.

Plant.

148

There are sixty-four species in all, two in the United States.
Trematodon ambiguum, Hornsch.

Habit and habitat.—Wet sandy places on hills ; in peat-bogs, ditches, etc., of Alpine regions.

Name.—The specific name *ambiguum,* doubtful, was given to this species at the time it was classified in the genus *Dicranum* (1792) and expressed the doubt as to its rightful position, which was determined in 1803.

Plants (gametophyte).—Short, ½ to 1 inch long.

Leaves.—Open, lance-shaped, channelled ; *apex* long and slender ; *base* concave, oval-oblong ; *margins* entire, inrolled; *vein* extending beyond the leaf-blade (excurrent).

Leaves at the base of the pedicel.—Large, oblong, with a short tapering point. Perichætial leaves.

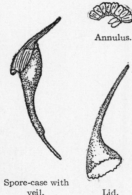

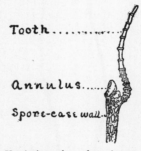

Annulus.

Tooth............

Annulus........

Spore-case wall.

Plant stripped of leaves to show two male and one female cluster.

Spore-case with veil.

Lid.

Vertical section of peristome showing two cells of the annulus at the base of a single tooth.

T. ambiguum.

Habit of flowering.—Male and female flowers in different places on the same plant (*autoicous*) ; male flowers terminal on a basal branch, bracts small, taper-pointed.

Veil (calyptra).—Translucent, slit on one side (*cucullate*).

Spore-case.—Oblong, straw-coloured or orange-brown ; in length equal to or shorter than the slightly arched neck (*collum*) which is swollen on one side at the base.

Pedicel (seta).—Long, twisted, ½ to 1½ inches long, straw-coloured.

Lid (operculum).—Conical at the base ; beak, long and oblique.

Teeth (*peristome*).—Cleft to near the base or in the middle only; segments sometimes irregularly torn.

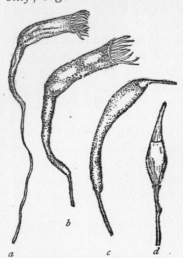

T. ambiguum. (*a*) and (*b*) old spore-cases; (*c*) mature spore-case; (*d*) young spore-case.

Annulus.—Large, rolling back when mature.

Spores.—Mature in July and August.

Trematodon longicollis, Michx.

Trematodon longicollis, the long-necked *Trematodon,* may be distinguished from *Trematodon ambiguum* by the neck, which is twice as long as the spore-case, by the shorter plants, and by the slender character of the teeth and the leaves at the base of the pedicel. The specific name *longicollis* is compounded of two Latin roots, *longum,* long, and *collum,* a neck.

THE LITTLE FORK-MOSSES

Genus DICRANELLA, Schimp.

The species of this genus are generally small with slightly branching stems. The leaves are very long and narrow from a broader often clasping base and are never curled, but spread on all sides or turn in one direction. Usually they are smooth with the margins plane and the vein broad.

The spore-cases are erect or inclined, symmetrical or unequal on yellow or red pedicels. They have lids with long awl-like points.

The peristome consists of sixteen large teeth, two-cleft to about the middle, closely cross-barred and marked with fine parallel bars running lengthwise.

There are one hundred and twelve species in all, thirty-two known in North America.

The generic name *Dicranella,* is the diminutive of *Dicranum,* from δίκρανος, a fork.

Dicranella heteromalla, Schimp.

Habit and habitat.—Forming silky, green tufts of moderate size on rocks, clay banks, naked soil and roots of trees.

Name.—The specific name *heteromalla* is derived from the Greek ἑτερόμαλλος, having hair only on one side, referring to the habit the leaves have of turning to one side.

Plants (gametophyte).—Stems simple or forking, ½ to 2 inches high.

Leaves.—Glossy, crowded, turned to one side, lance-shaped from the base; *apex* slender, awl-shaped, toothed or entire.

Leaves at the base of the pedicel (perichætial leaves).—Abruptly and narrowly awl-shaped from a half-clasping base.

Habit of flowering.—Male and female flowers on separate plants (*dioicous*).

Veil (calyptra).—Split up one side.

Spore-case.—Egg-shaped or oblong with the summit inclined. The base tapers to form a short neck (*collum*) and is slightly constricted under the mouth. Plaited when dry.

Pedicel.—Slender and pale yellow, ½ to 1 inch long.

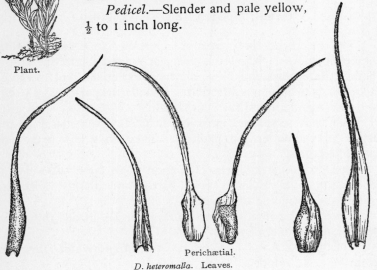

Plant.

Perichætial.

D. heteromalla. Leaves.

151

Lid (operculum).—Long-beaked.

Teeth (peristome).—Showy, red, two- or three-forked to the middle.

Annulus.—Simple, very narrow.

Spores.—Mature from November to February.

Distribution.—North America, Europe and Asia.

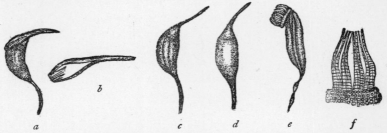

a   *c*   *d*   *e*   *f*

D. heteromalla. (*a*) Spore-case with veil; (*b*) veil; (*c*) and (*d*) spore-cases with lid; (*e*) spore-case with peristome; (*f*) portion of peristome.

FORK-MOSSES

Genus DICRANUM, Hedw.

The species of this genus are universally distributed, and include some of our most easily recognised mosses. They

Tuft of Dicranum scoparium

usually grow in dense tufts or cushions on the ground or on old decaying logs or even on rocks. About two hundred and thirty-four species are known in all ; about sixty-three are found in North America, six of these within the limits of New York City. Their showy dark-green or glossy yellow-green cushions are often conspicuous in damp shady places and consist of numerous more or less erect and forking stems, often crowded together and covered with a felt of reddish hairs at least below, with lance-shaped often curved leaves above that spread all about the stem or turn to one side.

152

WOOD PATH
"The moss upon the forest bark
Was polestar when the night was dark"

The *leaves* have a slender apex with a vein usually broad and extending into the apex. The character of the vein and the cell-structure are relied upon for perfect classification of the species. The *cells* vary from short to linear oblong in the upper part of the leaf, to long and narrow in the lower part ; four-sided, inflated, orange or brown, in the angles of the base. The leaves at the base of the pedicel are sheathing and abruptly pointed. The *spore-cases* are erect or turned to one side, the base, which is often swollen so as to be unsymmetrical, tapers to an erect pedicel, long and smooth. An *annulus* is generally present. The *lid* is conical with a long beak. The *peristome* is single, of sixteen teeth, two-cleft to the middle and red-brown at the base.

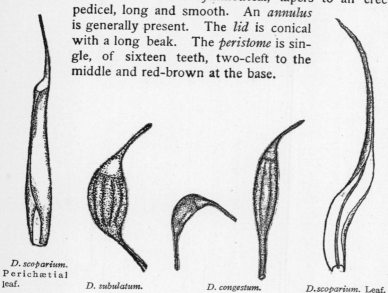

D. scoparium.
Perichætial
leaf.   *D. subulatum.*   *D. congestum.*   *D. scoparium.* Leaf.

The name of the genus is derived from a Greek word, δίκρανος, a flesh-hook or fork, from a supposed resemblance of its teeth to that instrument. The American Indians call Fork-mosses "Women's heads," "because when you trample them under foot they spring right up again."

Although at first glance the *Dicranums* appear to have their spore-cases on the sides of the plants, they truly belong to the group of mosses which bears them on the summits of the stems (*acrocarpi*) and not to the group which bears them on the sides of the stems (*pleurocarpi*), for a closer examination shows that a side stem grows on after the spore-case has

153

begun to develop, leaving the spore-case and pedicel behind on the apex of the main stem. The felt of hairs on the stems serves as a sponge through which water may creep to the upper parts of the plants.

> " How glorious are the summer woods,
> Where the bright Broom Fork-moss grows,
> With their gush of love-born melody,
> And their world of verdant boughs."

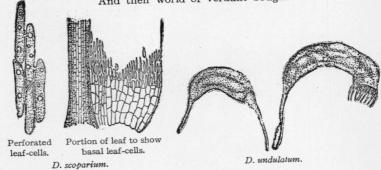

Perforated leaf-cells.

Portion of leaf to show basal leaf-cells.

D. scoparium.

D. undulatum.

Whip Fork-Moss, *Dicranum flagellare,* Hedw.—See Plate XIV.

Habit and habitat.—Growing in bright green, dense tufts producing fragile, small-leaved branches (*flagellæ*) in the axils of the upper leaves. Common on decayed trunks in deep woods.

Name.—The specific name *flagellum,* the Latin for " whip," refers to the young branches, which are so small as to be easily overlooked. They fall away as the plant dries.

Plant (gametophyte).—Repeatedly branching ; stems 1 to 2 inches high ; covered with a thick felt of hairs.

Leaves.—Forming little clusters on the summits of the stems ; lance-shaped, convolute ; *apex* toothed, turned back from the stem, the upper twisted when dry ; *margin* below entire, incurved ; *vein* broad, compressed, extending to the apex ; *cells* inflated at the basal angles, yellow-brown, four-sided. The leaves of the " whips " have no vein.

Leaves at the base of the pedicel (perichœtial leaves).—Rolled about the pedicel.

Habit of flowering.—Male and female flowers on separate plants (*dioicous*).

154

Plate XIII

THE BROOM-MOSS, *Dicranum scoparium*, Hedw.

Veil (calyptra).—Split on one side.

Spore-case.—Erect symmetrical, long, cylindrical, grouped lengthwise when dry.

Pedicel (seta).—Pale, twisted to the left when dry.

Lid (operculum).—Conical, with long oblique beak.

Annulus.—Narrow.

Teeth (peristome).—Sixteen, narrow, cleft nearly to the base.

Spores.—Mature in autumn.

Distribution.—North America, Asia, Africa ; rare in Great Britain.

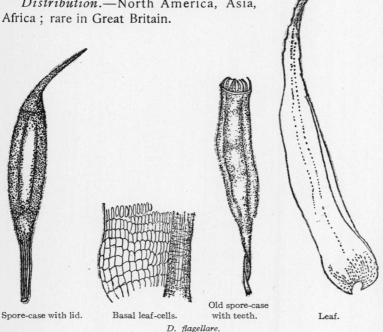

Spore-case with lid. Basal leaf-cells. Old spore-case with teeth. Leaf.

D. flagellare.

The Broom-moss, *Dicranum scoparium,* Hedw.—See Plate XIII.

Habit and habitat.—The Broom-moss, *Dicranum scoparium,* is a conspicuous species. It commonly grows in the woods forming large and symmetrical cushions on the ground, although it may extend in large patches over decaying stumps and logs or on the ground where there is a rich vegetable mould. The long-

155

beaked spore-cases, tilted on one side, commonly point one way, and the leaves also are all turned to one side pointing in the same direction as the beaks. Children fancy they resemble duck heads and see in them flocks travelling toward the water. Some call them soldiers and sing "The troops of Dicranum are tilting their lances."

Name.—The specific name *scoparium*, the Latin for "broom," is suggested by the resemblance of the plants to small counter-brooms.

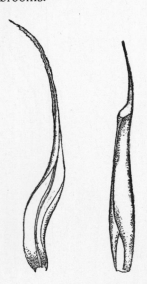

D. scoparium. Leaves.

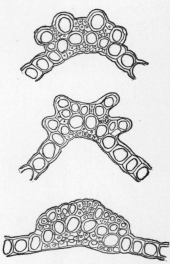

D. scoparium. Sections of vein toward apex of leaf.

Plant (gametophyte).—Large ; *stems* 2 to 5 inches high in loose yellow, rarely green, tufts, covered with rootlets to the newest growth, forking once or twice.

Leaves.—Glossy, turned to one side, or scythe-shaped, rarely erect, crowded at the tops of the stems ; *apex* awl-shaped ; *base* lance-shaped ; *vein* compressed, with four-toothed ridges on the back toward the apex ; *margin* sharply serrate and wavy toward the apex ; *cells* perforated, elongated in the upper part, narrow and worm-like toward the base, large, four-sided and orange-coloured at the angles.

Leaves at the base of the pedicel (perichætial leaves).—Sheathing at the base.

Habit of flowering.—Male and female flowers on different plants (*dioicous*).

Veil (*calyptra*).—Thin, smooth, beaked and split up one side.

Spore-case.—Long, with summit somewhat inclined, rarely erect, cylindrical, somewhat incurved, arched and grooved when dry.

Pedicel (*seta*).—Solitary, golden-yellow.

Lid (*operculum*).—Conical at the base, gradually narrowed into a strong beak, reddish, and as long as the spore-case.

Teeth (*peristome*).—Sixteen, dark-red, cleft to the middle.

Annulus.—None.

Spores.—Mature in summer.

Distribution.—North America, Europe, Asia.

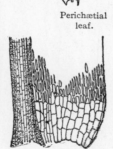

Perichætial leaf.

Tuft of *D. scoparium.*

Perforated leaf cells

Basal leaf-cells.

D. scoparium.

Genus FISSIDENS, Hedw.

The species of this genus are metallic green, plume-like, simple or sparingly branched, growing in mats upon shady wet banks and rocks ; sometimes on tree-trunks, and sometimes floating in water.

The leaves grow in two opposite rows (*distichous*), and are double below as if folded together, they are winged along the back and expanded toward the apex into a vertical simple blade; the vein extends to or beyond the apex ; the cells are small and filled with leaf-green.

The spore-cases are erect, horizontal or pendent, always smooth and terminal, unless they have been thrust to one side by the growth of a branch at the base of the pedicel.

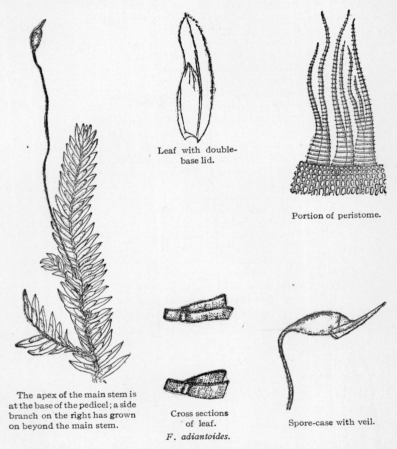

Leaf with double-base lid.

Portion of peristome.

The apex of the main stem is at the base of the pedicel; a side branch on the right has grown on beyond the main stem.

Cross sections of leaf.

F. adiantoides.

Spore-case with veil.

The *peristome* is single with sixteen teeth, red at the base and cleft at the apex, a character which has suggested the generic name from the Latin *fissus*, split, and *dens*, a tooth. When dry the teeth are incurved. The *annulus* consists of from one to four rows of large cells.

Five hundred and seventy-eight species are known in all, seventy-four in North America. The genus is represented throughout all the tropical and temperate regions of the world. It is probably to this pretty moss that Mungo Park, the African traveller, referred when he wrote the lines :

" Sad, faint and weary, on the sand
Our traveller sat him down ; his hand
Cover'd his burning head.
Above, beneath, behind, around,
No resting for the eye he found ;
All nature seemed as dead.
One tiny tuft of moss alone,
Mantling with freshest green a stone,
Fix'd his delighted gaze ;
Through bursting tears of joy he smiled,
And while he raised the tendril wild,
His lips o'erflowed with praise.
Oh ! shall not He who keeps thee green,
Here in the waste, unknown, unseen,
Thy fellow-exile save ?
He who commands the dew to feed
Thy gentle flower, can surely lead
Me from a scorching grave.
Thy tender stalks, and fibres fine,
Here find a shelter from the storm;
Perhaps no human eye but mine
Ere gazed upon thy lovely form.
He that form'd thee, little plant,
And bade thee flourish in this place,
Who sees and knows my every want,
Can still support me with His grace.'

Leaf.

Cross section of
leaf.

Stem to show distichous
leaves.

F. taxifolium.

159

Fissidens adiantoides, Hedw.

Habit and habitat.—In bright or dark-green mats on moist shady ground, wet rocks and roots of trees. Varying according to locality.

Name.—The specific name is compounded of ἀδίαντος, maidenhair, and the suffix οἰδ, like, referring to the habit the leaves of the maidenhair have of shedding water, ἀδίαντος, being compounded of ἀ, without, and διαίνω, wet.

Plant (gametophyte).—Stems 1 to 5 inches long ; branches growing from the apex or base of the stem, with root-like fibres at their base.

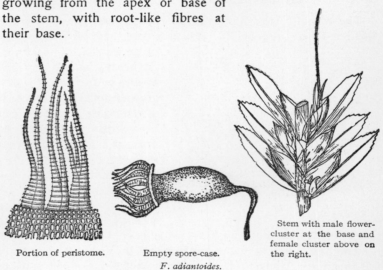

Portion of peristome.   Empty spore-case.
F. adiantoides.

Stem with male flower-cluster at the base and female cluster above on the right.

Leaves.—Numerous, close, overlapping like shingles, linear-oblong, clasping at the base ; apex taper-pointed and tipped with a short point continuous with the vein, the wing long and continuous ; margins transparent, irregularly and minutely serrate.

Habit of flowering.—Male and female flowers on different parts of the same plants (*autoicous*) ; male flower-clusters small, axillary, bud-like.

Veil (calyptra).—Split on one side.

Spore-case.—Oval, red-brown, much constricted under the orifice when empty.

Pedice.—Red, ½ to 1 inch long, appearing as if attached to the side of the stem.

Lid (operculum).—Conical, with a long beak.

Teeth (peristome).—Red, sixteen, each cleft into two slender segments with numerous cross-bars; inclined when dry.

Annulus.—One or two rows of large cells.

Spores.—Mature in December.

Distribution.—Universal.

WHITE MOSSES

Genus LEUCOBRYUM, Hampe

The white mosses are found in conspicuous greenish-white cushions about the roots of trees, in woods and on the borders

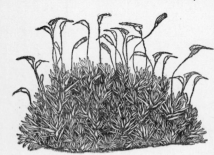

Leucobryum vulgare.

of swamps. The moist cushions are soft and spongy and decidedly greener than the dry, which are so brittle that they can be readily crumbled to dust; and so colourless that they lead one to think they are parasitic or sapro-phytic plants. The change from brittle to soft is due to large cells in the leaves being filled alternately with water and air.

The pale colour is due to the fact that the cells which contain leaf-green and active cell-contents are relatively small and are hidden between transparent cells many times as great. This arrangement of the cells is a contrivance for protecting the

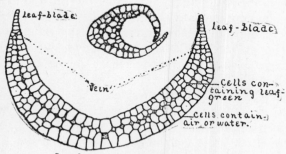

Leucobryum vulgare. Cross-section of leaf.

161

delicate leaf-green bearing cells from the fierce heat of the sun, and for providing a means by which water may be quickly transferred to all parts of the plants.

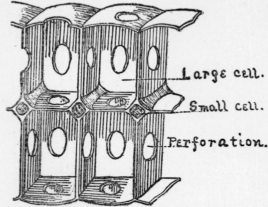

Leucobryum vulgare. Model to show structure.

The walls of these large colourless cells are very thin and are punctured with small holes which communicate with the holes of adjacent cells, so that the moment the plants are moistened, the cells fill with water by capillary attraction. The large cells when filled with water serve as reservoirs to the adjacent small cells, making it possible for the leaf-green to do its work of assimilating plant food. The greater transparency of the water-filled cells makes the leaf-green of the small cells more apparent from the exterior and gives the plants their deeper hue, when wet.

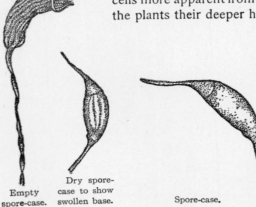

Empty
spore-case.

Dry spore-
case to show
swollen base.

Spore-case.
Leucobryum vulgare.

Leaf.

HAIRY-CAP MOSS, *Polytrichum commune*, L.

Roadsides in the woods and the slopes to the lake are carpeted with sturdy Hairy-caps

The name *Leucobryum*, from the Greek λευκός, white, and βρύον, a moss, was suggested by the pallid colour.

The leaves are lance-shaped with an awl-like apex and a vein occupying the width of the leaf with the exception of a few rows of cells on each side.

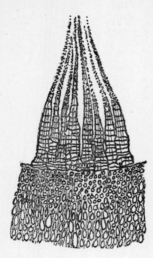

The spore-cases are exserted on long pedicels, they are erect or have the summit somewhat inclined, and the base more or less swollen on one side. When dry the wall is grooved lengthwise.

The lids have an awl-like beak and the teeth are two-parted and purple at the base.

The genus is universal, with seventy-four species in all, nine of them being known in North America.

L. glaucum. Portion of peristome.

Common White Moss, *Leucobryum vulgare,* Hampe.

Habit and habitat.—Conspicuous in white cushions about the roots of trees in woods and on the borders of swamps. It is not uncommon to find on the terminal leaves of female plants

(*a*) Young plant. (*b*) Terminal leaves.

Leucobryum vulgare.

minute tufts of root-like hairs developing a cluster of young plants, which may fall to the ground and form a new colony.

Name.—From the Latin, *vulgaris,* common.

Plant (*gametophyte*).—Whitish ; stems 2 to 8 inches high, two-forked with the primary branches of equal height and the secondary in clusters (*fastigiate*).

Leaves.—Half-clasping at the base, lance-shaped, and tubular from the middle upward ; *vein* occupying most of the leaf blade ; *apex* acute or obtuse with a short, sharp point.

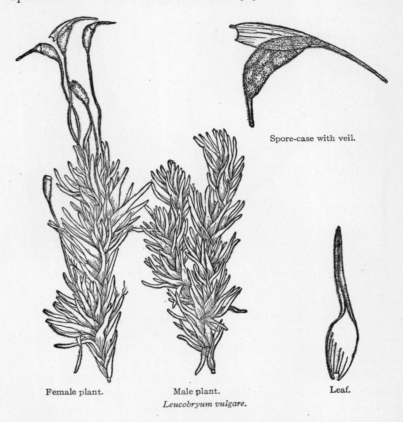

Spore-case with veil.

Female plant.   Male plant.   Leaf.

Leucobryum vulgare.

Habit of flowering.—Male and female flowers on separate plants (*dioicous*). The male plants in distinct tufts, and more slender, with the flower-clusters terminal, in a rosette of six oval bracts.

Veil (*calyptra*).—Large, white.

Spore-case.—Oblong-egg-shaped, chestnut colour, black when old, slightly wrinkled lengthwise when dry. The base (*collum*) distinctly swollen on one side.

Pedicel (seta).—Dark-brown, twisted to the left when dry ; ½ to ¾ of an inch long.

Lid (operculum).—Conical, long-beaked, oblique.

Annulus.—None.

Teeth (peristome).—Sixteen, lance-shaped, red at the base, cleft to below the middle into two unequal forks.

Spores.—Mature in winter or early spring.

Distribution.—Common all over the world, except in Asia.

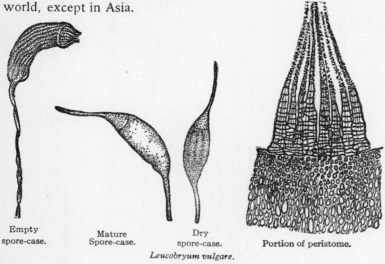

Empty spore-case.   Mature Spore-case.   Dry spore-case.   Portion of peristome.

Leucobryum vulgare.

THE EIGHT-TOOTHED WHITE MOSSES

Genus OCTOBLEPHARUM, Hedw.

The **Genus Octoblepharum** very much resembles the genus *Leucobryum*, the principal difference being that the genus *Octoblepharum* has but eight teeth instead of sixteen. This characteristic gives it its name from the Greek ὀκτὼ, eight, and βλεφάρον, eyelash.

There are fifteen species in all, eight of them in North America.

The Eight-toothed White Moss, *Octoblepharum albidum,* Hedw.

Habit and habitat.—In small white cushions on bark and on shady rocks.

Name.—The specific name *albidum*, white, refers to the colour of the leaves.

Plant (gametophyte).—Spongy, soft when wet, brittle and white when dry.

Leaves.—Close, thick, composed, except on the borders, of two or three superimposed layers of large porous cells without leaf-green, these separated by a layer of simple, narrow cells containing leaf-green.

Veil (calyptra).—Large, split on one side.

Spore-case.—Erect.

Pedicel (seta).—Short.

Lid (operculum).—Plane at the base with an oblique and awl-shaped beak.

Natural size.

Spore-case with
eight teeth.

O. albidum.

Leaf.

Teeth (peristome).—Eight, short, broadly lance-shaped, pale-yellow and transparent.

Spores.—Mature in spring.

Distribution.—Common in the warmer parts of the world except Europe.

Genus CERATODON, Brid.

The species of this genus are small erect plants growing in bright or dark-green cushions on soil or in the crevices of rocks.

The leaves are lance-shaped and keeled, with entire or toothed margins, and a vein extending to or beyond the apex.

166

The mature spore-cases are long-egg-shaped, erect or slightly arched, with a short neck. They are dark or pale-red with wine-red or yellow pedicels, and short-beaked, conical lids, becoming deeply furrowed, inclined, and contracted below the mouth when old.

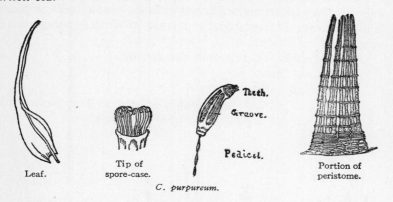

Leaf.   Tip of   Teeth.   Portion of
           spore-case.   Groove.   peristome.
                          Pedicel.

C. purpureum.

There is but one row of teeth, each tooth being cleft into two equal and strongly jointed segments, which suggest the generic name *Ceratodon*, a compound of two Greek words, κέρας, κέρατος, a horn, and ὀδών, a tooth. The two characteristics by which one may feel sure that his moss is a horn-tooth, are the cleft teeth and the shape and grooving of the spore-cases.

There are eighteen species in all, one common in North America.

The Purple Horn-tooth Moss, *Ceratodon purpureum,* Brid. —See Colour Plate IV.

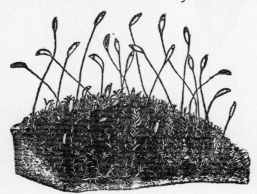

C. purpureum.

Habit and habitat.—Look for the Purple Horn-tooth Moss on rocky ledges in open sunny places of the woods, in pastures and along roadsides, and in vacant city lots. Bright-green cushions of this moss may be found in depressions of the rocks during

167

February and March. At this time the pedicels are often numerous and well-grown and their wine-red colour makes the moss conspicuous even while the spore-cases themselves thus early in the season are but little larger in diameter than the pedicels and are concealed by their veils. With the approach of warmer weather they mature rapidly still carrying their transparent veils. These are discarded before a great while and then the spore-cases and their conical short-beaked lids are glossy and wine-red. Later the lids fall, exposing a fringe of horn-like teeth about the rim. The spore-cases finally become deeply furrowed, inclined, and contracted below the mouth and in this condition may be found during most of the year.

Name.—The specific name *purpureum* is the Latin for "purple," It refers to the colour of the spore-cases and pedicels.

Plant (*gametophyte*). —Slender, erect, branching from the base of the pedicels; *stems* ½ to *3* inches long.

Leaves.—Lance-shaped, keeled; *vein* extending to or beyond the apex; *margin* somewhat irregularly toothed reflexed, opaque; *surface* with slight protuberances; *cells* distinct.

Leaf.

C. *purpureum.*

C. *purpureum.*

Habit of flowering.—Male and female flowers on separate plants (*dioicous*).

Veil (*calyptra*).—Smooth, transparent, split on one side.

Spore-case.—Long, egg-shaped with a short neck, dark-red, erect, somewhat arched; four- or five-angled and deeply furrowed when dry.

168

Pedicel.—Slender, wine-red, erect.

Lid (operculum).—Conical, short-beaked.

Teeth (peristome).—Purple, each split into two equal, strongly cross-barred segments, with tiny projections toward the apex.

Annulus.—Large, rolling back as the lid falls.

Spores.—Mature in early spring, when they are ousted by the shrinking of the wall tissue.

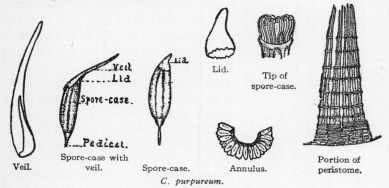

Veil. Spore-case with veil. Spore-case. Annulus. Lid. Tip of spore-case. Portion of peristome.

C. purpureum.

Distribution.—Almost universal.

Variety *Xanthopous.*—Greek ξανθός, yellow, and πούς, a foot; has a pale-yellow pedicel.

Variety *Aristatus.*—Latin "awned"; has the spore-case and pedicel pale and the mid-vein of the leaf extending beyond the apex of the leaf blade.

Variety *Minor.*—Latin "smaller"; is said to have narrower teeth jointed only from the middle downward.

Genus POTTIA, Ehrh.

The species of this genus are small and grow in tufts or cushions on the ground or in crevices of rocks. The stems are simple or sparingly branched from the base. The leaves are oval to oblong and obovate, soft, opaque, smooth or covered with tiny projections; the *apex* is usually taper-pointed, or hair-pointed; the *base* transparent; the *vein* round in section.

The cylindrical to obovate spore-case has sometimes a very short pedicel and

P. truncata. Leaves.

sometimes a long one. The peristome may have imperfect teeth or none or sixteen tiny flat ones.

There are about eighty-three species in all, fourteen in North America.

The genus was named for Professor D. F. Pott, a German botanist.

Pottia truncata, Fuern., l. c.

Habit and habitat.—Common in loose bright-green tufts in fields and gardens and along hedge-rows.

Name.—The specific name is the Latin *truncata*, cut off squarely, and refers to the abrupt summit of the spore-case which appears as if it had been sliced off.

Plant (gametophyte).—Small, ¼ of an inch high and simple, or longer and branching.

Leaves.—Long-oval with the narrow end attached to the stem, concave, smooth; *apex* taper-pointed, tipped with a sharp point; *margin* flat; *vein* extending below

P. truncata.

or beyond the apex.

Habit of flowering.—Male and female flowers on the same plant (*monoicous*).

Veil (calyptra).—Split on one side, smooth.

Spore-case.—Egg-shaped, broad end up (truncate).

Pedicel.—Short, red.

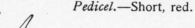

Spore-cases with veils.   Veil.   Spore-cases.   Lid with columella.   Spore-case with lifted lid.

P. truncata.

Lid (operculum).—Plano-convex with an oblique beak, falling with the columella attached.

Teeth (peristome).—None.

Spores.—Brown, mature in fall and winter.

Distribution.—North America, Europe, Asia.

PLATE XIV

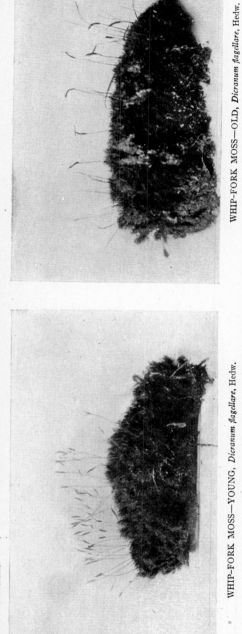

WHIP-FORK MOSS—OLD, *Dicranum flagellare*, Hedw.

WHIP-FORK MOSS—YOUNG, *Dicranum flagellare*, Hedw.

ORTHOTRICHUM

DITRICHUM PALLIDUM

Genus DITRICHUM, Timm, (1788)
LEPTOTRICHUM, Hampe, (1842)

The species of this genus are smooth and glossy plants growing in pale yellow-green tufts on soil or on rocks. The plants are dwarf, or tall and slender with lance-shaped, long-pointed leaves, and oval or cylindrical, erect spore-cases on long and straight, rarely flexuous, pedicels.

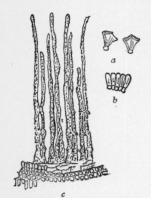

Ditrichum pallidum. (*a*) cells from annulus ; (*b*) annulus ; (*c*) portion of peristome.

The peristome has a compound annulus, and a single row of purple teeth cleft to the base into two slender, cross-barred segments, which have suggested the name of the genus.

The generic name *Leptotrichum,* used by some for the genus, from λεπτὸς, narrow, and θρὶξ, τριχὸς, a hair, has been shown by Hampe to be untenable, having previously been given to a genus of fungi. It has been replaced by *Ditrichum,* from δις, two, and θρὶξ, τριχὸς, a hair. This name has also the right of priority,

There are seventy-two species in all, seventeen in North America.

Ditrichum pallidum, *Leptotrichum pallidum,* Hampe, l. c.— See Colour Plate XIV.

Habit and habitat.—Common in loose tufts, pale or yellow-green, on bare sandy or clay-soil, in fields or by roadsides.

Name.—The specific name *pallidum,* pale, refers to the colour.

Plant (gametophyte).—Slender, erect.

Leaves.—Open, erect, spreading or curved to one side, lance-shaped at base and prolonged to an awl-shaped apex ; *vein* extending beyond the apex and distinctly toothed.

Habit of flowering.—Male and female flowers on the same plant (*monoicous*) ; the male flower-clusters bud-like at the apex of the stem.

Veil (calyptra).—Split up one side.

Spore-case.—Long, egg-shaped, brown.

Pedicel.—Bright yellow, 1 to 2 inches long.

Lid (operculum).—Conical, short-beaked.

171

Teeth (peristome).—Dark-red, each tooth divided into two unequal forks, free or united by the cross-bars.

Annulus.—Double.

Spores.—Very small, smooth, mature in early spring.

Distribution.—Nearly universal, but not found in Great Britain.

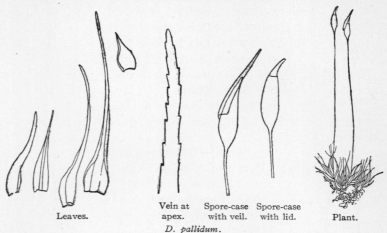

| Leaves. | Vein at apex. | Spore-case with veil. | Spore-case with lid. | Plant. |

D. pallidum.

THE LITTLE-BEARD MOSSES

Genus BARBULA, Hedw.

The species of this genus are found in tufts or cushions tinged with rusty-brown, on stone walls, rocks, tree-trunks and the ground.

The leaves usually much curled and twisted when dry are 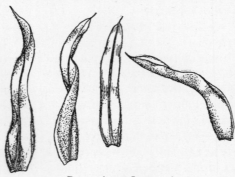 small, and gradually lance-shaped from an oval base, with a round vein vanishing below or rarely extending beyond the apex ; the basal cells are small rectangular and transparent ; the upper are small, round or four-sided, often obscure.

B. cæspitosa. Leaves.

172

The spore-cases are egg-shaped or cylindrical on long pedicels, and have lids with either long or short beaks. The

peristome consists of a very short membrane with sixteen short, straight, imperfect teeth, or of sixteen long teeth each cleft to the base into two long slender forks very much twisted.

B. cæspitosa.
Tip of spore-case to show twisted teeth.

The generic name from *barba*, a beard, refers to the long twisted teeth of some species.

There are in all three hundred and ninety-four species, nineteen being found in North America.

The Claw-leaved Barbula, *Barbula unguiculata*, Hedw.

Habit and habitat.—Common and variable in soft bright or dirty-green tufts on damp black soil, along fences, on rocks, stones, etc.

Name.—The specific name *unguiculata* from the Latin *unguis*, a claw, refers to the sharp-pointed leaves.

Plant (gametophyte).—Variable, ¼ to 1 inch high.

Leaves.—Narrowly oblong, *apex* obtuse with an abrupt sharp point; *vein*

B. cæspitosa.
Fertile plant.

rough with tiny points and passing beyond the apex; *margin* rolled back from the middle downward; *cells*, the *upper* obscure, nearly square, the *basal* longer, small, narrow, transparent.

Leaves at the base of the spore-case (perichætial leaves).—Transparent to near the apex.

Barbula unguiculata.

Habit of flowering.—Male and female flowers on separate plants (*dioicous*); male plants more slender, flower-clusters terminal and bud-like, bracts broadly egg-shaped.

173

Veil (*calyptra*).—Narrow, long-beaked.

Pedicel (*seta*).—Brown-red or purple, variable in length.

Spore-case.—Oblong-elliptical or sub-cylindrical, regular or incurved.

Lid (*operculum*).—Conical, beak long, straight, or curved.

Teeth (*peristome*).—Long and slender, deep-red and twisted two or three times.

Annulus.—None.

Spores.—Mature in winter or spring.

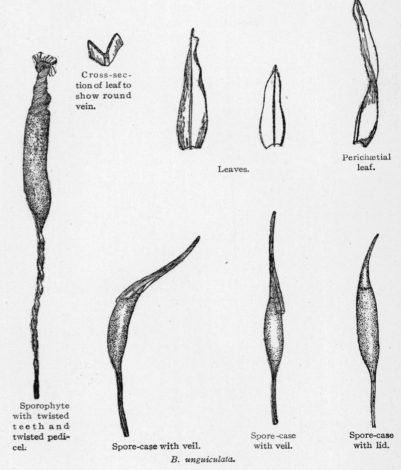

Cross-section of leaf to show round vein.

Leaves.

Perichætial leaf.

Sporophyte with twisted teeth and twisted pedicel.

Spore-case with veil.

Spore-case with veil.

Spore-case with lid.

B. unguiculata.

174

UMBILICARIA VELLEA, (L.) Nyl.

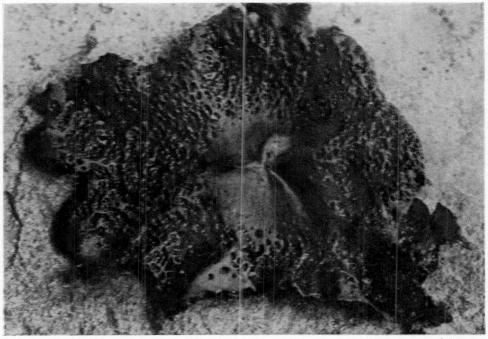

ROCK TRIPE, *Umbilicaria Muhlenbergii*, (Ach.) Tuckerm.

The Tufted Barbula, *Barbula cæspitosa,* Schwaegr.

Habit and habitat.—Common and variable, roots of trees in grassy places.

Name.—The specific name *cæspitosa,* from the Latin *cæspes,* turf, refers to the tufted manner of growth.

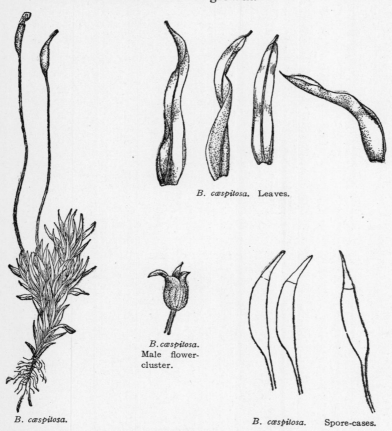

B. cæspitosa. Leaves.

B. cæspitosa.
Male flower-
cluster.

B. cæspitosa. Spore-cases.

B. cæspitosa.

Plant (gametophyte).—Loosely tufted, soft, variable in size.

Leaves.—Long and narrow, more or less wavy, curled or bent in various directions and with a very narrow wavy point when dry; *apex* bearing a short sharp point; *vein* strong, yellow, prolonged beyond the leaf-blade; *cells,* the basal loose and transparent, the upper green and indistinct.

Habit of flowering.—Male and female flowers on the same

175

plant (*monoicous*); male flowers in axillary buds, with short pedicels and two or three leaves.

Veil (*calyptra*).—Split up one side.

Spore-case.—Red, thin, long, egg-shaped, more or less incurved.

Pedicel.—Long and slender, twisted when dry.

Lid (*operculum*).—Conic, taper-pointed.

Teeth (*peristome*).—Basilar membrane none or scarcely visible; teeth very long, purple, twice or three times twisted.

B. unguiculata. Tip of spore-case with twisted teeth.

Annulus.—None.

Spores.—Minute, greenish, translucent, smooth; mature in May and June and late summer.

Distribution.—Hills of the Southeastern States; also in Europe, Asia, Africa, South America

Genus TORTULA, Hedw.

The plants of this genus are variable in size with simple stems forming yellow-green tufts on walls, rocks, or rarely on trees.

The leaves are oblong or spatulate and are covered with tiny protuberances. The apex is obtuse with the vein extending

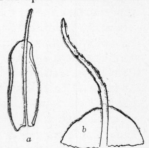

T. princeps. (*a*) Leaf. (*b*) Apex of leaf tip with transparent awn.

T. princeps. Portion of peristome.

beyond as a point or as a long transparent hair. Toward the apex the cells are six-sided, opaque and filled with chlorophyll grains; toward the base they are transparent and elongated.

The spore-cases are erect, oblong or cylindrical and somewhat incurved on usually long pedicels. The

T. ruralis. Tip of spore-case. (*a*) Basilar membrane. (*b*) Teeth.

peristome is sometimes absent; when present, it consists of thirty-two thread-like teeth remotely cross-barred and covered with tiny protuberances. The teeth are either straight, incurved, or spirally twisted, all united at the base into a distinct tubular more or less elongated basal membrane. The spores are small and nearly smooth.

The generic name *Tortula,* the diminutive of the Latin *tortus,* twisted, refers to the teeth.

Tortula princeps, De Not.

Habit and habitat.—In tall, loose, red-brown tufts on rocks, walls, and sometimes trunks of trees. A fine moss, easily known by its interrupted stems and dense, broad, rust-coloured leaves.

Name.—The specific name *princeps,* the Latin for "chief" refers to the striking character of the moss. It is described under the name of *Barbula Muelleri,* B r u c h a n d Schimp., in Lesquereux & James Manual.

Plant (gametophyte).—*Stems* repeatedly interrupted by new growths with root-like fibres at their bases.

Leaves.—Soft, dense, broad and rust-coloured in interrupted rosettes along the stem and at the summits of the branches; *apex* obtuse; *margin* rolled back to below the middle; *vein* red, extending beyond the apex in a slender transparent, faintly spiny hair-point; *cells* at the base loose, rectangular and transparent.

T. princeps.
Spore-case
with veil.

T. princeps.
Tip of
spore-case.

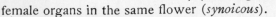

T. princeps.

Habit of flowering.—Male and female organs in the same flower (*synoicous*).

Veil (calyptra).—Split on the side.

Spore case.—Cylindrical, brown, arched like a bow.

Pedicel.—Red.

Lid (operculum).—Long and conical.

Teeth (peristome).—The lower half tubular and pale, the teeth red.

177

Annulus.—Double.

Spores.—Mature in spring.

Distribution.—Headquarters in the Mediterranean basin; rare in England, common in the western states of North America.

Tortula ruralis.

T. ruralis. Tip of spore-case. (*a*) basilar membrane; (*b*) twisted teeth.

Tortula ruralis is much like the preceeding, but smaller, with flowers dioicous. It grows on thatched roofs or stony ground, in tall cushions 1 to 3 inches deep; bright green above and bright red-brown below. The awn at the apex of the leaf is strongly spiny, transparent above and often red at the base, sometimes equalling the rest of the leaf. The spore cases are narrowly cylindrical with a lid half as long and a stout red pedicel about an inch long.

T. ruralis. Awn at the apex of the leaf.

Genus GRIMMIA, Ehrh.

The species of the **Genus Grimmia** sometimes form conspicuous gray tufts, often hoary from the white hair-points which terminate the leaves; sometimes they form soft fragile patches on exposed rocks of higher mountain regions. The tufts vary in size from little dense cushions one-third of an inch high, to the mats of *Gr. hypnoides,* whose stems attain a length of eight inches.

The dingy colour of their leaves, tipped with long or short white hairs is their most striking character. The chlorophyll is not only absent from the hair-point but often from the apex of the leaf-blade as well, thus adding to the grayish-white appearance of the tufts. The plants are usually short, with forked stems, crowded with lance-shaped leaves, frequently thickened along the margin, which is mostly entire; the *vein* is percurrent or extends into the transparent hair; the *cells* of the lower part are rectangular, of the upper part small, often obscure.

178

The generic name was given in honour of J. F. C. Grimm, a German botanist, who was a physician of Gotha.

The spore-cases are oval and smooth, borne on arched or straight pedicels. The peristome consists of sixteen red, lance-shaped teeth, entire or cleft at the apex and often perforated below.

There are about two hundred and forty species known at present, fifteen of them in North America.

Grimmia apocarpa, Hedw.

Habit and habitat.—Loosely tufted to form olive-green or black tufts on rocks or stone walls or even on roofs. There are varieties which grow in streams.

Name.—The specific name *apocarpa* from ἀπὸ, *without* and καρπός, *a fruit*, was given by J. G. Hedwig, in 1787, to describe the hidden spore-case.

Plant (gametophyte).—Robust, the stems one inch long, branching in pairs, free from root-like fibres.

Leaves.—Lance-shaped, open when moist, erect when dry; *apex* sometimes slightly toothed, the upper leaves usually prolonged into a short, rough hair about one-quarter as long as the leaf; the *base* is concave,

G. apocarpa, becoming keeled upward; *margin* recurved; the *vein*
Plant with
immersed continued into the transparent hair, or vanishing below
spore-case. the apex; *cells*, the basal rectangular, then narrow, the upper rounded.

Leaves at the base of the pedicel (perichœtial leaves).—Broader, thinner; *vein* narrow; *apex* with or without short point.

Habit of flowering.—Male and female flowers on separate part of the same plant (*autoicous*); male flower-clusters bud-like.

Veil (calyptra).—Very small, not reaching below the lid, lobed at the base.

Spore-case.—Egg-shaped, almost concealed in the leaves at the base, red.

Pedicel.—Very short.

G. apocarpa. *Lid (operculum).*—Bright-red, tipped with *G. apocarpa.*
Spore-case Spore-case
with lid. a sharp point; *columella* attached to the lid with veil. and falling with it.

Annulus.—None.

Teeth (peristome).—Arising below the mouth, large, purple-red, entire or perforated, spreading when dry.

Spores.—Mature in winter.
Distribution.—Universal.

THE TORN-VEIL MOSSES

Genus RACOMITRIUM, Brid.

The species of the **Genus Racomitrium** are usually of large size, with stems branching in pairs, the branches simple and all

Racomitrium lanuginosum.

reaching the same height, or unequal, in lateral clusters. They are widely and loosely tufted on rocks in mountainous r e g i o n s. Many of the species resemble the *Hypnum* mosses on account of their long prostrate stems, their numerous short branches, and their apparently lateral spore-cases.

R. lanugino-sum. Veil.

The name is from the Greek ῥάκος, a shred, and μιτρίον, a veil, referring to the torn base of the veil.

The *leaves* are not tufted at the top of the stems but are close, nearly equal, long, lance-shaped, concave and channelled, with an *apex* blunt or ending in a fine point or hair; the *margin* is recurved; the *cells* are usually obscure, rounded or four-sided in the upper part, and long and narrow in the lower part.

The spore-cases are oblong cylindrical, narrowed at the orifice and usually erect on erect pedicels. The *lids* are small and more or less beaked and the peristome consists of a single row of sixteen long teeth cleft two or three times to below the middle, or

Portion of peristome.

R. lanuginosum. Vertical section o f peristome with two cells of the annulus at the base of one tooth.

divided into two thread-like, knotty, nearly equal segments, erect when dry, rarely spreading. The *annulus* is compound, rolling back when the lid falls.

Eighty-one species are known at present, twenty in North America. They are mostly distinguished from the species of the genus *Grimmia* by the peculiar narrow and wavy cell-structure of the leaf-base in conjunction with their habit of growth.

The Woolly Torn-veil Moss, *Racomitrium lanuginosum,* Brid.

Habit and habitat.—Common on the tops of walls and on rocks in mountainous regions. The thick grayish-white tufts extending in wide patches.

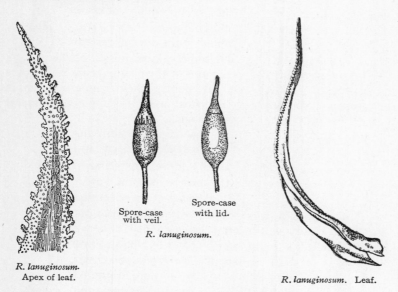

Spore-case with veil.

Spore-case with lid.

R. lanuginosum.

R. lanuginosum. Apex of leaf.

R. lanuginosum. Leaf.

Name.—The specific name *lanuginosum*, woolly, was applied by Bridel to describe the white appearance due to the transparent tips of the leaves.

Plant (gametophyte).—Long and slender, stems 1 to 12 inches long, prostrate, branches in pairs, the side branches numerous.

Leaves.—Close, long-spreading, erect or recurved narrowly lance-shaped, bent to one side toward the apex; *apex* tapering to a white transparent hair-point often longer than the leaf-blade;

181

vein narrow; *margin* from the middle upward a pellucid membrane bearing tiny protuberances, and bordered with hair-like teeth, wavy when dry; *cells*, those of the margin very small, dot-like; those of the leaf-blade narrow.

Habit of flowering.—Male and female flowers on separate plants (*dioicous*).

Veil.—Resembling a bishop's mitre, long-beaked, rough at the apex only.

Spore-cases.—Oblong, egg-shaped, pale-brown, finally darker.

Pedicel.—Short, $\frac{1}{5}$ to $\frac{1}{2}$ of an inch long on a lateral branchlet.

Lid (operculum).—Tapering from a conical base.

Teeth (peristome).—Long, cleft into two forks; orange-red.

Annulus.—Broad.

Spores.—Mature in summer.

Distribution.—Universal.

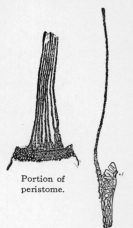

Portion of peristome.

Vertical section of peristome showing two cells of the annulus at the base of one tooth

R. lanuginosum.

HEDWIG'S MOSS
Genus **HEDWIGIA**, Ehrh.

The species of the **Genus Hedwigia** have two-forked stems with roots at the base. They are usually found in hoary fragile patches on rocks.

The leaves are broad, oval, veinless, and coarsely toothed or fringed on the margins.

The spore-cases are globular, immersed with almost no pedicel and no peristome.

There are ten species in all, three in North America.

The generic name was given in honour of J. G. Hedwig, a distinguished German botanist, who lived in 1782.

H. ciliata. Plant stripped of leaves to show two male flower-clusters on the stem and one spore-case surrounded with three fringed leaves.

H. ciliata. Leaf.

Hedwig's Fringe-leaf Moss, *Hedwigia ciliata*, Ehrh.
Habit and habitat.—In small or wide patches, loosely tufted,
and hoary-green; common on rocks.
Name.—The specific name *ciliata*,

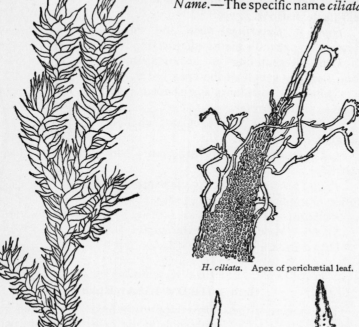

H. ciliata. Apex of perichætial leaf.

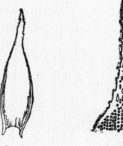

Leaf.   Apex of leaf.
H. ciliata.

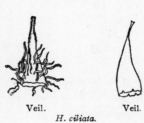

Veil.   Veil.
H. ciliata.

H. ciliata. Sterile plant.

183

referring to the fringed perichætial leaves, is derived from the Latin *cilium*, an eyelash.

Plant (gametophyte).—Pale-green, *stems* slender, 1 to 4 inches long, at first erect, then procumbent, repeatedly twice-forked.

Leaves.—Spreading all round when moist, crowded and overlapping like shingles when dry, broadly lance-shaped; *apex* recurved, translucent by the absence of leaf-green; *margins* wavy, *base* growing down the stem and yellow at the point of attachment; *cells* with tiny projections.

Leaves at the base of the spore-case (perichætial leaves).—Thin and transparent, taper-pointed, fringed on the margins.

Habit of flowering.—Male and female flowers on one plant (*monoicous*).

Veil (calyptra).—Small, covering the lid, conical, with or without hairs.

Spore-case.—Immersed, globular, light-brown, red at the mouth.

Pedicel.—Almost none.

Lid (operculum).—Convex, with or without an obtuse point in the centre.

Annulus.—None.

Teeth (peristome).—None.

Spores.—Mature in spring.

Distribution.—Universal.

H. ciliata. Plant stripped of leaves to show spore-case surrounded with three fringed leaves; two male flower-clusters on the stem.

Spore-case.

Spore-case without lid.

H. ciliata.

THE CURLED-LEAF MOSSES

Genus ULOTA, Mohr

The species of the **Genus Ulota** usually grow in small rounded cushions, which live year after year on trees but never on soil. They are common on the trunks and small stems of mountain trees.

184

SCARLET-CRESTED CLADONIA, *Cladonia cristatella*, Tuckerm.

BROWN-FRUITED CUP CLADONIA, *Cladonia pyxidata*, (L.) Fr.

The leaves are narrowly lance-shaped from a broad oval base and are usually curled when dry. It is this character which gives them their generic name from ὀυλότης, curled.

The cells are very narrow, coloured and thickened along the median line while the marginal cells below are transparent in several rows.

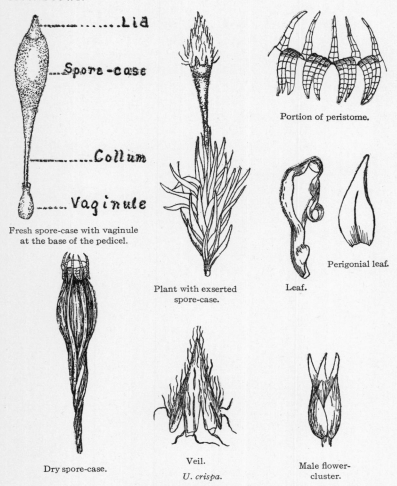

Lid

Spore-case

Collum

Vaginule

Fresh spore-case with vaginule at the base of the pedicel.

Portion of peristome.

Perigonial leaf.

Plant with exserted spore-case.

Leaf.

Dry spore-case.

Veil.
U. crispa.

Male flower-cluster.

The veils are conical bell-shaped, usually covered with erect, yellow hairs; they are lobed at the base and folded lengthwise in plaits.

185

The spore-cases are exserted on straight pedicels; they are pear-shaped, narrowed at the base into a long neck, 8-striate and twisted to the left when dry.

The peristome is single or double, the outer of the sixteen white teeth usually united in pairs; the inner of 8 to 16 narrow processes alternate with the teeth or wanting.

There are fifty-seven species in all, sixteen in North America.

The Curly-leaved Ulota, *Ulota crispa,* Brid.—See Plate XV.

Habit and habitat.—In small dense round cushions, yellow-green on the surface and rust-colour within. Common in mountain woods on trunks and branches of trees, especially beeches, firs and birches.

Name.—The specific name from the Latin *crispus,* curled, refers to the special curling of the dry leaves.

Plant (gametophyte).—Small, erect.

Leaves.—Linear, lance-shaped from an enlarged oval concave base; *apex* narrow or hair-like, curled when dry; *cells* at base long and narrow, worm-like, thick-walled, on the margin enlarged and 4-sided.

U. crispa.
Leaves.

Habit of flowering.—Male and female flowers on same plant (*monoicous*); male flower-clusters bud-like.

Veil (calyptra).—Yellow, bell-shaped, split at the base, plaited lengthwise and covered with soft hairs.

U. crispa. Sporophyte spore-case with a long neck and tooth, pedicel short with vaginule.

Spore-case.—Pale-green or light-brown, thin-walled, pear-shaped, narrowed end extending almost to the base of the pedicel, constricted under the mouth and deeply grooved when dry and empty.

Pedicel (seta).—Short and erect.

Lid (operculum).—With a comparatively short beak.

Teeth (peristome).—The outer of eight pairs, at first spreading, then recurved, the inner eight, rarely sixteen.

186

THE CURLY-LEAVED ÚLOTA, *Úlota crispa*, Mohr.
The lichen is *Parmelia saxatilis*, (L.) Fr.

Spores.—Mature in August.

Distribution.—Universal.

The Bud-leaved Ulota, *Ulota phyllantha,* Brid.

Ulota phyllantha grows in dense cushions ½ to 1½ inches high, green or yellow above and rich red or brown below.

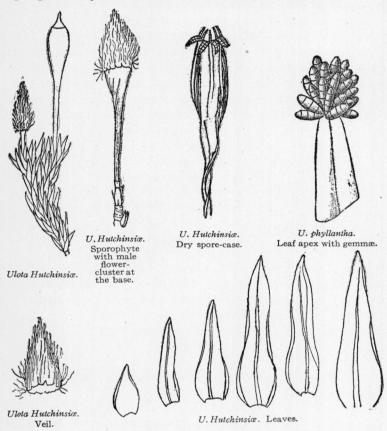

Ulota Hutchinsiæ.

U. Hutchinsiæ.
Sporophyte
with male
flower-
cluster at
the base.

U. Hutchinsiæ.
Dry spore-case.

U. phyllantha.
Leaf apex with gemmæ.

Ulota Hutchinsiæ.
Veil.

U. Hutchinsiæ. Leaves.

The leaves are acutely pointed with percurrent vein, upon the apex of which are abundant red-brown, club-shaped and jointed gemmæ which have suggested the specific name from the Greek φύλλον, a leaf, and ἄνθος, a flower or young bud.

This moss has been found on the highest plant-line of Chimborazo as well as close to sea-level, and is widely distributed over the world.

187

Hutchins's Ulota; *Ulota Hutchinsiæ*, Schimp.

Habit and habitat.—The plant grows in dark red-brown tufts, rigid and fragile. They are common on granite rocks in the mountains.

Name.—The specific name was given by Wilhelm Philipp Schimper in honour of Miss Hutchins, who first collected the plants on the lake shore near Bantry, Ireland.

Leaves.—Close and overlapping like shingles, rigid and appressed when dry; erect or slightly spreading when moist; oblong, lance-shaped; *apex* obtuse; *base* oval or oblong; *margins* turned back; *vein* strong; *cells*, the basal linear or worm-like, the marginal somewhat 4-sided, the upper small.

Habit of flowering.—Male and female flowers on the same plant (*monoicous*); the male flower-clusters bud-like.

U. Hutchinsiæ. Portion of peristome with four cilia and six teeth in pairs.

Veil (*calyptra*).—Very hairy.

Spore-case.—Oval, narrowed to a very long neck 8-furrowed the whole length, hardly contracted at the mouth.

Pedicel (*seta*).—Long.

Lid (*operculum*).—Conical, taper-pointed.

Teeth (*peristome*).—Eight; long, lance-shaped, in pairs, entire or split at the apex, reflexed when dry; the inner segments eight, a little shorter than the teeth.

Spores.—Mature in summer.

Distribution.—Common in mountainous regions

MOSSES WITH STRAIGHT-HAIRED VEILS

Genus ORTHOTRICHUM, Hedw. (See Plate XIV.)

The species of the **Genus Orthotrichum** grow in round cushions on rocks, trees and walls. The plants are usually erect, with branching stems having radicles at the bases.

The leaves are lance-shaped, lapping like shingles, rarely twisted when dry, the surface is covered with minute protuberances, or is rarely smooth in the upper part; the margin is recurved; the cells toward the apex of the leaf are dot-like and contain chlorophyll, toward the lower part they are longer and transparent; the veil is bell-shaped, more or less split at the base and keeled or deeply grooved throughout, it may be naked or may have a few straight hairs, a character which suggested the name *Orthotrichum*, from ὀρθός, straight, and θρὶξ, τριχός, hair. The spore-cases are immersed or exserted on a short pedicel and have usually, when dry, 8 to 16 grooves running lengthwise, but they may be smooth. The pedicels are generally short with an enlarged base (*vaginule*) crowned with a minute cup-like sheath. The peristome is simple or double, the outer consisting of 16 single teeth or 8 pairs, with either no annulus or a very narrow one.

In all there are two hundred and thirty-five species, fifty-seven being found in North America.

Orthotrichum strangulatum, Beauv.

Habit and habitat.—In small, loose dirty-green tufts ¼ of an inch deep; on trees, rarely on rocks.

Name.—The specific name *strangulatum*, strangled, refers to the constriction under the mouth of the spore-case.

Plant (*gametophyte*).—One-quarter of an inch long.

Leaves.—Linear lance-shaped from an oblong base, keeled; *apex* pointed or blunt; *margins* rolled back; cells, the *upper*, round, small, close, with slight protuberances; the *basal*, long and quadrangular.

Leaves at the base of the pedicel (*perichætial leaves*).—Longer, erect, somewhat sheathing.

Habit of flowering.—Male and female flowers on the same plant (*monoicous*).

Veil (*calyptra*).—Resembling a bishop's mitre (*mitriform*) furrowed and nearly naked.

Spore-case.—Oblong egg-shaped,

Plant.

Portion of peristome, with two cilia and four teeth.

O. strangulatum.

189

half-emergent, dirty-brown when old, strongly constricted under the mouth.

Lid (operculum).—Conical, obtusely short-pointed.

Teeth (peristome).—The outer eight double teeth, dirty-yellow, granulose, reflexed when dry; the *inner*, of eight filiform strong segments.

Spores.—Mature in May and June.

Distribution.—North America only.

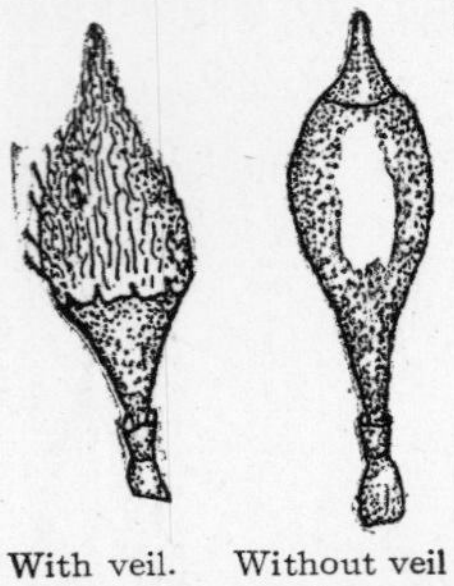

With veil.   Without veil
Mature sporophyte.
O. rupestris.

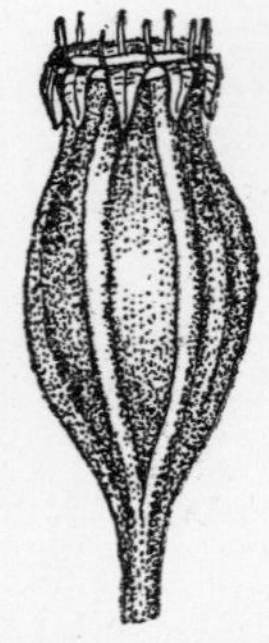

O. strangulatum
Dry spore-case.

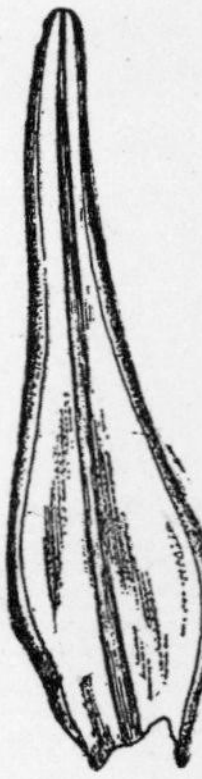

O. strangulatum.
Leaf.

O. rupestris.
Dry sporo-
phyte with-
out lid.

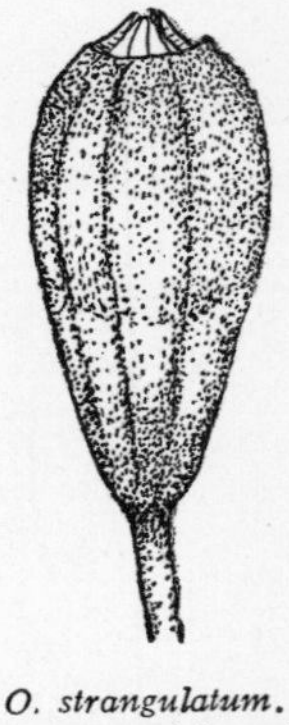

Mature sporo-
phyte with
veil.
O. strangulatum.

O. strangulatum.
Spore-case without lid.

O. rupestris. Plant.

THE EXTINGUISHER MOSSES

Genus ENCALYPTA, Schreb.

The species of the **Genus Encalypta** grow on bright-green cushions on rocks or on the ground.

The leaves are linear, spatulate or tongue-shaped and are

190

covered with tiny double-pointed projections. The cells toward the base are thin and transparent, while those toward the apex are small and opaque with leaf-green.

The spore-cases are borne on long solid pedicels; they are regular, erect and ribbed or twisted when dry with conic and long-beaked lids.

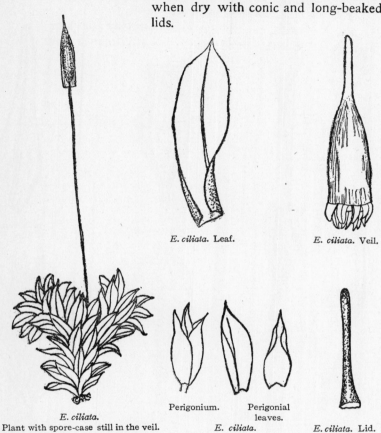

E. *ciliata*. Leaf.

E. *ciliata*. Veil.

E. *ciliata*.
Plant with spore-case still in the veil.

Perigonium.

Perigonial leaves.
E. *ciliata*.

E. *ciliata*. Lid.

The veils are large, cylindrical and bell-shaped, longer than the spore-cases, tapering at the apex and sometimes fringed at the base. This character suggested the generic name, from the Greek ἐνκαλυπτὸς, veiled. The peristome is variable, having no teeth or a single or double row. The spores are large and beset with small projections.

191

In all there are thirty-nine species, sixteen being found in North America.

The Extinguisher Mosses with Fringed Veils, *Encalypta ciliata,* Hedw.

Habit and habitat.—In loose bright or pale-green tufts on shaded rocks and soil; not rare.

Name.—The specific name *ciliata,* from the Latin *cilium,* an eyelash, refers to the fringed base of the veil.

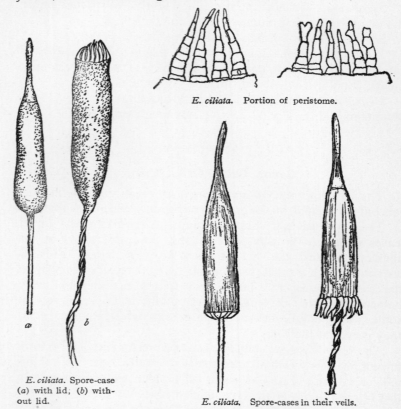

E. ciliata. Portion of peristome.

E. ciliata. Spore-case (*a*) with lid; (*b*) without lid.

E. ciliata. Spore-cases in their veils.

Plant (gametophyte).—Stems ½ to 2 inches high, thick, covered with rooting filaments, simple or sparingly branched.

Leaves.—Soft, large, crowded, recurved-spreading, oblong, egg-shaped or tongue-shaped, slightly concave; *apex* short, taper-pointed with a tiny sharp point; *margin* wavy; *vein* pale-yellow,

192

vanishing below the apex or passing into it; *cells*, toward the base loose, red, the marginal of several rows narrower and paler.

Habit of flowering.—Male and female flowers on one plant (*monoicous*).

Veil (*calyptra*).—Straw-colour, descending far below the base of the spore-case, bordered at the base by lance-shaped solid white or orange segments.

Pedicel.—Long; yellow or pale-red.

Spore-case.—Cylindrical, smooth, slightly constricted under the mouth when dry, the neck short and indistinct.

Lid (*operculum*).—Conic, with a long slender beak.

Teeth (*peristome*).—Rarely absent, single, of 16 narrowly lance-shaped red teeth, sometimes divided into two irregular segments, connivent when dry, incurved when moist.

Distribution.—Mountain regions of New England, the Rocky Mountains and the Pacific slope, Europe and Africa.

FOUR-TOOTHED MOSSES

Genus GEORGIA, Ehrh.

The species of the **Genus Georgia** are erect, growing in clusters but not matted, on the ground, on rotten wood and sandstone.

The lower leaves are small, distant and scale-like; the upper leaves are longer, broadly lance-shaped, close and tufted at the apex of the stems; the vein reaches to below the apex; the cells are somewhat six-sided, less crowded and linear rectangular at the base. Linear root-leaves (*frondiform*) or whip-like leafy branches are often present. These frondiform leaves appear in some species only in the protonemal stage, while in other species they persist at the base.

The spore-cases are cylindrical or oval on long slender, smooth, brown pedicels which are straight or abruptly bent. The lids are conical with mitre-like veils. The four teeth arising from just below the rim of the box are a conspicuous character of the genus. They are formed by the splitting of a solid mass of pithy tissue within the lid into four slender triangular segments, red and slightly furrowed on the back. A cross section of a tooth shows it to be triangular and composed externally of large transparent cells and internally of small thick-walled pointed cells. There is no annulus.

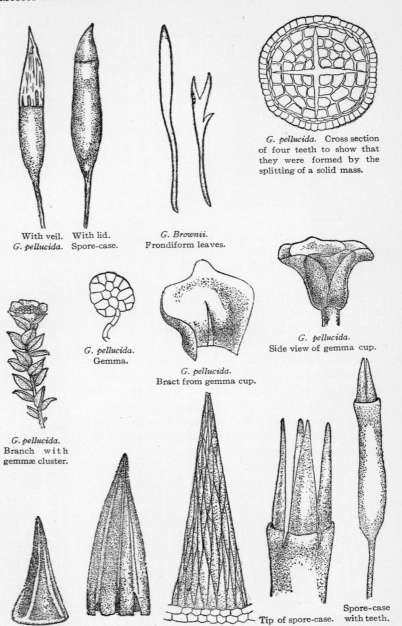

G. *pellucida*. Cross section of four teeth to show that they were formed by the splitting of a solid mass.

With veil.
G. *pellucida*.

With lid.
Spore-case.

G. *Brownii*.
Frondiform leaves.

G. *pellucida*.
Gemma.

G. *pellucida*.
Bract from gemma cup.

G. *pellucida*.
Side view of gemma cup.

G. *pellucida*.
Branch with gemmæ cluster.

G. *pellucida*. Lid.

G. *pellucida*. Veil.

G. *pellucida*. Tooth.

Tip of spore-case.
G. *pellucida*.

Spore-case with teeth.

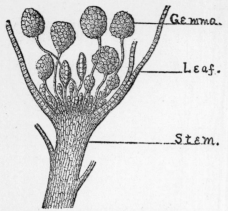

G. pellucida. Vertical section of gemma cup showing gemmæ with slender stems and cut edges of leaves on either side.

There are but two species known and both of these are found in North America.

The genus was named by Friedrich Ehrhart, in honour of King George III. of England, whom he considered one of the greatest patrons of botany.

Georgia pellucida, Rabenh.—See Colour Plate III.

Habit and habitat.—Erect, rather densely crowded, bright-green above, red below. On decayed wood in damp places, common.

Name.—The specific name *pellucida* from the Latin *per*, through, and *lucida*, transparent, refers to the texture of the leaves, which are very translucent.

Plant (gametophyte).—Stems of two kinds, (1) the fertile ½ to 1 inch long, pale red, simple or branching in pairs, fibrous at the base with crowded leaves tufted at the summit of the stem; (2) gemmæ-bearing, the gemmæ disk-like with short stalks, greenish, transparent, inclosed in a rosette of 4 to 5 bracts.

Leaves.—The *lower* leaves are small, remote, erect, appressed, broadly lance-shaped

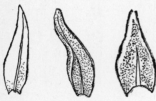

G. pellucida.
Lower leaves of fertile plant.

G. pellucida.
Upper leaf of gemmæ plant.

G. pellucida.
Perichætial leaf.

and red; the *upper* leaves are larger, broader, not lying against the stem; *margin* entire; *vein* vanishing below the apex; *cells* round-hexagonal above, elongated and rectangular at the base. It is not an uncommon thing to find gemmæ which have fallen from the cups, entangled and growing among the leaves.

Leaves at the base of the pedicel (perichætial leaves).—Lance-shaped, sheathing elongated, rather obtuse.

Habit of flowering.—Male and female flowers on the same plant (*monoicous*); male flower-clusters bud-like at the apex of the shoots which arise in pairs.

Veil (calyptra).—White below, more solid and red above, mitreform, reaching to the middle of the spore-case, irregularly folded lengthwise into 8 or 9 ridges, somewhat ragged at the base.

Spore-case. — Erect, elongated, cylindric, pale-brown with the mouth red.

Pedicel (seta). — Straight, smooth, purple; when dry twisted to the left in the lower part, to the right above, ½ to ¾ of an inch long.

Lid (operculum). — Thin, conical, straight or oblique,

Annulus.—None.

Teeth (peristome).—Four, erect, brown, pyramidal, grooved lengthwise on the back, arising from below the rim of the spore-case.

Columella.—Slender, cylindrical.

Spores.—Small, smooth, green, mature from July to September.

Distribution. — Widely in America, Europe and Asia.

G. pellucida. Fertile plant, with male branch at the left.

196

Georgia geniculata, Girgens.

Georgia geniculata may be distinguished from *G. pellucida* in having the pedicel suddenly bent near the middle, a character which suggested the specific name *geniculata* from the Latin *geniculum*, a little knee.

It is found in Japan and in North America.

Gemmæ-bearing branch.
G. pellucida.

G. geniculata. Sporophyte with four teeth and a twisted spiny pedicel.

G. geniculata. Plant with two spore-cases on bent pedicels; male branch on the right.

197

FOUR-TOOTHED MOSSES

Genus TETRADONTIUM, Schwaegr.

This genus was established by Schwaegrichen, but differs so little from the genus *Georgia* that many think it should not be considered a separate genus.

There are two species in all, one in North America.

It differs from *Georgia* in having both teeth and stems shorter, in having the spore-case oval instead of cylindrical and in having the veil cover the spore-case.

The name is derived from the Greek τέτρα, four, and ὀδὼν, a tooth.

Tetradontium repandum, Schwaegr.

Habit and habitat.—Very small, growing in loose clusters on shaded rocks.

Name.—The specific name *repandum*, the Latin for "curved," refers to the margin of the mouth of the spore-case.

Plant (gametophyte).—Stems very short, bearing little gemmæ at the base of thread-like leafy branches.

Leaves.—Ovate-lance-shaped, rigid, red-brown, closely overlapping like shingles.

Leaves at the base of the pedicel (perichætial leaves).—Ovate and oblong, very concave, *vein* obscure; scales about the male flowers (*perigonium*) smaller, thinner, vein absent.

Habit of flowering.—Male and female flowers on the same plant (*monoicous*).

Veil (calyptra).—Conical, resembling a bishop's mitre and covering the spore-case to the base.

Spore-case.—Thick, oval, the margin of the orifice somewhat notched between the teeth.

Georgia pellucida. Spore-case with veil.

Tetradontium repandum Spore-case with veil.

Tetradontium repandum. Female plant with thread-like branch at the base.

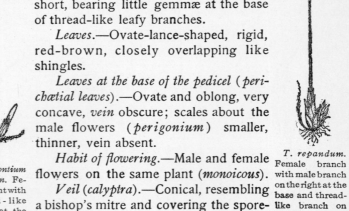

T. repandum. Female branch with male branch on the right at the base and thread-like branch on the left.

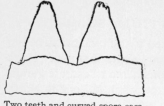

Two teeth and curved spore-case margin.

Perigonium and perigonial leaves.

Perichætial leaves.

Leaf.

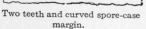

Tetradontium repandum.

Pedicel (seta).—Thick and rigid.

Lid (operculum).—Conical, erect, short.

Teeth (peristome).—Simple, of four short, triangular teeth.

Spores.—Mature in autumn.

Distribution.—Near Glen House and at Dixville Notch, White Mountains.   Very rare.

Genus SCHISTOSTEGA, Mohr

The **Genus Schistostega** contains but one species; this is found growing in bright-green patches on the ground in caverns and grottoes and under the shade of rocks.   The protonema is persistent, and shines with a weird light in the semi-darkness where it grows.   The most striking character of the moss is the highly refractive power of the protonema cells.   These are able to converge the feeble rays of light which enter the caves and

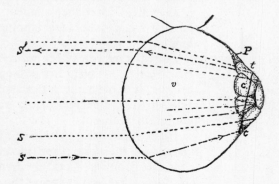

Vertical section of a protonema to show paths of refracted and reflected light rays; (*S*) an incident ray refracted to *t*, then reflected from *t* to *t* and again reflected and refracted from *t* to *S¹*; (*v*) clear cell contents; (*c*) chlorophyll grains; (*P*) plasma.

T. repandum. Thread-like branch.

199

grottoes so that they fall upon the chlorophyll grains and enable them by light-energy to build up plant foods from gases and water. When searching for this moss one must be careful not to intercept the rays of light which enter the cave and then one may be fortunate enough to get the feebly reflected rays which

Protonema in natural position, very highly magnified. Illumination from above.

Veil.

Three cells of protonema from L to show position of chlorophyll grains when the light rays enter perpendicular to the surface.

Spore-case with lid.

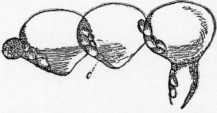

Three cells of protonema to show position of chlorophyll grains when light rays enter obliquely.

Schistostega osmundacea

Spore-case with lid raised showing spores.

S. osmundacea.

emerge from it. The four diagrams if taken in order with their legends, will give one a clear idea of how the light rays are refracted and reflected by the cell-contents and of how the chlorophyll grains move to that part of the cell which is illuminated.

Schistostega osmundacea, Web. & Mohr.

Plant (gametophyte).—Living but one year, produced from a persistent, thread-like growth *(protonema); stems* tender and delicate, usually simple, ¼ of an inch high with root-like filaments at the base. Two forms are found, the *barren* which are naked below and have two rows of vertically placed leaves above, the *fertile* which resemble the barren or are naked except for a small tuft of terminal leaves.

S. osmundacea. Fertile plant.

S. osmundacea. Barren plant with male branch at the left.

N a m e .—The specific name *osmundacea* suggests a resemblance to the ferns of the same name.

L e a v e s .—Oblong-pointed, confluent at the base; *cells* large, rhomboidal, containing leaf-green.

Habit of flowering.— Male and female on separate plants *(dioicous)* male flower-clusters bud-like.

Veil (calyptra).—Minute, narrow, resembling a bishop's hat, covering the lid only.

Spore-case.—Small, almost spherical, soft.

Spore-sac (sporangium).—Distinct.

Columella.—Present, thick.

201

Pedicel.—Long and soft.

Lid (operculum).—Small, convex, with a red border.

Teeth (peristome).—None.

Spores.—Minute, maturing in the spring.

Species.—But one known.

Distribution.—It has been found in northern and central Europe and in New York and the White Mountains.

THE QUARTETTE MOSS
Genus TETRAPLODON, Bruch & Schimp.

The plants of the **Genus Tetraplodon** are perennial, growing in densely crowded cushions.   They closely resemble the plants

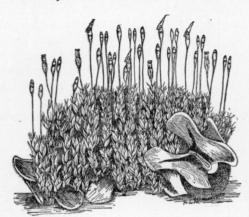

T. mnioides.   Growing on porcupine bones.

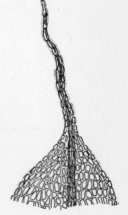

T. mnioides.   Leaf apex.

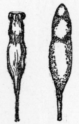

Empty spore-case.   Mature spore-case.   *T. mnioides.*

of the genus *Splachnum*, but differ principally in that the enlarged part (*apophysis*) of the pedicel under the spore-case is not inflated and is of the same colour and consistency as the spore-case. The plants are peculiar in their choice of habitat, being invariably found on animal substances. *Tetraplodon angustatus* is said to have been found growing on an old stocking near

T. mnioides. Peristome of sixteen double teeth.

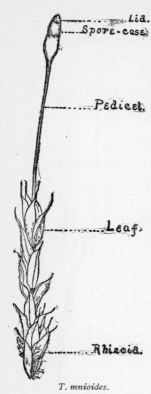

Lid.
Spore-case.

Pedicel.

Leaf.

Rhizoid.

T. mnioides.

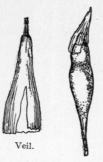

Veil.

T. mnioides.

the summit of Ingles-borough, Yorkshire, and also on an old hat on Mt. St. Bernard, Switzerland. The stems are branching and bear root-like filaments. The leaves are lance - shaped or oval-oblong, and are prolonged i n t o an awl-like point.

The spore-cases are small and erect with conical-convex, obtuse lids. They are borne on pedicels which are enlarged just under the spore-case to form a club-shaped apophysis. The apophysis is of importance as an assimilating and trans-piring organ and is the only part of the moss which bears pores (*stomata*).

The peristome is single with sixteen dark-purple double teeth r e f l e x e d when dry. These a r e at f i r s t in groups of four, and af-terward in pairs, a character which has suggested the generic name *Tetraplodon* f r o m the G r e e k τετραπλόος, four-fold, and ὀδούς, ὀδόντος, a tooth.

Nine species are known in all, four being found in North America.

Tetraplodon mnioides, Bruch & Schimp.

Habit and habitat.—Growing in dense tufts on decaying animal matter in mountainous regions.

The specimen illustrated was found on porcupine bones in

T. *mnioides.* Plant stripped of leaves to show (♂) male and (♀) female flower-clusters.

T. *mnioides.* Leaf.

203

Vermont. The specific name *mnioides* is derived from μνίον, moss, and the suffix οἰδ, like.

Plant (gametophyte).—Robust, pale-green, ½ to 3 inches high, stems branched, covered with matted root-like filaments below.

Leaves.—Crowded, ovate-lance-shaped or narrowly obovate-lance-shaped; *apex* pointed, suddenly narrowed into a flexuous yellow awn; *vein* prolonged to form the awn; *margin* yellow, entire.

Habit of flowering.—Male and female flowers on one plant (*monoicous*).

Veil (calyptra).—Small, conical, usually split up one side.

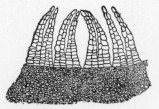

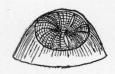

T. mnioides. Portion of peristome to show teeth.

T. mnioides. Tip of spore-case to show position of teeth when closed.

T. mnioides. Peristome with reflected teeth.

Spore-case.—Short-cylindrical, fawn-colour, with a cylindrical green apophysis, both become dark-red, and the spore-case is contracted below the mouth when empty.

Pedicel (seta).—Stout, orange to red, variable in length, $\frac{1}{2}$ to 2 inches long. Enlarged under the spore–case.

Lid (operculum).—Obtusely conic.

Teeth (peristome).—Reflexed when dry, orange-red.

Spores.—Small, mature in summer.

Distribution.—Universal.

COLLAR MOSSES

Genus SPLACHNUM, Linn.

The species of the **Genus Splachnum** are easily recognised by the extraordinary enlargement of the pedicel at the base of the spore-cases. They are perennial and grow in tufts, invariably on the dung of animals. The branches are soft and slender with broadly lance-shaped leaves, the lower distant and open; the upper tufted; all with a vein.

A THALLOID HEPATIC. *Marchantia polymorpha*, L.

One of the group which "in relation to the evolution of the higher plants stands as a key or link between the lower or simpler
and the higher or more complex"

The name is the Greek σπλάγχνον, used by Dioscorides for some lichen or non-flowering plant.

The spore-cases are small, oval or short-cylindrical with convex mammillate lids, and a central column (*columella*) capped and generally exserted after the falling of the lid.

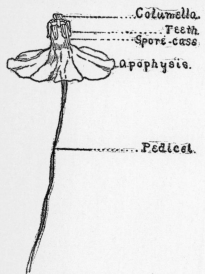

S. luteum.

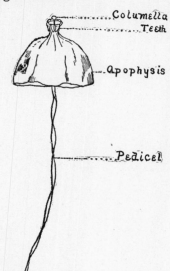

S. rubrum. Sporophyte with spore-case open showing the exserted columella and bell-shaped apophysis.

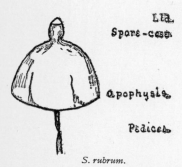

S. rubrum.

S. rubrum. Fertile plant, all but the lower part of the pedicel removed.

The pedicels are long and very much enlarged under the spore-case, the enlarged portion (*apophysis*) increasing after maturity and becoming pear-shaped, round or umbrella-like and diversely coloured. There are sixteen linear teeth in pairs

205

(*geminate*), orange-coloured and formed of two layers, the outer thicker and covered with tiny protuberances. The spores are minute.

S. rubrum. Male plant.

S. rubrum. Tip of spore-case with columella exerted and teeth reflexed.

S. rubrum. Leaf.

S. rubrum. Veil.

Eight species are known in all, five of them in North America.

The Red Collar-moss, *Splachnum rubrum,* Linn., l. c.

Habit and habitat.—Chiefly on dung in peat-bogs.

Name.—The specific name, Latin *rubrum,* red, refers to the colour.

Plant (*gametophyte*).—Living but one year, small, the male plants smaller.

Leaves.—Large, open; *apex* recurved; *base* narrowed from an enlarged middle, above more abruptly narrowed to a long taper-point; *margin* distinctly serrate from below the middle; leaves of the male plant smaller.

Habit of flowering.—Male and female flowers on separate plants (*dioicous*).

Veil (*calyptra*).—Small, conical, slightly split or mostly entire at the base, soft and falling early.

Spore-case.—Small, oval and ending abruptly at the summit as if cut off, thin, membranous and dirty-yellow.

Pedicel (*seta*).—Very long and red, enlarged just below the spore-case to form a purple, bell-shaped or umbrella-like portion (*apophysis*).

Lid.—Highly convex.

Teeth (*peristome*).—Sixteen, large, densely cross-barred, joined in pairs at the base and sometimes at the apex.

Spores.—Small, mature in summer.

Distribution.—In the Rockies and in Maine, also in Europe.

The Yellow Collar-moss, *Splachnum luteum*, Linn., l. c.

The Yellow Collar-moss differs from the Red Collar-moss in having the margins of the leaves not so coarsely toothed and in having the enlarged portion of the pedicel under the spore-case convex, umbrella-like, bright-yellow, and ½ an inch in diameter. The pedicel is often six inches long.

The name is from the Latin *luteum*, a weed, probably a yellow one as the derivatives all signify "yellow." This moss is also found on dung in bogs. The spores are mature in autumn.

THE BLADDER-CAP MOSS

Genus PHYSCOMITRIUM, Brid.

The species of the **Genus Physcomitrium** rarely live more than one year. They have a delicate texture and grow in loose tufts. The plants are sparingly branched, and bear comparatively large, soft, obovate or spatula-shaped, taper-pointed leaves

Plant.

P. turbinatum.

Leaf.

with large transparent cells. The spore-cases are ovate or spherical, and erect upon immersed or exserted pedicels. They have convex lids but no teeth, and the spore-sac (*sporangium*) is free from the spore-case wall, adhering to it only by thread-like strands. The veils are lobed at the base and scarcely descend to the middle of the spore-case.

The generic name *Physcomitrium* is a combination of two

207

Greek words, φύσκων, a fat paunch, and μιτρίον, a conical cap. The two words together describe the veil (*calyptra*) as a conical cap with an inflated base.

Top-moss, *Physcomitrium turbinatum,* Muell. ined.—See Plate XVI.

Habit and habitat.—Top-moss is everywhere common in old fields and grassy open places in gardens. It is conspicuous both with and without spore-cases, and may be easily recognised from its picture. In September and October the bright-green rosettes of both male and female plants may be found in loose

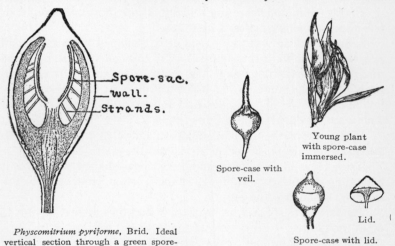

Spore-sac.
wall.
Strands.

Spore-case with veil.

Young plant with spore-case immersed.

Lid.

Spore-case with lid.

Physcomitrium pyriforme, Brid. Ideal vertical section through a green spore-case.

P. turbinatum.

clusters growing on the ground in protected spots, and if examined with a compound microscope, may reveal the archegonia and antheridia. About the middle of May the same locality should show colonies of plants with their perfect spore-cases on slender pedicels (*setæ*). One is almost sure of finding this moss about flower-pots in green-houses where the ground has not been too recently worked over. The shape of the spore-cases, the contraction below the mouth of the dry spore-case and the amount of thickening of the elongated cells about the mouth, and the degree of roughness of the spores, all depend upon the stage reached in their development before they become dry and shrivelled; and again the stage in their development depends upon the amount of rain and heat in their environment.

The differences resulting from changes in environment were shown in an interesting manner by plants examined from pots which were under steam-pipes in comparative darkness in the New York Botanical gardens. In September the plants were small with pedicels only about half an inch long. In January the pots were removed to benches with bottom heat and more light and then plants were developed with pedicels twice as long, paler of colour, and with spore-cases more top-shaped and smaller.

Name.—The specific name, *turbinatum*, the Latin for "pointed like a top," refers to the top-shaped spore-case.

Plants (gametophyte).—Light-green, *stems* short and simple, or taller and branching, $\frac{3}{10}$ to 1 inch long.

Leaves.—Broadly-lance-shaped or egg-shaped with the broad end tapering toward the stem (*obovate*); *margin* serrate above the middle; *vein* vanishing below the apex or extending beyond to form a tapering point. *Cells*, the *lower* oblong, the *upper* rhomboidal or hexagonal, the *marginal* longer and narrower, often yellow and inflated at their upper ends.

Veil (calyptra).—Conical, oblique, and cleft unequally 5- to 8-lobed and beaked, covering about half the spore-case.

Spore-case.—Erect, green and round pear-shaped when fresh; becoming dark-brown, and urn-shaped, often contracted below the rim, when dry and empty.

Pedicel (seta).—Erect or twisted, sometimes arched, ¼ to ¾ of an inch long.

Lid (operculum).—Convex or tipped with a small nipple (*mammillate*) occasionally with an acute point (*apiculate*).

Teeth (peristome).—None; the rim is bordered by 8 to 12 rows of transversely, elongated cells, the uppermost very narrow and orange-coloured.

Annulus.—Persistent, of transparent, bladder-like cells incurved after the falling of the lid.

Spores.—Rough, maturing in spring.

Distribution.—Ontario to Florida, west to the Rocky Mountains.

CORD MOSSES

Genus FUNARIA, Schreb.

The species of the **Genus Funaria** are short, simple, or branching, growing in clusters on the ground. The leaves are variable; with loose transparent cells. The spore-cases are pear-shaped, erect and symmetrical, or oblique and curved on long pedicels, straight or arched above. The pedicels twist one about another when dry, a habit suggesting the generic name *Funaria*, from the Latin *funis*, a cord. The lids are plano-convex. Sometimes there is a compound annulus which rolls back as the lid falls.

The teeth are sometimes rudimentary but more generally they are double, the outer sixteen obliquely curving to the right and connected at the apex by a small mesh-like disk. The outer surface of the teeth is pale and granulose and the inner face is marked with prominent purple cross-bars. The inner membrane is divided into sixteen more or less rudimentary segments opposite to the outer teeth and adhering at the base. They are yellow and lance-shaped with longitudinal median line.

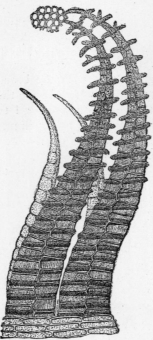

F. hygrometrica. Portion of peristome with two inner teeth and with two outer teeth attached to a terminal disk.

The spore-sac is much smaller than the spore-case and is attached to it by loosely entangled filaments. The spores are often very large.

Seventy-nine species are known in all, fourteen being found in North America.

The Pale Funaria, *Funaria flaricans*, Michx.—See Plate XVI.

This species is found in the Middle and Southern States. It differs from *Funaria hygrometrica* in being paler in colour. The leaves are more abruptly narrowed into a long flexuous point, the mouth of the spore-case is more enlarged and less oblique.

The Water-measuring Cord-moss, *Funaria hygrometrica*, Sibth.—See Colour Plates III and XVI.

Habit and habitat.—Like Cinderella, the Cord-moss is to be found among the ashes. One may look for it where picnic fires have been, or in wood-lots which have been swept by flames. One may also expect to find it in vacant lots used as dump

TOP MOSS
Physcomitrium turbinatum, Muell. *ined.*

THE PALE FUNARIA
Funaria flaricans, Michx.

THE WATER–MEASURING CORD–MOSS, *Funaria hygrometrica*, Sibth.

grounds, or even on the crumbling mortar of old stone houses and neglected walls.

Name.—The specific name *hygrometrica* is a compound of two Greek words, ὑγρὸς, water, and μετρικὸς, measuring, and refers to the habit the

Spores.

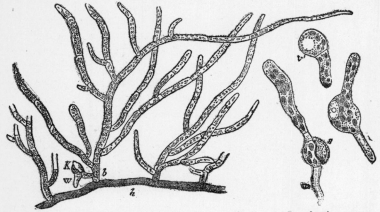

(*b*) Branching protonema with a moss plant starting at (*k*); (*w*) rhizoid; (*h*) a primary filament of protonema.

Funaria hygrometrica.

Germinating spores.
(*v*) Vacuole; (*w*) rhizoid
(*s*) spore wall.

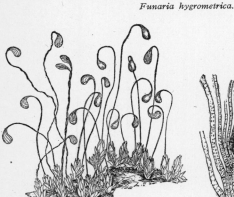

F. hygrometrica.

F. hygrometrica.

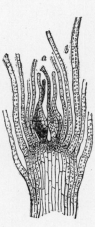

F. hygrometrica. Female flower in vertical section. (*a*) archegonium; (*b*) leaf.

F. hygrometrica. Plant with immature spore-case still in its veil.

211

plants have of twisting and untwisting their pedicels as they are alternately moistened or dried.

F. hygrometrica. Leaf.

Plant (*gametophyte*).—The young plants are found in the fall. They are yellow-green with simple or branching stems, living but one year, or continuing by new growths.

Leaves.—Variable; tufted at the apex of the stem, usually erect and pressed together; oblong egg-shaped; *apex* short-pointed; *margin* entire; *vein* reaching the apex.

Habit of flowering.—Male and female flowers on the same plant (*monoicous*); terminal; the male on primary stems, the female on secondary.

L. pyriforme.
(See page 217.)

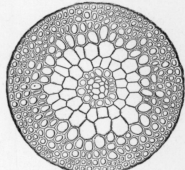

F. hygrometrica. Cross section of young pedicel.

Veil (*calyptra*).—Conical, shining, inflated at the base, split up one side, composed of bladder-like cells.

Spore-case.—When immature, erect, nearly symmetrical; when mature, pear-shaped, with the small end narrowed to an elongated and curved neck (*collum*). One side is more swollen than the other (*gibbous*); leathery, reddish, and deeply furrowed when old.

Spore-sac.—Much smaller than the spore-case, attached to it by loosely tangled threads.

Pedicel (*seta*).—Straight or arched above, 1 to 2½ inches high, twisting and untwisting with the changes in the humidity of the air.

Lid (*operculum*).—Small like a flat saucer. *F. hygrometrica.* Annulus.

212

F. hygrometrica. Plant with two sporophytes.

Annulus.—Compound, rolling back as the lid falls.

Teeth (peristome). — The *outer teeth* sixteen, obliquely curving to the right, with horizontal prominent purple cross-bars on the inner face

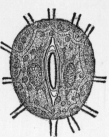

F. hygrometrica. Breathing pore from the spore-case.

(*trabeculate*): pale and granular on the outer face, connected at the apex by a small disk with mesh-like veins (reticulated); the inner teeth sixteen, lance-like or more or less rudimentary, opposite to the outer teeth and adhering at the base, yellowish with a line

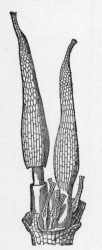

Tip of female shoot with archegonia, two containing sporogoniums half-grown. The one on the left has severed the upper part of the archegonium wall, calyptra, from the base.

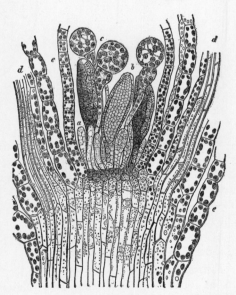

F. hygrometrica. Vertical section through a male flower: (*a*) young antheridium in vertical section. (*b*) old antheridium in vertical section; (*c*) paraphysis; (*d*) vein of leaf in section; (*e*) blade of leaf in section.

213

running from apex to base, distinctly beset with minute points (*papillate*).

Spores.—Of medium size, maturing all summer.
Distribution.—Universal.

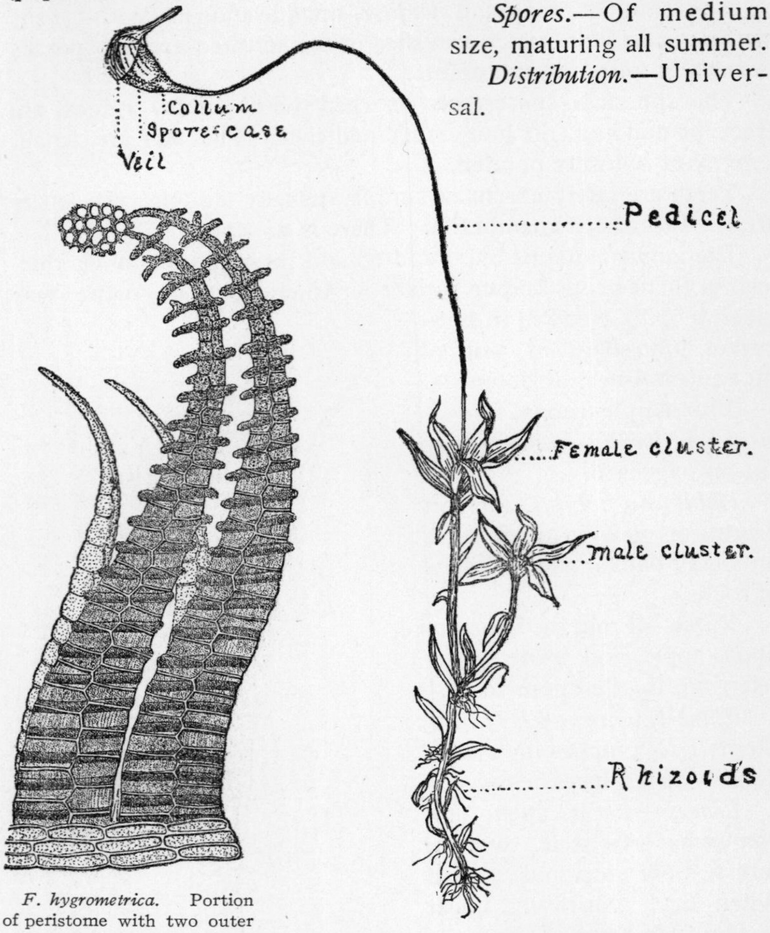

Collum

Sporecase

Veil

Pedicel

Female cluster.

Male cluster.

Rhizoids

F. hygrometrica. Portion of peristome with two outer teeth attached at their tips to a reticulated disk; and two innner teeth free.

F. hygrometrica. A plant with a female branch supporting a sporophyte on the left; a male branch with male flower-cluster on the right.

Genus BARTRAMIA, Hedw.

The species of the **Genus Bartramia** live from year to year, their erect, two-forked stems with soft felted hairs toward the base forming extensive tufts on soil and rock, or occasionally on trees.

The leaves are long and narrow, opaque and yellowish-green; with a round vein which vanishes in the serrated apex or passes beyond to form a rough point.

The spherical spore-cases marked with parallel ridges are erect, or nodding, on long erect pedicels. The lids are small, convex or obtusely pointed.

Teeth are rarely absent or simple, usually double, the outer attached to basilar membrane. There is no annulus.

The genus contains one hundred and three species in all, thirteen of them being known in North America. The name was given by J. G. Hedwig in honour of John Bartram, one of the earliest American botanists.

The Apple-moss, *Bartramia pomiformis*, Hedw.—See cut on page 216.

Habit and habitat.—In soft bright or yellow-green tufts on shady banks and in clefts of rocks.

Name.—From the Latin *pomum*, apple, and *forma*, form, referring to the spore-cases.

Plant (g a m e t o p h y t e).—Stems 1 to 3 inches high with densely felted hairs below.

Leaves.—Long, open, and somewhat twisted w h e n moist, more erect and crisped when dry. Narrowly linear and awl-like from a paler base; *vein* extending beyond the apex to form a spiny awn; *margin* sharply serrate above, rolled back from the middle downward.

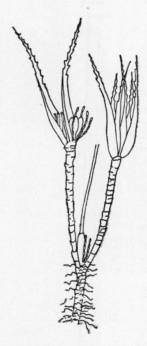

B. pomiformis. Plant stripped of leaves to show antheridia, archegonia, and paraphyses on the left branch; the base of an old pedicel lies between the two branches.

Habit of flowering.—Male and female flowers on the same plant (*monoicous*).

Veil (calyptra).—Conical, split up one side, falling early.

Spore-case.—Spherical, grooved longitudinally.

Pedicel (seta).—Slender, $\frac{1}{2}$ an inch high.

Teeth (peristome).—Outer teeth regular, densely cross-barred, inner segments shorter than the teeth and cleft, cilia imperfect or none.

Annulus.—None.

Spores.—Mature in spring.

Distribution.—Universal.

B. pomiformis.   *Bartramia pomiformis.*   *B. pomiformis.* Leaves.

THREAD-MOSS

Genus LEPTOBRYUM, Schimp.

The species of the **Genus Leptobryum** live but one year, the plants are unbranched above, new growths coming only from the base. The generic name from the Greek λεπτὸς, slender, and βρύον, a moss, refers to the slender character of the plants.

The leaves are narrow, glossy, and turn in different directions. The apex is like an awl and the cells are narrowly rhomboidal above, looser toward the base and rectangular-six-sided.

The spore-cases are inclined or pendent, long-necked and thin-coated with convex lids tipped with a small point. The teeth are double, the intermediate hair-like segments having crossbars projecting beyond the edge.

There are but few species known at present, one of these is found in North America.

216

The Pear-shaped Thread-moss, *Leptobryum pyriforme,*
Schimp.—See cuts on page 218.

Habit and habitat.—In dense silky green patches on shady
rocks and walls, and sandy or turfy soil, also on burnt and decaying trees. Common.

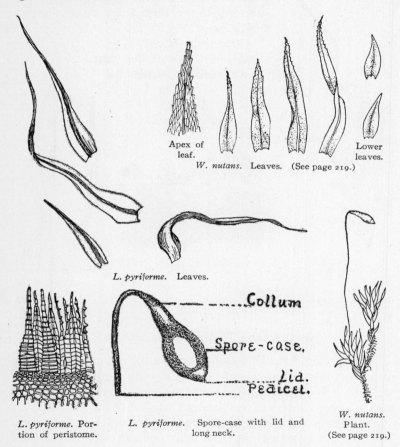

Apex of
leaf.

Lower
leaves.

W. nutans. Leaves. (See page 219.)

L. pyriforme. Leaves.

Collum

Spore-case.

Lid.

Pedicel.

W. nutans.
Plant.
(See page 219.)

L. pyriforme. Por-
tion of peristome.

L. pyriforme. Spore-case with lid and
long neck.

Name.—The specific name *pyriforme* is from the Latin *pyrum,*
a pear, and *forma,* form, referring to the spore-case.

Plant (gametophyte).—Slender, simple, stem short. One-
half to one inch high.

Leaves.—The lower distant, narrowly lance-shaped, the upper
tufted and longer; *apex* awl-like, flexuose, serrate; *cells above,*

217

narrow and long, *below*, broader.   *Vein* dilated at the base, extending below the apex.

Habit of flowering.—Male and female flowers together, (*synoicous*).

Spore-case.—Pear-shaped or oval, yellow-brown, glossy, symmetrical, neck long.

Pedicel.—Red, slender, 1 to 2 inches long.

Lid (*operculum*).—Convex, with a tiny nipple.

L. *pyriforme.*
Apex of leaf.

Teeth (*peristome*).—Pale yellow, lance-shaped, segments of the inner membrane keeled and perforated; the thread-like segments bearing little knots on the edges.

Annulus. — Broad, rolling back as the lid falls.

Spores. — Mature in May and June.

Distribution.—Universal.

Genus WEBERA, Hedw.

The members of this genus are similar to those of the genus *Bryum,* the essential characters which separate the two are that *Webera* has rhomboidal-hexagonal, narrow, and more or less linear leaf-cells with a slender vein, while *Bryum* has rhomboidal-hexagonal, smooth, usually broad and loose cells, with a solid, round vein generally passing beyond the apex of the leaf.

The name was given by J. G. Hedwig, a German botanist, in honour of G. H. Weber.

W. *albicans.* Stem.
(See page 220).

L. *pyriforme*
Annulus.

W. *nutans.* Spore-case.

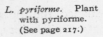

L. *pyriforme.* Plant with pyriforme.
(See page 217.)

WEBERA NUTANS, Hedw.

WEBERA ALBICANS, Schimp, l. c.

Webera nutans, Hedw.—See Plate XVII. Also see cuts on page 217.

Habit and habitat.—This pretty moss is common, growing in soft cushions on moist ground, in peat bogs and swamps and in fissures of rocks.

Spore-case.   Lids.   Annulus.

W. nutans.   Inner membrane.

Name.—The specific name *nutans,* the Latin for "nodding," describes the spore-case.

Plant (gametophyte).—Yellow-green; stem slender and flexible, ½ to 2 inches high.

Leaves.—The *lower* ovate-lanceolate, *margin* entire; the *upper* linear-lanceolate, serrate at the apex; *vein* thick, reddish, glossy, vanishing below the apex.

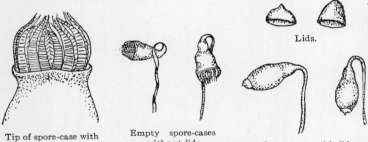

Lids.

Tip of spore-case with two rows of teeth.

Empty spore-cases without lids.

Spore-cases with lids.

W. albicans. (See page 220.)

Habit of flowering.—Male and female flowers on the same plant (*monoicous*).

Spore-case.—Oblong-ovate with a broad opening, yellow-brown, short-necked, inclined or pendent.

Pedicel.—Glossy red, often two inches high.

Lid (operculum).—Highly convex, with a tiny nipple.

Teeth (peristome).—Dark orange, pale and thread-like at the apex, the segments of the inner membrane pale-yellow, split, slender segments (*cilia*) 2 to 3 strongly jointed, as long as the teeth.

W. albicans.
Male plant.

Annulus.—Large, rolling back as the lid falls.

Spores.—Mature in summer.

Distribution.—Almost universal.

Webera albicans, Schimp.— See Plate XVII.

Habit and habitat.— This pretty moss grows in soft tufts of a light-green colour in wet sand on the borders of streams, and in swampy land along wheel ruts.

Name.—The specific name *albicans*, whitish, has reference to its peculiar pale-green colour.

Plant (gametophyte).— Simple, erect or inclined; 1 to 4 inches long; *stem* reddish or dark-purple.

Leaves.—The *lower* ovate, oblong and taper-pointed, the upper oblong-lanceolate, soft, yellowish or pale-green; *vein* vanishing below the apex; *margin* serrate near apex; leaves around the male flowers broad and concave at the base, open and lanceolate above.

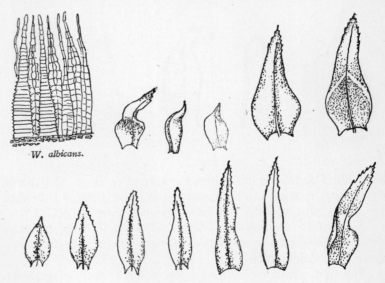

W. albicans.

W. albicans. Leaves.

Habit of flowering.—Male and female flowers on separate plants, male flowers in a disk-like head.

Spore-case.—Inclined or pendent, short-pear-shaped, inflated

220

at the neck (*collum*); green with a bloom, becoming brown; somewhat round and wide-mouthed when empty.

Pedicel.—Long, generally reddish and bent at the base.

Lid (operculum).—Conical with a nipple (*mammillate*).

Teeth (peristome).—Large, orange-coloured.

Annulus.—None.

Spores.—Mature in spring and early summer.

Distribution.—Almost universal.

Genus BRYUM, Dill.

The plants of the **Genus Bryum** live on from year to year on the ground or on rocks, seldom on trees. The stems are covered with small red-brown filaments.

The generic name is an ancient word for moss used both by Gaius Plinius, "The Elder," a Roman naturalist, who perished in the eruption that destroyed Pompeii, and by Pedanius Dioscorides, a Greek physician, who was the founder of

B. argenteum. Leaf.
    Spore-case with lid.
    Spore-case without lid. *B. roseum.*
    B. argenteum. Portion of peristome.

botany and flourished in the first and second century. The name *Bryum* was restricted to the present genus by Johann Dillenius, a German, who was the first professor of botany at Oxford.

The leaves are smooth with a solid round vein generally extending beyond the apex; the cells are smooth, six-sided and more or less elongated.

The spore-cases are leathery, pear-shaped, narrowing down to a solid neck (*collum*) with breathing pores (*stomata*) on the surface; they are regular or rarely recurved. They have convex lids with a tiny blunt point at the centre and are borne on long and stout pedicels.

221

The peristome is double, the outer teeth are long and linear or lance-shaped, marked with many cross-bars internally, prominent below; the inner membrane is divided above into keeled segments adherent to or free from the teeth, and separated by usually two to five hair-like divisions (*cilia*) mostly with spurs attached at intervals to the margin.

The annulus is large, compound, and rolls back as the lid falls.

There are 800 or more described species, one hundred and thirty-two in North America.

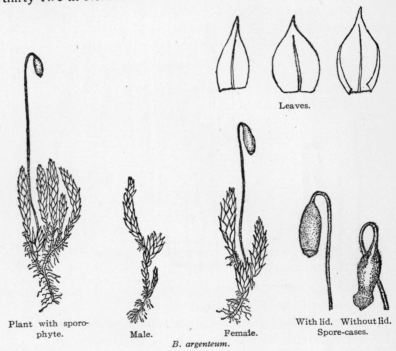

Leaves.

Plant with sporophyte.　　Male.　　Female.　　With lid.　Without lid.
Spore-cases.

B. argenteum.

The Silvery Bryum, *Bryum argenteum,* Linn.

Habit and habitat.—In green or silvery-white irregular cushions, on exposed ground, roofs, pavements, burnt places and almost everywhere except on trees.　Very common.

Name.—The specific name refers to the colour.　Latin *argenteum,* silvery.　Johann Dillenius, a German botanist, called this moss "Catkin-stemmed Silver Moss" from its resemblance to the catkins of a poplar tree.

222

Plant (*gametophyte*).—Stems short, ½ to 1 inch high covered with root-like filaments; there are numerous shining catkin-like branches, each tipped with a brush of hairs.

Leaves.—At the apex of the stem, oblong-lance-shaped, taper-pointed, silvery-gray; stem and branch leaves broadly oval, or inverted oval, deeply concave; *apex* abruptly pointed; *margin* entire, flat; *vein* (*costa*) vanishing above the middle; cells loose.

Habit of flowering.—Male and female on separate plants (*dioicous*). Male flowers terminal.

Veil (*calyptra*).—Narrowly hood-like, falling before the spore-case ripens.

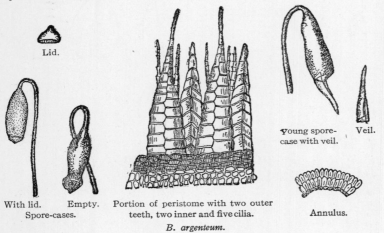

Lid.

With lid.   Empty.
Spore-cases.

Portion of peristome with two outer teeth, two inner and five cilia.

B. argenteum.

Young spore-case with veil.   Veil.

Annulus.

Spore-case.—Abruptly pendulous, oblong, deep purple when ripe, constricted under the mouth when old.

Pedicel.—Long and curved at the summit, ½ inch high, dark red when mature.

Lid (*operculum*).—Convex, slightly pointed, dark-orange.

Teeth (*peristome*).—As in the genus. Inner membrane yellow.

Annulus.—Present.

Spores.—Mature in fall and winter.   Rarely fruiting in Great Britain.

Distribution.—Found in America, Europe and Asia.   This is one of the five mosses which Sir Wm. Jackson Hooker found in the early part of the 19th Century at "Ultima Thule" of Antarctic vegetation.

The Rose Bryum, *Bryum roseum,* Schreb.—See Plate XVIII.

Habit and habitat.—*Bryum roseum* is one of the largest and showiest of the *Bryums* known outside the tropics. It is found in shaded woods at the bases of trees and decayed logs. Under favourable circumstances this species forms tufts, but usually the plants are scattered among other mosses.

Name.—The specific name refers to the rose-like arrangement of the crown leaves, Latin *roseus,* a rose.

Plant (gametophyte).—Fine and large,

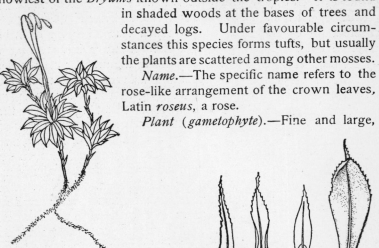

Plant with stolons.

B. roseum.

Leaves.

stems 1 to 2 inches long, with few branches; creeping *stems* (*stolons*) present, from which new plants arise.

Leaves.—At the apex crowded to form a rosette, each leaf spatulate; *apex* taper-pointed; *margin* acutely toothed from the middle upward, reflexed to the base, wavy when dry; *vein (costa)* broad and reddish at the base, narrowed upward and produced beyond the apex; *cells* loose and filled with chlorophyll. *Stem-leaves* lying close to the stem, oblong-lance-shaped, small and thin.

Apex of leaf.

Male flower and bracts.
Bryum roseum.

Male plant.

PLATE XVIII

THE ROSE BRYUM. *Bryum roseum.* Schreb.

Habit of flowering.—Male flowers in separate tufts from the female flowers (*dioicous*), arranged at the apex of the stems and surrounded with radiating leaves.

Veil (*calyptra*). — Split up one side.

Spore-case.—Single or in clusters, oblong-conical, pendent, and slightly incurved, solid and not constricted under the mouth when dry.

With lid. Without lid.
B. roseum.

B. roseum. Portion of peristome.

Pedicel (*seta*).—Dark purple, long and solid. 1 to 1½ inches high.

Lid (*operculum*).—Slightly convex with a tiny nipple in the centre, dark-purple.

B. roseum.
Annulus.

Teeth (*peristome*). — Very long, inner segments orange-coloured, perforated along the keel.

Annulus.—Compound, rolling back as the lid falls.

Spores.—Mature in autumn.

Distribution.—On the Eastern and Western slopes of North America, also in Europe, Asia and Africa.

Genus MNIUM, Linn.

The species of the **Genus Mnium** are handsome mosses, usually tall and robust, with large, translucent leaves. They may be looked for about the bases of trees, on lawns, along roadsides, and in damp woods. They are especially attractive on the banks of mountain brooks or in the cool water of bubbling springs. The beginner may recognise some members of the genus by the dainty rosettes on the summits of the male plants,

M. punctatum. Var. elatum.

M. affine. Apex of leaf—spiny border, single.

each rosette made of pale-green leaves with a beaded centre of darker green. Some species have the fertile stems erect with branches growing from near their bases or from creeping stems. The branches are often different from the main stems, being fern-like, prostrate, or curved with rooting tips so as to form successions of miniature arches.

The great Swedish botanist, Carolus Linnæus, named the group from the Greek μνίον, an ancient word for "moss."

M. cuspidatum. Spiny border, single.

M. hornum. Spiny border, double.

M. punctatum. Border entire.

M. cuspidatum. Spiny border, single.

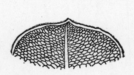

M. punctatum. Apex of leaf

M. hornum. Apex of leaf.

The leaves of all the *Mniums* are dainty and fresh and their cell-structure and their colour are so delicate that it will repay one to examine them with a hand lens or the low power of a compound microscope. The leaves are usually large, rounded, more or less elliptic or tongue-shaped; the margin usually has a distinct border and is frequently spiny toothed; the vein either vanishes below or extends beyond the apex; the cells are smooth, rounded-hexagonal or rarely elongated.

226

The spore-cases are more or less pendulous, on long and slender, often clustered pedicels. They are oblong-cylindrical or oval, never pear-shaped. The lids are convex, long-beaked, taper-pointed, or tipped with a tiny blunt point. The annulus is usually conspicuous, rolling back as the lid falls.

The peristome is double, the outer teeth being long and narrow or lance-shaped, closely cross-barred below, with the bars evident on the inner surface; the inner membrane is keeled and reaches to the middle of the outer teeth, where it divides into large segments alternating with two or three thread-like

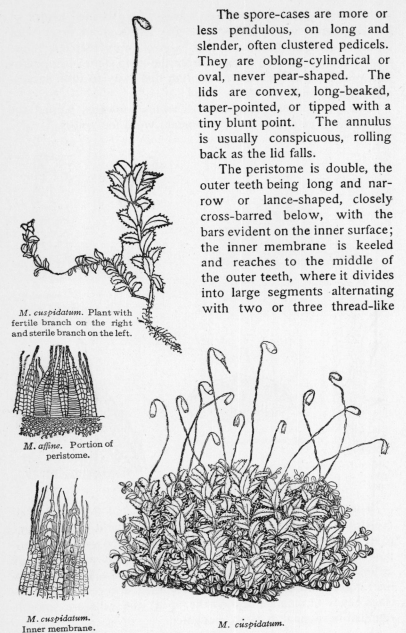

M. cuspidatum. Plant with fertile branch on the right and sterile branch on the left.

M. affine. Portion of peristome.

M. cuspidatum. Inner membrane.

M. cuspidatum.

227

segments (*cilia*). Sometimes the cilia have spurs attached at intervals to the margins.

There are ninety-nine species in all, thirty-three in North America. Of the fifteen species which appear in the Eastern States, five will be found with entire borders to the leaves, five with a single row of teeth, and five with a double row.

The Pointed Mnium, *Mnium cuspidatum,* Hedw.

Habit and habitat.—The Pointed Mnium (*Mnium cuspidatum*) is one of the prettiest of the genus and is to be found in shaded places on the ground in almost every state and territory in the Union.

Name.—J. G. Hedwig, a German botanist, named this species from the Latin *cuspidatum,* a point, on account of the apex of the leaves.

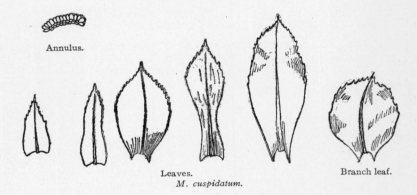

Annulus.

Leaves.
M. cuspidatum.

Branch leaf.

Plants (gametophyte).—Simple, the young shoots bright pale-green, the older stems dark-green, the sterile shoots prostrate or somewhat erect.

Leaves.—All with a short sharp point at the apex, *vein* extending beyond the apex to form the point. *Stem-leaves* with the base growing downward on the stem (*decurrent*) oval-oblong or obovate-spatulate ; *branch-leaves* smaller, rounded-oval; all much crisped when dry; *margin* with 3 to 5 rows of yellow cells, and a single row of spiny teeth in the upper half.

Leaves at the base of the pedicel (perichœtial leaves).—Spatulate.

HEPATIC. DRY.
Frullania Eboracensis, Gottsche

HEPATIC, MOIST.
Frullania Eboracensis, Gottsche

HEPATIC.
Porella platyphylla

HEPATIC.
Ptilidium ciliare, Nees

Habit of flowering.—Male and female flowers in the same cluster (*synoicous*).

Veil (*calyptra*).—Split up one side.

Spore-case.—Solitary, somewhat pendulous, oval-oblong.

Pedicel.—Solitary, pale.

Lid (*operculum*).—Conical, obtuse.

Annulus.—Narrow, rolling back as the lid is pushed off.

Teeth (*peristome*).—The outer yellow, the inner orange, solid, the segments open on the keel, thread-like and sharp-pointed at the apex; cilia usually three between each tooth.

Spores.—Mature in spring.

Distribution.—In almost every state of the Union, also in Europe.

Mnium affine, Bland.

Habit and habitat.—Common on shaded banks and roots of trees. Bright, pale-green, loosely tufted with long sterile shoots arched or prostrate.

Name.—The specific name, *affine*, from the Latin *affinis*, related, refers to the resemblance of this species to *Mnium cuspidatum* with which it has often been confused.

Plant (*gametophyte*).—One to two inches high with brown filaments at the base.

Leaves.—Spreading, recurved and crisped on the borders when dry; *the lower stem-leaves* round egg-shaped with the narrow end next to the stem; the *middle stem-leaves* oblong egg-shaped, growing more or less down the stem; the upper

M. cuspidatum.
Inner membrane.

Stem with leaves.   Apex with vein and marginal cells.   Spore-case
                                                                       without lid.

M. cuspidatum.

229

stem-leaves inverted egg-shaped and long spatulate crowded into a rosette; *margins* acutely toothed all round; *vein* extending beyond the apex to form a sharp point.

Habit of flowering.—Male and female flowers on separate plants (*dioicous*); male plants terminating in disks.

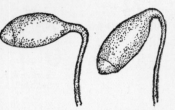

M. cuspidatum.   Spore-cases with lids.

Veil (*calyptra*).—Split up one side.

Spore-case.—Clustered, 1 to 3, rarely 5 to 6; pendent, oblong; green until fully ripe, then yellow-brown.

Pedicel (*seta*).—Slender, 1 to 1½ inches long.

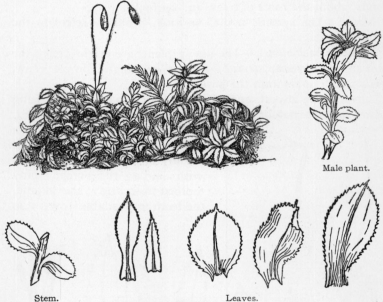

Male plant.

Stem.   Leaves.

M. affine.

Lid (*operculum*).—Convex, short, sharp-pointed.

Teeth (*peristome*).—As in the genus.   The outer yellow, the inner orange.

Annulus.—Narrow, rolling back as the lid falls.

Spores.—Mature in spring.

Distribution.—Universal.

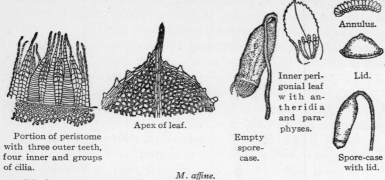

Portion of peristome with three outer teeth, four inner and groups of cilia.

Apex of leaf.

Empty spore-case.

Inner perigonial leaf with antheridia and paraphyses.

Annulus.

Lid.

Spore-case with lid.

M. affine.

Mnium hornum, Linn.

Habit and habitat.—Robust in dense tufts, on damp earth in woods, about the roots of trees, and on rocks.

Name.—The specific name, *hornum*, probably refers to the horny border.

Plant (gametophyte).—The young plants are bright-green, the older are dark-green; *stems*, 1 to 2 inches high, simple erect; *sterile shoots*, erect from the base.

Leaves.—The lowest minute, the upper gradually increasing in size, the terminal forming a rosette, all oblong-lance-shaped, *apex* more or less acute with a sharp little point; *base* growing slightly down the stem; *margin* with a strong red border, spiny toothed from below the middle, the teeth in a double row; *vein*

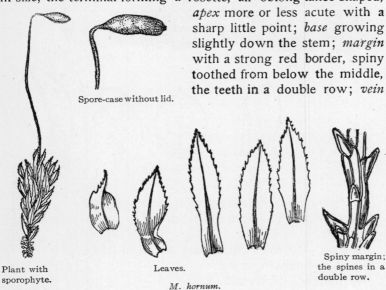

Spore-case without lid.

Plant with sporophyte.

Leaves.

Spiny margin; the spines in a double row.

M. hornum.

231

vanishing below the apex, spiny above at the back; *cells* thick-walled.

Habit of flowering.—Male and female flowers on separate plants (*dioicous*).   Male flowers surrounded with a rosette of leaves.

Veil (*calyptra*).—Split up one side.

Spore-case.—Narrowly oval with a narrow tapering neck somewhat pendulous, finally horizontal, somewhat inflated when empty, pale-yellow with a red rim.

Pedicel (*seta*).—Solitary, 1 to 1½ inches long, arched above.

Lid (*operculum*).—Conical, tipped with a short, sharp point.

Annulus.—Narrow.

Teeth (*peristome*).—As in the genus.

Spores.—Mature in spring.

Distribution.—Europe, Africa, and North America.

The Dotted Mnium, *Mnium punctatum*, Hedw.

Habit and habitat.—The Dotted Mnium may be looked for about cold springs and along the borders of mountain brooks.

It grows in loose dark or yellowish green tufts, each plant standing stiff and erect with rusty-brown hairs.

The leaves are large, not very close together on the stem and of a delicate translucent green.   A hand lens will show them to have a hard, brown, entire margin notched at the rounded apex, and a tiny little point in the notch.

M. hornum. Spore-case with lid and with a bract on the pedicel.

The fruits are not often found, but when present are oval, green cylinders with sharp-pointed lids, horizontal or inclined on slender pedicels.

Name.—The specific name, the Latin *punctatum*, dotted, was given by J. G. Hedwig, on account of the cell structure.

Plant (*gametophyte*).—Tall, robust, 3 to 6 inches high, the dark-green sterile shoots erect; all covered the whole length with brown filaments.

Leaves.—Remote on branches and stems, open, turned back from the stem, large, the *lower* round, oval, inserted onl

M. hornum. Apex of leaf to show spiny margin.

PLATE XIX

MNIUM PUNCTATUM, variety *Elatum*, Bruch. & Schimp.
The stolons are Mnium affine

by the enlarged vein; the *upper* 4 to 6 in a rosette, each leaf broadly oval, tapering toward the base; *apex* slightly notched, with a sharp point in the notch; *margin* entire, brown, thick and hard; *vein* purplish, abruptly vanishing near apex, extending down the stem.

Stem.　　Stem with hairs.

M. punctatum.

Habit of flowering.—Male and female flowers on separate plants (*dioicous*); male plants more slender than the female, with but few stem leaves, and the leaves at the summit arranged as a rosette about the male flowers (*antheridia*).

Veil (*calyptra*).—Split up one side, remaining on the spore-case all winter but falling early in the spring.

Spore-case.—Oval, green when mature, brown when older, ovate-oblong, somewhat pendulous, finally horizontal.

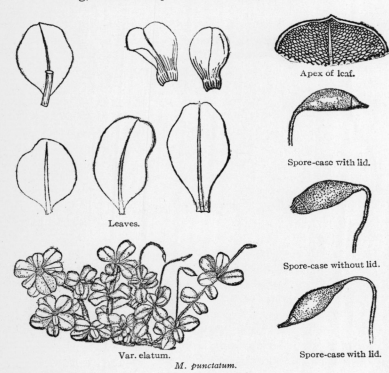

Apex of leaf.

Spore-case with lid.

Leaves.

Spore-case without lid.

Var. elatum.

M. punctatum.

Spore-case with lid.

233

Pedicel.—Long and pale, usually solitary.

Lid (operculum).—Acutely beaked.

Annulus.—Narrow, rolling back as the lid is pushed off.

Teeth (peristome).—As in the genus.

Spores.—Mature in spring.

Distribution.—America, Europe, Asia.

Mnium punctatum, variety elatum, Bruch & Schimp., (See Plate XIX), has the stem taller, often 6 to 8 inches high, and more branching and for this reason called *elatum,* the Latin for "raised."

Genus AULACOMNIUM, Schwaegr.

The species of the **Genus Aulacomnium** are erect, in dense cushions on marshy ground or in cracks of rocks. Some species will be easily

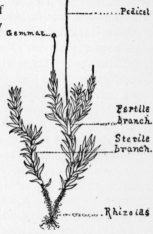

A. *heterostichum.*
Old spore-cases.

A. *androgynum.*

A. *androgynum.* Plant with sterile branches on the left and gemmæ-bearing branches on either side of the sporophyte.

A. *androgynum.*
Head of gemmæ.

recognised by their leafless branches terminated by round clusters of loose granular bodies (*gemmæ*). Each gemma is an aggregate of cells and resembles the early stage in a developing leaf. They fall to the ground and there develop into new plants.

The leaves are oblong or lance-shaped with tiny projections on the cells.

Oblong nodding spore-cases, conspicuously ribbed when old, are borne on slender pedicels. The ribbing of the cases has suggested
the name *Aulacomnium*, from the Greek αὖλαξ,
αὖλακος, a furrow, and μνίον, moss. There
are two rows of teeth, the inner with long
cilia.

Nine species are known in all, five of them
in North America.

Aulacomnium androgynum, Schwaegr.

M. punctatum, var. elatum. Margin of leaf.

Habit and habitat.—In dense tufts, green
above, rust-brown within, owing to the num-
erous felted hairs on the stems. Found on bare earth, roots of
trees, fissures of rocks, on plains or mountains. A tiny Western
humming-bird uses this moss for its nest.

Name.—The specific name, *androgynum*, hermaphrodite, was
given from a mistaken idea that the moss was produced only by
asexual methods, that is, by the gemmæ, which are not the result
of fertilisation. The name is a compound of the Greek ἀνὴρ,
ἀδυρὸς, man, and γυνῆ, woman.

Plant (gametophyte).—Dull-green, stems slender, rarely 1½
inches high, bearing red-brown felt-like filaments, and usually
producing slender leafless shoots terminating with round heads
of tiny granular bodies (*gemmæ*).

Leaves.—Narrowly taper-pointed; *apex* toothed; *cells* small,
round, with tiny projections on each face.

Habit of flowering.—Male and female flowers on separate
plants (*dioicous*). Male flower-clusters terminal, bud-like.

Veil (calyptra).—Reaching the middle of the spore-case;
long-beaked, split up one side.

Spore-case.—Brown, cylindrical-oblong, furrowed when old;
erect, finally horizontal.

A. androgynum. Spore-case
with lid.

Pedicel (seta).—¾ of an inch long.

Lid (operculum).—Large, conical.

Annulus.—Compound, r o l l i n g
back as the lid falls.

Teeth (peristome). — As in the
genus.

Spores.—Mature in summer.

Distribution.—America, Europe.

235

Aulacomnium palustre, Schwaegr.

Habit and habitat.—In loose or dense tufts 1 to 5 inches deep, yellow or dirty-green above, red-brown within. Found on borders of swamps, on plains, or on mountains.

Name.—The specific name *palustre,* Latin, *palus,* a swamp, refers to the habit of the moss.

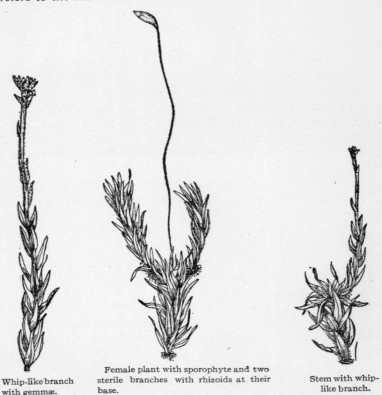

Whip-like branch with gemmæ.

Female plant with sporophyte and two sterile branches with rhizoids at their base.

Stem with whip-like branch.

A. palustre.

Plants (gametophyte).—Robust, closely covered with red-brown felted filaments, often producing whip-like branches with clusters of bud-like growths at the apex.

Leaves.—Usually crowded, more or less crisped and twisted when dry, narrowly lance-shaped; *apex* obtuse or pointed; *margin* finely toothed toward the apex, rolled back below; *vein* vanishing below the apex; *cells* with tiny projections on both faces.

236

BUXBAUMIA APHYLLA, L.

AULACOMNIUM HETEROSTICHUM, Bruch. & Schimp.

Habit of flowering.—Male and female flowers on separate plants (*dioicous*). Male flower-clusters bud-like.

Veil (*calyptra*).—Split up one side.

Spore-case.—Oblong, unsymmetrical.

Pedicel.—1 to 2 inches long.

Lid (*operculum*).—Conical.

Annulus.—Large, compound, rolling back as the lid falls.

Teeth (*peristome*).—Long, acute, the segments of the inner membrane about as long, with 3 to 4 cilia intermediate.

Spores.—Maturing in early summer.

Distribution.—Universal.

Aulacomnium heterostichum, Bruch & Schimp.—See Plate XX.

A. androgynum.
Old spore-case.
(See page 235.)

Annulus.

Lid.

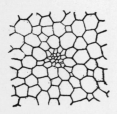

Spore-case
with lid.

Veil.

Habit and habitat. — In wide pale-green tufts on shady banks and slopes in the woods.

Name.—The specific name, *heterostichum*, is a compound of two Greek words, ἕτερος, other, and στίχος, rank, referring to two kinds of leaves.

Plant (*gametophyte*).—Stems densely covered with red-brown filaments (*tomentose*).

Leaves. — Inclined to one side; lower obovate, *upper* gradually longer and obovate-oblong, incurved on one side; *apex* nearly flat, obtusely pointed (*apiculate*);

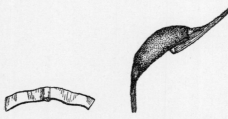

Cross section of central
strand of stem.
A. palustre

Cross section of leaf.
A. heterostichum.

Spore-case with veil.

margin saw-toothed from the middle upward; *vein* (*costa*) yellow-brown, vanishing below the apex.

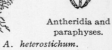

Male flower.

Habit of flowering.—Male and female flowers on one plant (*monoicous*). The male flower-clusters, sessile along the stems, and with rootlets at the base. The inner leaves of the clusters broadly ovate-concave, abruptly pointed and veined.

A. heterostichum.
Stem.

Veil (*calyptra*).—Split up one side.

Spore-case.—Oblong, slightly incurved and inclined.

Pedicel (*seta*).—Short, erect.

Lid (*operculum*).—Convex, obtusely short-beaked.

Annulus.—Large, rolling back as the lid falls.

Teeth (*peristome*).—Large, the inner segments open, but not disjoined, cilia 2 to 3.

Spores.—Mature in June.

Distribution.—Asia, Japan, North America.

Annulus.

Old spore-case.
A. heterostichum.

Antheridia and
paraphyses.

A. heterostichum.

A. heterostichum.   Leaves.

238

POLYTRICHACEÆ

The Polytrichaceæ form a large family which has been divided into some three tribes, nine genera, and about two hundred species, if the plants of the whole world are considered.

The species are often of large size and are probably the most highly developed of all the mosses. One may look for the American species by roadside banks, in fields and open woods. They grow in conspicuous patches and may be easily recognised by their mitrate or hood-like veils, their long wiry pedicels, their regularly cylindrical or angular spore-cases with mouths covered by a thin membrane bordered with 32 or 64 blunt teeth, and by their firm and rigid leaves with delicate vertical blades of cells (*lamellæ*) on the upper surface.

KEY TO GENERA

Veil.—Hood-like, spore-case symmetrical or nearly so; leaves wavy and crisp when dry, lamellæ few (2 to 8), straight, teeth 32 . . . . *Catharinea.*

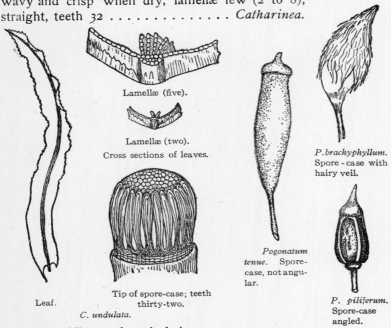

Lamellæ (five).

Lamellæ (two).
Cross sections of leaves.

P. brachyphyllum.
Spore-case with hairy veil.

Pogonatum tenue. Spore-case, not angular.

Leaf.

Tip of spore-case; teeth thirty-two.

C. undulata.

P. piliferum.
Spore-case angled.

Veil.—Mitrate, densely hairy.

Spore-case not angular, teeth often 32 . . . *Pogonatum.*

Spore-case 4- to 6-angled, teeth 64 . . . . *Polytrichum.*

239

CATHARINE MOSSES

Genus CATHARINEA, Ehrh.

The members of this genus will always attract attention from their habit of growing in extensive patches in partly shaded places. The leafy part of the plant is erect and large enough to

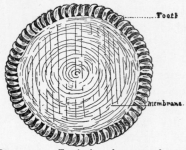

P. commune. Teeth sixty-four, summit of spore-case. (See page 239.)

form soft and luxuriantly green areas very conspicuous when beset with slender pedicels bearing either pale immature spore-cases or shining rich-coloured mature ones. The genus was founded by Friedrich Ehrhart in honour of Catharine II, Empress of Russia. The leaves are strap-shaped or oval-oblong, rich in

leaf-green and wavy when fresh, and curled or twisted in various directions when dry; the apex is acute or obtuse and the base is not sheathing; the vein bears a few lamellæ toward the apex.

The veils are split up one side and are sometimes rough.

Pogonatum. Teeth thirty-two. (See p. 239.)

The spore-cases are oval cylindrical, nodding, or arched, with long-beaked lids and are borne on long exserted pedicels.

The little column (*columella*) within the spore-case is terminated by a disk-like membrane (*epiphragm*).

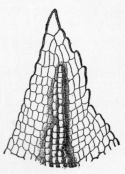

C. undulata. Apex of leaf with lamellæ.

The peristome is simple, of 32 tongue-like teeth united at the base; the tips are united by their inner faces to processes on the edge of the epiphragm so that the epiphragm hangs down from them by the length of the processes.

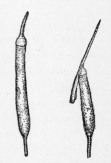

With lid.   With veil.
C. angustata. Spore-cases.

240

There are about forty-eight species known in all, nineteen being found in North America.

The Slender Catharinea, *Catharinea angustata*, Brid.—See Plate IV.

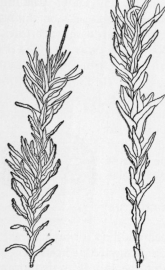

Apex of leaf.

Habit and habitat. — Very common in conspicuous patches on the ground at the bases of trees, along roadsides, and in woods. The fruits and the bright red rosettes of the male plants may be found in winter. In cold or dry weather this moss curls up its leaves so as to protect the upper delicate surface from frost and too rapid evaporation.

C. angustata. Leaf.

Name. — The specific name *angustata*, the Latin for "narrowed," refers to the slender habit of the plant.

Plant (gametophyte).—Simple or forked, erect, bearing one to three spore-cases.

Leaves.—Long, narrowly strap-shaped, wavy on the borders. *Apex* serrate; *base* not sheathing; *margin* serrate only in the upper half. Lamellæ 5 to 7.

Female plant.   Male plant
C. angustata.

Habit of flowering.—Dioicous, male flower on one plant, female flowers on another.

Veil (calyptra).—Membranous, split up one side, hairy at the summit.

Spore-case.—Nearly erect, narrowly cylindrical, green or dark-purple, shining.

Pedicel (seta).—Red, about one inch high.

Lid (operculum).—Dome-like, abruptly long-beaked.

Teeth (peristome).—Thirty-two, blunt, connected at the base, attached by the tips to the disk at the summit of the columella.

241

Spores.—Mature in winter.

Distribution.—North America, Europe, Asia.

The Wavy-leaved Catharinea, *Catharinea undulata,* Web. & Mohr.

Catharinea undulata differs from *C. angustata* in the leaves being more acute and with margins toothed throughout. Also it is a rather larger plant with less-prominent lamellæ and with a monoicous inflorescence.

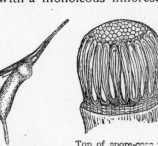

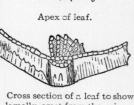

Apex of leaf.

Spore-case with veil.

Top of spore-case with the teeth un ... near their tips to an epiphragm.
C. undulata.

Cross section of a leaf to show lamellæ erect from the vein.

Leaf.

HAIR-CAP MOSSES

Genus POGONATUM, Beauv.

The **Pogonatum** mosses grow in tufts on the ground, often with a green felt of thread-like cells (*protonema*) at the base. The plants are short and simple, or long and robust; with branches starting below the leaves at the base of the pedicel, or half-way up to the stem. The male plants continue to grow from the centre of a terminal rosette of bracts.

The leaves are erect or spreading, the upper-half lance-shaped or strap-shaped; the base is clasping, with large pale cells; the margins are entire or serrate; the vein is broad, with numerous lamellæ occupying almost the entire width of the leaf-blade, and with their terminal cells smooth or bearing tiny projections (*papillose*).

The generic name *Pogonatum,* from the Greek πώγων, a beard, refers to the veil, which is hairy and almost covers the spore-case.

The spore-cases are cylindrical, but not angular. They are

242

P. brevicaule. Top of spore-case with 32 teeth united by their tips to a membrane.

P. Alpinum. Leaf with serrate margin and numerous lamellæ.

P. brevicaule. Stem with perichætial leaves.

P. brevicaule. Spore-case with veil.

P. urnigerum. Spore-case with lid.

P. brevicaule. Spore-case with lid.

nearly symmetrical, erect, or turned to one side, with flat lids having a central point. They are borne on erect pedicels.

The peristome is simple, of 32 blunt teeth, orange in the middle, united at the base and appearing as if attached at the apices to a membranous disk (*epiphragm*).

There are one hundred and fifty-six species known in all, nine in North America.

The Short-stemmed Hair-cap Moss, *Pogonatum brevicaule*, Beauv.—See Colour Plate IV.

Habit and habitat.—The short-stemmed *Pogonatum* is remarkable because of its habit of retaining the protonema, which persists as a bright-green felt covering the ground at the base of the plants. It binds the crumbling earth so that one may gather it in sheets. As the moss commonly grows in clay-banks, in ditches, and in places rather insecure, it may be that the habit of retaining the protonema has been evolved in the struggle for existence to enable it to live in situations too insecure to be occupied by other mosses.

243

Name.—The specific name *brevicaule*, from the Latin *brevis*, short, and *caulis*, stem, refers to the height of the plant.

Plant (gametophyte).—Short, simple; ¼ to ½ of an inch high. The male plants are minute and bud-like.

Leaves.—Five or six, erect, lance-shaped; *apex* awned; *base* broad, transparent; *margin* serrate, with appressed teeth; *lamellæ* few, 5 to 6 cells deep, the terminal one smooth

Leaf.

Blunt teeth.   Lid.

P. brevicaule.

and elliptic in section. *Male-cluster leaves* erect, curved back from the middle, lapping as shingles, broadly obcordate; *vein* passing beyond the apex to form a sharp point.

Leaves at the base of the pedicel.— Sheathing, long, membranous, abruptly narrowed to a long, erect, obtusely serrate point.

Section of lame*llæ.*
P. brevicaule.

P. brevicaule. Plant with a sporophyte.

Habit of flowering.—Male and female flowers on separate plants (*dioicous*). Male plants bud-like.

Veil (calyptra).—Hairy, reaching to the base of the spore-case.

Spore-case.—Cylindrical, broadest at the mouth, contracted below the mouth when dry, rough with tiny projections (*papillose*).

Pedicel (seta).—Twisted, 1 to 2 inches long.

Lid (operculum).—Flat, with a point at the centre.

Teeth (peristome).—White, simple, of 32 blunt teeth.

Spores.—Mature in winter.

Distribution.—North America; Eastern States, north to New-foundland, west to Ontario.

The Short-leaved Hair-cap Moss, *Pogonatum brachyphyllum,* (Michx.) Beauv.

Habit and habitat.—The short-leaved *Pogonatum* is found on sandy or loamy soil. The plants do not grow close together, but scattered somewhat, on a persistent green felt of slender alga-like threads.

Name.—The specific name *brachyphyllum* is compounded of the Greek βραχὺ, short, and φύλλον, a leaf.

Plants (gametophyte).—Olive-green or dark-brown when old; *stems* rigid, short, ⅖ to ⅕ of an inch long.

Leaves.—In rosettes at the summit of the stems, curved, appressed and brown when dry, very short, strap-shaped; *apex* blunt; *margin* entire; *vein* broad; *lamellæ* numerous, 6 to 7 cells deep, irregular, the terminal cell smooth, elliptic in section; base clear with large cells.

P. brachyphyllum.
Spore-case with veil.

P. brachyphyllum.
Spore-case with lid.

Habit of flowering.—Male and female flowers on separate plants (*dioicous*).

Veil (calyptra).—Hairy, dirty-brown, reaching to the middle of the spore-case.

Spore-case.—Yellow-brown, erect or curved, broadest at the mouth, rough with tiny projections.

Pedicel (seta).—Erect, short 1 to 1½ inches long, twisted.

Lid (operculum).—Flat, beak short, blunt-pointed.

Teeth (peristome).—Simple and blunt. Thirty-two in number.

Spores.—Mature in winter.

Distribution.—Pine barrens of New Jersey, south to Florida and Louisiana.

The Hair-like Hair-cap, *Pogonatum capillare,* (Michx.) Brid.

Habit and habitat.—Pale-green plants growing rather close together.

Name.—The specific name *capillare* is the Latin for "hair-like," referring to the slender character of the stem, leaves and teeth.

245

Plant (*gametophyte*).—Simple, or increasing by shoots from the summit of the main stem, 1 to 3 inches high, naked below, loosely leafy above.

Leaves.—Curled when dry, spreading when moist, $\frac{1}{5}$ to $\frac{2}{5}$ of an inch long, broadly lance-shaped; base transparent; *margin* serrate, with many-celled, triangular teeth; *lamellæ* numerous, 30 to 35, cells of the lamellæ 5 to 7 deep, the terminal broadest in section with tiny projections on the flat surface.

Habit of flowering.—Male and female flowers on separate plants (*dioicous*).

Veil (*calyptra*).—Hairy, covering the spore-case to the base.

Spore-case.—Erect, egg-shaped, $\frac{1}{10}$ of an inch long, with tiny projections on the surface, not contracted below the mouth when dry.

Pedicel (*seta*).—One-half to one and a half inches long, slender, flexuous, erect.

Lid (*operculum*).—Hemispherical at the enlarged base, abruptly straight-beaked.

Teeth (*peristome*).—Thirty-two in number, long and narrow.

Spores.—Mature in winter.

Distribution.—Rare in the mountains of New York, common in the mountains of New England; also along the Gaspé Coast to Newfoundland, west to the Rocky Mountains.

The Urn-bearing Hair-cap Moss, *Pogonatum urnigerum*, (L.) Beauv.

Habit and habitat.—Pale-green or with a bloom, growing in wide mats but not crowded. On the banks and by streams.

Name.—The specific name *urnigerum*, urn-bearer, refers to the spore-case.

Plants (*gametophyte*).—Erect, 1 to 3 inches high, the branches reaching the same height and densely leafy, each branch of the female plant bearing a spore-case. Male plants continue to grow from the centre of the terminal rosette.

Leaves.—Pale-green or brown, lance-shaped, erect when dry, spreading when wet; *apex* acute; *base* short, clasping; *vein* extending slightly beyond the apex of the leaf as an awn; lamellæ numerous, 40 to 50; 6 *cells* high, the terminal oval, with tiny projections (*papillose*), lower leaves scale-like.

Habit of flowering.—Male and female flowers on the summits of separate plants (*dioicous*).

246

Veil (*calyptra*).—Yellow-brown, covering the spore-case.

Spore-case.—Erect, red-brown, cylindrical or egg-shaped, contracted below the mouth when dry, the surface rough with tiny projections (*papillose*), the neck nearly smooth.

P. urnigerum. One row of lamellæ cells, the terminal cell papillose.

Pedicel.—Red-yellow, slender, 1 to 1½ inches long.

Lid (*operculum*).—Broad, conical, beak short and straight, surface rough with tiny projections.

Teeth (*peristome*).—Thirty-two, symmetrical, short and broad.

Spores. — Mature in autumn and winter.

P. urnigerum. Spore-case with lid.

P. urnigerum. Leaf.

Distribution.—Universal.

The Alpine Hair-cap Moss, *Pogonatum Alpinum*, (L.) Roehl.

Habit and habitat.— Growing in wide mats on rough stony and grassy places on all mountains. This is a pretty moss, larger than most Hair-cap mosses and may be readily distinguished from the others by its smooth spore-case, narrower at the mouth than below, obliquely inclined to the red pedicel, and by its veil which does not reach to the base of the spore-case.

Name.—The name refers to its habit of growing in mountain regions.

Plant (*gametophyte*).—Erect, 2½ to 7 inches high, the branches attaining an equal height, and densely leafy; stems naked and subterranean at the *base*. Male plants 1 to 2½ inches high.

P. Alpinum. Vertical row of cells from lamellæ, terminal cell papillose.

Leaves. — Erect, or recurved, narrowly lance-shaped; *apex* awl-shaped, spiny on the back; *base* white, sheathing, *margins* incurved, red, serrate; *lamellæ* numerous

P. Alpinum. Leaf.

247

20 to 30, covering most of the upper half of the blade, 6 to 7 cells deep, the terminal cell oval in section with tiny projection (*papillose*).

Leaves at the base of the pedicel (perichætial leaves).—Sheathing, longer; without lamellæ.

Habit of flowering.—Male and female flowers on the summits of separate plants, (*dioicous*).

Veil (calyptra).—Hairy, not covering the spore-case.

Spore-case.—Nearly cylindrical to egg-shaped, smooth, light-green, inclined or horizontal, somewhat curved.

Pedicel (seta).—Flexuose, 1 to 2 inches long.

Lid (operculum).—Small with a slender beak.

Teeth (peristome).—Thirty-two in number, blunt.

Spores.—Mature in late summer.

Distribution.—In mountainous regions.

HAIRY-CAP MOSSES

Genus POLYTRICHUM, Linn.

Found in extensive patches by roadsides and in open woods.

Brown and unattractive when dry, fresh and luxuriantly green when moist, owing to the habit of inrolling the thin margins of the leaves and folding them against the stem in dry air and of unrolling and turning them at right angles to the stem in damp air.

The **Genus Polytrichum** contains plants which were the first to be recognised as "plants with-

P. juniperinum.
Male plant.

P. juniperinum. Leaves with inrolled margins.

out flowers." Pliny called them "golden maiden-hair." They were dedicated to Venus and afterward to the Virgin Mary. Because of this fancied resemblance of the veils to a maiden's tresses, they were used to make a wash which was supposed to strengthen the hair.

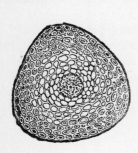

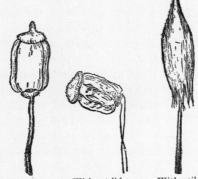

Polytrichum commune. Cross-section of stem.   With lid.   Without lid.   With veil.

P. commune. Spore-cases.

The plants are very tall, 1 to 18 inches high, and live on year after year, growing perpendicularly from the centre of the **male** (*antheridial*) flower-heads or from horizontal underground stems, or from the side of main stems.   The stems (see page 45) are stout, with almost woody fibres running up through them.

The leaves are long and slender, with a lance-shaped, awned apex and a membranous sheathing base; the *vein* is broad and covered by numerous thin green blades (*lamellæ*, see page 44), and the *margins* are entire or serrate, often inrolled.

The generic name *Polytrichum* is composed of two Greek words, πολὺς, many, and θρὶξ, a hair, and refers to the large mitrate, hairy veil which may partially or entirely cover the spore-case.

The spore-cases are erect or horizontal with 4 to 6 angles, a distinct basal portion (*apophysis*, see page 57), and lids conical or flattened-convex with a point at the centre.

M. juniperinum. Leaf with unrolled margins.

The peristome is single, of 64 short, rigid teeth united at the base and joined above to a thin circular disk (*epiphragm*) which terminates a central column.

The spores small and smooth.

There are ninety-nine species in all, about fifteen of them known in North America.

Genus POLYTRICHUM

KEY TO SPECIES

P. sexangulare.
Leaves.

P. juniperinum.
Leaf.

P. commune.
Leaf.

I.—Leaves entire, margins inflexed, apex obtuse, *P. sexangulare.*

Apex rough-awned.

Awn coloured brown or red, short. Leaves spreading when moist, somewhat re-curved . . *P. juniperinum.*

Awn whitish, transparent, long . . . . . . *P. piliferum.*

II.—Leaves serrate.

Marginal cells of lamellæ not enlarged in section, higher than broad.

Spore-case egg-shaped, ob-scurely angled.

Lid beaked . . . . . *P. gracile.*

Spore-case oblong, 4- to 6-angled.

Lid acutely conic, *P. formosum.*

Marginal cells of lamellæ en-larged, broader than high, 2 to 1 . . . . . *P. Ohiense.*

Marginal cells of lamellæ semi-lunar, with two prominent horns at corners, *P. commune.*

P. piliferum.
Leaf.

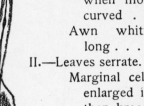

a *b*
P. Ohiense. *P. commune.*
Vertical rows of cells from lamella.
(*a*) Terminal cell broader than high; (*b*) terminal cell semilunar.

P. gracile.
Spore-case.

CLIMACIUM AMERICANUM, Brid.

CLIMACIUM DENDROIDES, Web. & Mohr.

Slender Hairy-cap, *Polytrichum gracile,* Dicks.

Habit and habitat.—The slender *Polytrichum* is not common. It may be found densely tufted—on the ground in woods, or on rocks.

Name.—The specific name *gracile* is from the Latin *gracilis,* slender.

Plant (gametophyte).—Light green, erect, 1 to 4 inches high, simple above, divided at the base and covered with soft matted hairs.

Leaves.— Spreading or erect when dry, broadly lance-shaped ; *apex* sharply taper-pointed ; *base* sheathing ; *vein* broad ; *margins* serrate ; *lamellæ* 30 to 40, not covering all of the leaf blade, 4 to 6 cells deep, the terminal cell elliptic in section.

Leaves at the base of the pedicel (perichætial leaves).—Sheathing, ½ an inch long.

Habit of flowering.— Male and female flowers on separate plants, (*dioicous*).

Veil (calyptra).— Orange, not quite covering the spore-case.

Spore-case. — Erect or horizontal, broadly egg-shaped; indistinctly six-angled, mouth small; *apophysis* obscure.

Pedicel (seta).—Slender, orange, 1½ to 2 inches long.

Lid (operculum).—Conic, beaked.

Teeth (peristome).—With 64 teeth often confluent and unequal.

Spores.—Mature in summer.

Perichætial
leaf.

Leaf.

P. gracile.

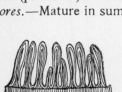

Portion of peristome. Spore-case with lid.

P. gracile.

Distribution.—From the mountains of Virginia to Newfoundland and west to the Rocky Mountains. Also in Europe, Asia and the Pacific Isles.

251

Ohio Hairy-cap, *Polytrichum Ohiense,* Ren. and Card.

Habit and habitat.—Found on the ground growing loosely in patches. Distinguished from *P. formosum** by the form of the spore-case, which is more or less narrowed toward the base and has an indistinct apophysis, but chiefly distinguished by the form of the marginal cells of the lamellæ, a character which separates it from all our other species of *Polytrichum.*

Name.—The specific name *Ohiense* refers to the fact that the type specimen came from Ohio.

Plant (gametophyte).—Erect, simple or divided, 1½ to 3 inches high, woolly below.

Spore-case.

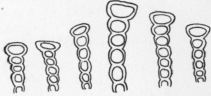

Vertical sections of lamellæ to show terminal cells.
P. Ohiense.

Leaves.—Spreading when moist, erect and slightly twisted when dry; *apex* narrowly taper-pointed, the awn spiny; *base* white, sheathing; *margin* serrate; *lamellæ* 30 to 40; *cells* 5 to 7 deep, the marginal cell much larger, broader than high, stirrup-shaped in section.

Leaves at the base of the pedicel (perichætial leaves).—Resembling the stem-leaves, longer and with a longer transparent base.

Habit of flowering.—Male and female flowers on separate plants (*dioicous*).

Veil (calyptra).—Pale, small, ragged, not concealing the spore-case.

Spore-case.—Erect, finally horizontal, with 4 to 6 acute angles, the base tapering into an indistinct apophysis.

Pedicel (seta).—Red below, paler above, 2 to 4 inches long.

Lid (operculum).—Conic and taper-pointed, bordered with orange.

Teeth (peristome).— Sixty-four.

---

*NOTE.—*Polytrichum formosum* seems to be rare in America, having been reported only from Miquelon Island, near Newfoundland.

Spores.—Rust colour, ripe in summer.

Distribution.—North Carolina to Prince Edward's Island, and west to Minnesota and British Columbia. Also in Norway and Sweden.

The Awned Hairy-cap, *Polytrichum piliferum,* Schreb.

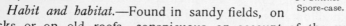

P. Ohiense
Spore-case.

Habit and habitat.—Found in sandy fields, on rocks or on old roofs, conspicuous on account of the white hair-like tips and the bluish-white bloom of the leaves; the plants in clusters but not matted together. The male flower-clusters surrounded with red bracts. The specific name *piliferum* is compounded of two Greek words, πιλος, hair, and φέρω, to bear, referring to the numerous white hairs of the leaves.

Plants (gametophyte).— Short, 1 to 1½ inches high, simple from subterranean creeping shoots, wiry and naked below, densely leafy above.

Leaves. — The upper long lance-shaped, the lower oval, appressed to the stem when dry, spreading when moist; *apex* smooth on the back, prolonged into a rough, hair-like awn; *margin* entire, inflexed upon the upper surface of the leaf-blade; *vein* red, becoming suddenly transparent at the apex; *lamellæ* about 30, 4 to 7 cells deep, the upper cell pointed in section.

Leaves at the base of the seta (perichætial leaves). — Narrowly tongue-shaped, erect, concave,

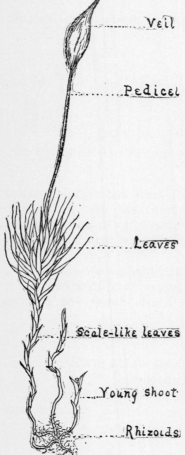

P. piliferum. Plant with sporophyte and with creeping shoots at the base.

253

without lamellæ; base sheathing, transparent, shorter than the awn.

Habit of flowering. — Male and female flowers on separate plants (*dioicous*).

Veil (*calyptra*).—Mitrate, covering the spore-case.

Spore-case. — Erect, finally horizontal, egg-shaped, 4-angled. Apophysis distinct, constricted above where it passes into the spore-case.

Pedicel (*seta*).—Erect, 1 to 1½ inches long.

Lid (*operculum*).—With a short stout beak, red or orange.

Teeth (*peristome*).—Symmetrical, sixty-four in number.

Spores.—Smooth, ripe in summer.

Distribution. — America, Europe and Asia.

P. piliferum.
Perichætial leaves.

P. piliferum.
Leaves.

Spore-case.

Perigonial leaves.
P. piliferum.

Vertical section of lamella to show pointed terminal cell.

Juniper Hairy-cap, *Polytrichum juniperinum,* Willd.—See Plate XXI.

Habit and habitat.—Common by damp sandy roadsides, or in peat-bogs. This is one of the Hairy-caps which in dry air turns its leaves up against the sun in order to protect the delicate lamellæ from his rays. It as well as *P. piliferum*, is conspicuous for its bluish-white bloom, but differs from *P. piliferum* in that the leaves are tipped with a short red awn instead of with one long, white, and hair-like.

Name. — Carl Ludwig Willdenow named this pretty moss *juniperinum* from its resemblance to tiny Juniper trees.

Plate XXI

JUNIPER HAIR-CAP, *Polytrichum juniperinum*, Willd.

Plant (gametophyte).—Simple or forked, erect, 1 to 4 inches high from subterranean shoots.

Leaves.—Erect, when dry, spreading when moist, lance-like; *apex* a rough red awn; *base* enlarged and sheathing; *vein* rough; *margins* entire, inflexed *lamellæ* 40 to 50, 5 to 6 *cells* deep; cells square in section, the terminal 3-toothed. Bracts of male flower-cluster short and abruptly awned.

P. piliferum.
Subterranean shoot.

P. juniperinum. Vertical sections of lamellæ to show *papillose terminal cell.*

Spore-case   Spore-case
with veil.   with lid.
P. juniperinum.

P. juniperinum.
Leaves.

P. juniperinum. Male plant with two years growth marked by the bracts of a terminal rosette.

Leaves at the base of the pedicel (perichætial leaves).—Sheathing, without lamellæ.

Habit of flowering. — Male and female flowers on separate plants (*dioicious*).

Veil (calyptra).—Large, covering the spore-case.

Spore-case. — Erect, finally horizontal, 4-angled; apophysis small, red, shield-like.

255

Pedicel (*seta*). — Red-orange, becoming brown, stout, glossy, 1½ to 2½ inches high.

Lid (*operculum*).—Red, flattened-convex with a short beak.

Teeth (*peristome*).—Pale, symmetrical, rather short, sixty-four in number.

Spores.—Ripe in summer.

Distribution.—From Florida to Alaska, also in Europe.

The **Common Hairy-cap,** *Poly-trichum commune,* L.—See Colour Plate X.

Habit and habitat.—This moss is widely distributed and attains its largest size in peat-bogs where it may usually be recognised by the long stems covered below by the silvery bases of the leaves and by the angular spore-case which bears a flat disk at the base. It has the distinction of being one of a few mosses which have served in the economy of the household. In the north of England the plants are made into small dusting brooms and mats. Withering states that the plants are used for bedding by bears, and Carolus Linnæus, the renowned Swedish botanist, is said,

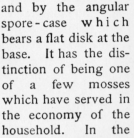

P. commune. Spore-case.

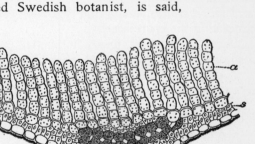

P. juniperinum. Spore-cases.

P. juniperinum. Cross section of leaf to show (*a*) lamellæ growing from the inner surface of the vein. (*s*) The vein. On the left, the blade is shown one cell thick and seven cells wide.

256

while on a trip in the North, to have used the dry
plants as stuffing for his pillow and mattress and to
have recommended it as not harbouring fleas and
infectious diseases.

Name.—The specific name *commune*, common,
describes the general distribution of this moss.

Plant (gametophyte).—Tall, 6 to 18 inches high;
dark-green or red-brown.   The male plants often with
the flower-heads in an ascending series of five to six,
marking the age of the plant; *stems* simple,
rarely forking; below, leafless, with the
basal portions of old leaves adhering;
growth erect from the centre of the male
heads or directly from the ground.

Leaves.—Crowded above, about ¾ of
an inch long; apex spreading and recurved,
lance-shaped and pointed, *base* enlarged,
white, glossy, sheathing; *vein* rough on the
back and bearing from 50-60 lamellæ on the
upper surface; *margin* inrolled when dry,
serrate; *lamellæ* 5 to 6 cells deep, the terminal the largest, semilunar or concave in
section.

Apex of leaf.   Leaf.
P. commune.

Leaves at the base of the pedicel (perichætial leaves).—White, ¾
of an inch long, without lamellæ; awn long and horny.

Habit of flowering.—Male and female flowers on separate
plants, (*dioicous*).

Veil (calyptra). — Covered with long silky hairs,
concealing the spore-case.

Spore-case.—Erect, finally horizontal,
4-angled; apophysis distinct, disk-like.

Pedicel (seta).—Stout,
2½ to 4 inches long.

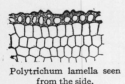

Polytrichum lamella seen
from the side.

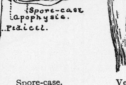

Spore-case.
P. commune.

Veil.   Veil on spore-
case.

Lid (*operculum*).—Flattened with an acute point at the centre.

Teeth (*peristome*).—Sixty-four, blunt at the apex, continuous at the base. United at the tips with a thin disk (*epiphragm*).

Spores.—Red-brown, ripe in summer.

Distribution.—Universal.

Lid.

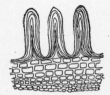

Portion of peristome.

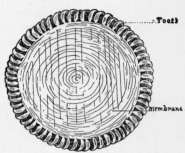

Summit of spore-case with 64 teeth around the thin disk.

P. commune.

Genus DIPHYSCIUM, Mohr

The species of the **Genus Diphyscium** are minute stemless plants growing scattered on the ground and on rocks. The leaves are strap-shaped or lance-shaped with a vein. The cells are **2** to **3** layers deep. The leaves at the base of the spore-cases are large, saw-toothed or cut into a ragged fringe.

D. foliosum. Growing on the ground.

D. foliosum.
Perichætial leaf.

The spore-cases are immersed or exserted on an inconspicuous pedicel, they are oval and taper-pointed, oblique and swollen on one side, with a conical lid. The outer teeth are none, or rudimentary and the inner membrane forms a pale blunt cone of 16 twisted folds.

The name, from δίς, twice, and φυσκίον, a vesicle, refers to the double wall of the spore case, which is due to the spore-sac being widely separated from the outer wall.

There are eleven species known in all, one of them being found in North America.

258

The Leafy Diphyscium, *Diphyscium foliosum,* Mohr.

Habit and habitat.—Dark-green, widely tufted; growing on clay soil and shady banks along roads, also on rocks.

Name.—From the Latin *foliosus,* leafy.

Plant (gametophyte).—Simple with short stems.

Leaves.—Strap-shaped, thick, or curled in various directions when dry, *vein (costa)* present; *margin* roughened with minute projections above and sometimes with a few distinct teeth, *cells* small and containing leaf-green.

Lid lifted to show teeth. Spore-case withou lid Top of spore-case with inner teeth. Top of spore case with outer teeth. Single plant. Perigonial leaf.

D. foliosum.

Leaves at the base of the spore-case.—Ovate lance-shaped, membranous, and without leaf-green; *vein* excurrent, forming a bristle point almost as long as the blade of the leaf.

Habit of flowering.—Male and female flowers on separate plants, *(dioicous).*

Veil.—Acute, conical, covering the lid.

Spore-case. — Immersed in colourless leaves; swollen on oneside, ovate, lance-shaped, yellowish-green.

Pedicel (seta).—Very short.

Lid (operculum).—Conical, acute.

Male plant.   Veil.
D. foliosum.

Teeth (peristome).—Double, the outer short, triangular, grainy, and with transverse bars, often perforated in the middle, pale-yellow, purple at the apex; the inner membranaceous, and forming a blunt cone of twisted folds.

Spores.—Small, mature in summer.

Distribution.—Europe, Asia and North America.

Genus BUXBAUMIA, Hall.

The species of the **Genus Buxbaumia** are tiny stemless plants growing scattered over decayed wood or on the ground.

The leaves are extremely minute, some broadly oval or oblong terminating in broad, spreading cilia.

The spore-cases are the conspicuous part of the plant, they are egg-shaped with a conical cap, depressed above, swollen on the lower side, and are borne obliquely on a thick pedicel covered with wart-like protuberances. The outer skin at the margin of the mouth is split into irregular fragments which roll back from the thickened rim which is formed of

B. aphylla. Young plant with spore-case with a veil and surrounded by leaves.

several layers of cells (the pseudo-annulus). The teeth are in several rows, the outer short and rudimentary; the inner membrane (*endostome*) is conical tubular, of 32 fan-like plaits, slightly twisted to the right.

There are five species known at present, three of them in North America.

Albrecht von Haller, the founder of the genus, named it *Buxbaumia* in honour of its discoverer, J. C. Buxbaum.

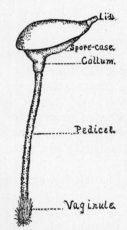

B. aphylla. Sporophyte with depressed spore-case; and hairy vaginule at the base of a rough pedicel.

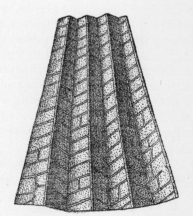

B. aphylla. Inner membrane.

260

Buxbaumia aphylla, L.—See Plate XX.

Habit and habitat.—Small stemless plants growing on earth and decayed wood. Coloured patches of a peculiar green-black felt appear at first, and on this felt, which under the microscope is shown to be a web of minute-branched threads (*protonema*), young plants, minute and spherical, appear. The moss has an annoying habit of disappearing from a station so that one cannot rely upon finding it the second time in the same locality. This sporadic habit and the scanty numbers of this moss invest its discovery with a charm known only to one who has collected it. The young spore-cases appear early in September. During the winter they remain green and with the warm days of early spring begin growth again and the colour changes from green to brown. By the middle of March the plants are ready to disperse their spores.

B. aphylla. Leaf.

Name.—The specific name *aphylla* is a compound of *à*, privative, without, and φύλλον, a leaf.

History.—In 1712, J. C. Buxbaum, a German botanist, discovered the curious plant on which the genus was founded. He collected it near Astrakhan, on the banks of the Volga, and says, "I wished to make it into a new genus and name it after my father, but called to mind the fox, who was derided by the others, because he begged the grapes, not for himself, but for his sick mother." It was for a time regarded as a fungus; but in 1741 Johann Dillenius correctly referred it to the mosses. Schimdel made a careful study of it in 1758, and Linnæus also wrote of it.

Plant (*gametophyte*).—Stemless, the male plants solitary in red-brown felt at the base of the female plant.

Leaves.—Extremely minute, oval or palm-shaped, soon disappearing; *margin* in shreds, or coarsely saw-toothed; *cells,* loose, colourless, long six-sided; leaves of the plant only two and without a shredded margin.

B. aphylla.
Veil.

Habit of flowering.—Male and female flowers on separate plants (*dioicous*).

Veil (*calyptra*).—Conical.

Spore - case. — Inclined, boat-shaped, and depressed above, swollen below, smooth, greenish-brown; *coat*, firm, glossy, and thickened on the

261

margin, rolling back at the mouth irregularly to form a crown-like border.

B. aphylla. Top of spore-case showing the peristome with cone of inner membrane rising from a cone of outer teeth.

Pedicel (seta).—Rigid, erect, straight, ½ inch high, deep purple, rough; the *base (vaginule)* thick, covered with rusty hairs.

Lid (operculum).—S h o r t, conic, obtuse, remaining for a time attached to the columella after separating at its margin.

Teeth (peristome).—The outer of short irregular teeth; the inner, a deeply plicate, funnel-shaped membrane.

Spores.—Very small, mature from April to September.

Distribution.—North America, Europe and Asia.

B. aphylla. Sporophyte with depressed spore-case and hairy vaginule at the base of rough pedicel.

THE FOUNTAIN MOSSES

Genus FONTINALIS, L.

The species as the name suggests grow either submerged or floating in streams and ponds.

Peristome with latticed cone protruding from outer teeth.

Stem.

Female branch with immersed spore-case at the summit.

F. antipyretica.

The plants are branched, often naked at the base. Every third leaf is directly over the first one counted; usually concave or keeled, with a base often auricled and growing slightly down the stem. They have no vein. The cells are linear, those of the basal angles more or less enlarged.

The spore-cases are oval or cylindrical with conical lids and are immersed in the leaves at the base.

The peristome is double, the outer of sixteen lance-shaped teeth, the inner of sixteen slender cilia united into a latticed cone.

There are about forty species in all, over twenty-five being known in the United States.

Fontinalis antipyretica, var. gigantea, Sulliv.

Habit and habitat.—Glossy, yellow-green or bronzed plants growing in fresh water.

Name.—The specific name *antipyretica* is a compound of the Greek ἀντί, against, and πυρεκτικὸς, fever, given because of a belief in its efficacy in fevers. The varietal name *gigantea* refers to its size.

Fontinalis antipyretica with tiny female branches.

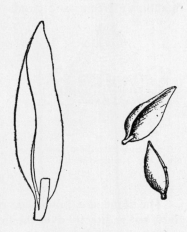

F. antipyretica. Leaves.

Plants. — One to two feet long, rooting only at the base and growing attached to stones, and roots of trees in streams.

Leaves.—Keeled and overlapping; *vein* none; *apex* finely toothed; *cells* of the basal angles enlarged.

263

Leaves at the base of the pedicel (perichætial leaves). — Overlapping, broad and blunt.

Perichætial leaves.   Veil.   Spore-case with lid.

F. antipyretica.

Habit of flowering.—Fruiting branch ½ an inch long, male and female flowers on separate plants.

Veil (calyptra).—Beaked.

Spore-case.—Cylindrical.

  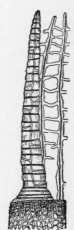

Top of spore-case with the inner teeth forming a latticed cone in the centre of the outer teeth.

Cone

Portion of peristome showing one outer tooth on the left and a portion of the inner membrane on the right.

F. antipyretica.

Lid (operculum).—Conical.

Teeth (peristome).—As in the genus.

Spores.—Mature in summer.

Distribution.—In temperate regions of both continents.

Genus NECKERA, Hedw.

The species of the **Genus Neckera** grow in extensive mats on tree-trunks or rocks. The primary stems are creeping, and the secondary are once or twice feather-branched, erect or pendent, often whip-like, and covered at the base with red-brown filaments.

N. pennata. Sporophyte with paraphyses at the base.

The leaves are glossy, translucent, often flat and generally wavy. The cells are minute rhomboidal, oblong in the upper part, linear in the middle and quadrate on the borders.

The spore-cases are immersed or exserted, with a short or somewhat elongated pedicel. They are erect and symmetrical with conical beaked lids.

The peristome is double, without an annulus, the outer teeth being long, linear, lance-shaped, and closely cross-barred. The inner membrane consisting of a basal portion with 16, often short, processes without intermediate cilia.

The genus was named by J. G. Hedwig in honour of J. N. Necker, a distinguished botanist. 158 species are known at present, 8 being found in North America.

The Feathered Neckera, *Neckera pennata,* Hedw.—See Colour Plate III.

N. pennata. Portion of peristome with four long outer teeth and three short inner.

Habit and habitat. — Growing in widely spreading pale-green matted tufts (*cespitose*) on tree trunks. It is a conspicuous moss on trees of the Adirondack woods. The older parts of the plants are shabby, while the newer parts are pale yellow-green and grow horizontally around the tree.

Name.—The specific name *pennata,* from the Latin *penna,* a feather, was suggested by the arrangement of the branches.

Plant. (*gametophyte*).—The primary stems are long, the secondary 2 to 4 inches long in opposite rows (*distichous*), close or distant, erect.

Leaves.—In the same plane with the branches, spreading, glossy, broadly lance-shaped, transversely wrinkled ; *apex* acute ; *margin* entire or slightly saw-toothed from the middle

265

upward ; *vein* faint and short, single, or two-forked, or want-ing ; *base* slightly unequal ; *cells* very small, rhomboidal-oblong, 4-sided at the basal angles.

N. *pennata*. Leaves.

Leaves at the base of the pedicel (perichætial leaves).—Long and sheathing, taper-pointed, surpassing the spore-case.

Habit of flowering.—Male and female flowers on the plant (*monoicous*).

Veil (calyptra).—Small, white, covering the lid only.

Spore-case.—Immersed, oval-oblong, dirty-yellow, brown when old, thin-walled.

Pedicel.—None, the cellular sheath at the base of the spore-case hairy.

Lid (operculum.)—Conical, beaked.

Teeth (peristome).—Pale-yellow, the outer of linear awl-shaped teeth from a narrowly lance-shaped base, cohering at the apex, densely cross-barred, irregularly divided, the inner segments rudimentary.

Perichætial leaves.

Old spore-case with-out lid.

(♀) Female branch. (♂) Male branch.

N. *pennata.*

Spores.—Mature in spring.

Distribution.—Common in North America ; universal.

Genus ANOMODON, Hook & Tayl.

The species of the **Genus Anomodon** are found on the roots of trees in woods, on rocks and on decayed logs.

The primary stems are prostrate, with horizontal shoots from the base and erect secondary stems irregularly branched. The stem-leaves are distant and minute, while the leaves of the branch-lets are crowded, spreading, or turned to one side, and have minute cells, usually with tiny protuberances on both faces.

266

The spore-cases are erect, cylindrical, regular, chestnut-coloured with conical beaked lids, and are borne on more or less elongated pedicels. Annulus narrow or wanting.

The peristome is pale, with narrowly lance-shaped teeth, and the segments of the inner membrane short, narrow and more or less irregular from a narrow base. The character of the teeth was not very well understood at first and so the genus was named *Anomodon*, from ἄνομος, irregular, and ὀδὼν, tooth, from the supposed unusual construction.

There are forty-nine species known in all, eleven being found in North America.

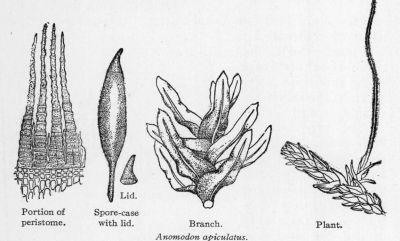

| Portion of peristome. | Spore-case with lid. | Branch. | Plant. |

Lid.

Anomodon apiculatus.

Anomodon rostratus, Schimp.

Habit and habitat.—Densely tufted, bright green at the surface, yellow-brown within. Growing on trees, roots, and limestone rocks.

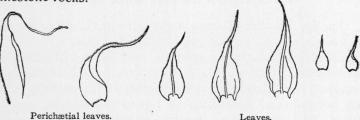

Perichætial leaves.   Leaves.

A. rostratus.

Name.—The specific name *rostratus,* beaked, refers to the lid.

Plant (gametophyte).—Primary stems brittle and bearing numerous thread-like branches, forming dense tufts.

Leaves.—Dense, overlapping as shingles, lance-shaped ; *apex* long-pointed ; *vein* solid, vanishing below the apex ; *base* oval.

Leaves at the base of the pedicel (perichætial leaves). — Long, white and thin ; apex of the inner leaves narrowed into a thread-like, reflexed point as long as the leaf-blade.

Habit of flowering.—Male and female flowers on separate plants (*dioicous*).

Veil (calyptra).—Split up one side.

Spore-case. — Red-brown, oval-oblong.

Pedicel (seta).—Short.

Old spore-case. Spore-case. Veil.
A. rostratus.

Lid (operculum).—Long-beaked.

Teeth (peristome).—The segments of the inner membrane about as long as the teeth, keeled, dirty-yellow, with cilia between, solitary, rudimentary or none.

Spores.—Mature in Fall.

Distribution.—North America, Europe and Asia.

Anomodon attenuatus, Hueben.

Habit and habitat.—In loose wide tufts on roots of trees and on rocks along streams ; common.

Name.—The specific name *attenuatus,* slender, refers to the branches.

Plants (gametophyte). — Irregularly branched and intricate, the branches short and rather obtuse; 1 to 2 inches high, or elongated and whip-like with minute leaves.

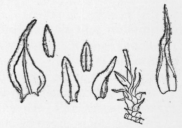

A. attenuatus. Perichætial leaves.

Leaves.—Spreading or turned to one side ; oblong lance-shaped from a widely oval base ; *apex* acute with a tiny sharp point ; *base* narrow at the

268

point of attachment and growing slightly down the stem; *margin* plane, minutely wavy, with papillæ ; *vein* translucent, vanishing below the apex ; surfaces densely covered with tiny protuberances.

Habit of flowering.—Male and female flowers on separate plants (*dioicous*).

Veil (*calyptra*).—Split up one side.

Pedicel (*seta*).—Twisted, ¾ of an inch long.

Spore-case.—Red-brown, shining, cylindrical, straight or slightly curved.

Lid (*operculum*).—Conic and beaked.

Teeth (*peristome*).—Narrowly lance-shaped; segments of the inner membrane, thread-like, fragile and irregular.

Annulus.—Narrow.

Spores.—Mature in autumn, not found in Britain.

Distribution.—North America, Europe and Asia.

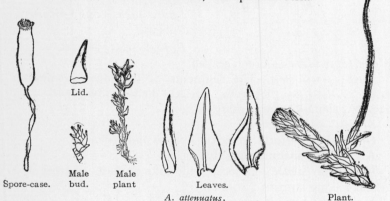

Spore-case.   Lid.   Male bud.   Male plant   Leaves.   Plant.

A. attenuatus.

Anomodon apiculatus, Bruch & Schimp.—See Plate XXII.

Habit and habitat.—Loosely and widely tufted on trees and rocks in mountains.

Name.—The specific name *apiculatus* from the Latin *apex, apicis*, refers to the short-pointed leaves.

Plants (*gametophyte*).—Green, with a bloom, dirty-red when old. Primary stems prostrate and whip-like ; secondary stems straight, simple or divided at the base.

Leaves.—Two-ranked, tongue-shaped, thick, opaque ; *apex* pointed; *margin* wavy; *vein* transparent, vanishing below the apex; *surface* covered with tiny protuberances; *base* oblong-oval with ear-like and fringed appendages; *cells* dense, minute, round.

Leaves at the base of the pedicel (perichætial leaves).— Long and sheathing, tongue-shaped toward the apex.

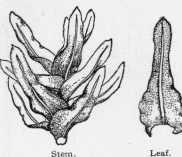

Stem.   Leaf.
A. apiculatus.

A. apiculatus.
Male flower-cluster.

Habit of flowering.—Male and female flowers on separate plants, (*dioicous*).

Veil (calyptra).—Split up one side.

Spore-case.—Egg-shaped or elliptical.

Pedicel (seta).—Short.

Lid (operculum).—Conic, beaked.

Teeth (peristome).—Narrowly lance-shaped and awl-shaped, cross-barred and knotty. Segments of the inner membrane very short from a very narrow base, sometimes wanting.

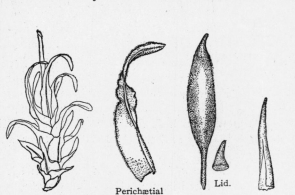

Female branch.   Perichætial   Lid.   Veil.   Portion of
leaf.   Spore-case.   peristome.
A. apiculatus.

Annulus.—None.

Spores.—Mature in autumn.

Distribution.—North America, Europe, Asia.

270

ANOMODON PICULATUS, Bruch. & Schimp.

TREE MOSSES

Genus CLIMACIUM, Web. & Mohr

The species of the **Genus Climacium** are large, resembling miniature evergreen trees. They are common in shady woods, in damp places on decayed logs, on roots of trees and on hummocks in swamps, and will be easily recognised from the photograph.

The primary stem is creeping, and the secondary erect and robust, with stout branches. The stem-leaves are scale-like ; the branch-leaves oblong lance-shaped with a thin vein, and the leaves at the base of the pedicel are long and sheathing.

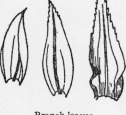

The spore-cases are clustered on long, erect pedicels ; they are cylindrical with a beaked lid and a long calyptra split up one side and embracing the base.

Stem leaf.

Branch leaves.

Perichætial leaf (base of pedicel).

C. dendroides.

The peristome is double, the outer teeth large and united at the base ; the inner keeled and perforated.

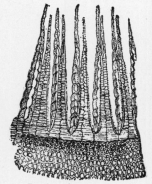

Spore-case with veil.

Top of spore-case with columella extending above the inner teeth.

Portion of peristome.

C. dendroides.

271

The generic name *Climacium* is derived from the Greek κλιμάκιον, a little ladder, referring to the appearance of the inner teeth.

Six species are known at present, two in North America.

Climacium dendroides, Web. & Mohr.—See Colour Plate IV ; also Colour Plate XV.

Habit and habitat.—Bright green, tree-like, found in wet places.

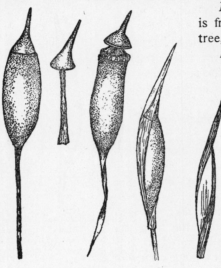

Name.—The specific name is from the Greek δένδρον, a tree, and εἶδος, like.

Plant (gametophyte).—Primary stem creeping, secondary simple, erect, often sharp-pointed at the apex, 2 to 4 inches high; branches clustered at the summit.

Leaves.—Stem-leaves broad, clasping; branch leaves narrower, oblong, folded lengthwise; *base* only

a   c   d   e

(*a*) Spore-case with lid ; (*b*) lid with columella ; (*c*) spore-case with lid lifted ; (*d*) spore-case with veil ; (*e*) veil.

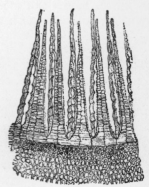

Cross-section of stem to show central strand.

Top of spore-case with columella extending above the inner teeth.

Portion of peristome with five outer and five inner teeth.

C. dendroides.

272

slightly growing down on the stem at the hollow basal angles; *apex* sharply serrate; *vein* vanishing below the apex.

Habit of flowering.—Male and female flowers on separate plants (*dioicous*).

Veil (*calyptra*).—Thin, smooth, extending below the spore-case.

Spore-case.—Erect, cylindrical, red-brown.

Pedicel (*seta*).—An inch long or more, deep-red.

Lid (*operculum*).—Straight, acutely beaked, remaining for some time attached to the central column of the spore-case.

Teeth (*peristome*).—As in the genus.

Annulus.—None.

Spores.—Olive-green, small, mature in the autumn and winter.

Distribution.—Common in North America, Europe, Asia and Africa.

Climacium Americanum, Brid.—See Colour Plate XV.

This species closely resembles the last, but may be distinguished by the long decurrent stem-leaves broadly eared at the base and coarsely serrate at the apex, as well

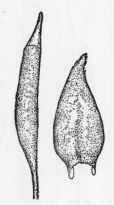

Spore-case   Stem
with lid.   leaf.

C. Americanum.

as by the longer and more narrowly cylindrical spore-cases with more abruptly, longer beaked lids.

HYPNUM RUSCIFOLIUM, Neck.

" Where, through some meadows, soft and green,
   Gemm'd with the daisy's silver bloom,
A gentle stream is wandering seen,
   'Mid flowering banks of rare perfume ;
There you may look beneath the waters
   Sweetly gliding on serene,
For one of Beauty's lovely daughters—
   Lovely though of humble mien ;
And where the stream, in childish glee,
   Leaps o'er the rocks with infant pride,
This little moss, in eddying swirl
   Of foaming waves, its head doth hide."

273

Genus HYPNUM, Dill.

The species of the **Genus Hypnum** in its wider sense all agree in having the peristome double and perfect, the outer of sixteen, strong, lance-shaped, taper-pointed and densely cross-barred teeth; the inner a broad membrane divided to the middle, or about, into sixteen, keeled, yellow segments, distantly cross-barred, entire, or cleft more or less along the keel, the segments generally separated by 1 to 3 filiform divisions (*cilia*) cross-barred and often bearing tiny spurs on the margin.

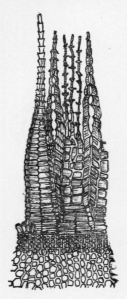

Hypnum triquetrum. Portion of peristome showing one outer tooth on the left with annulus cells at its base, two keeled inner teeth on the right with three spurred cilia between.

The difference in the species will perhaps better be understood by reference to the following synopsis of the sub-genera represented by the species which follow.

Dr. Johnston in speaking of the genus *Hypnum* said that perhaps it formed one-fourth of the vegetable clothing of Great Britain.

The word *hypnum* is the Greek ὕπνον, an ancient name for some sort of moss supposed to promote sleep.

SYNOPSIS OF SUB-GENERA

Thuidium.—Primary stems prostrate and irregularly divided; leaves with tiny protuberances (*papillose*); paraphyllia more or less numerous.

Stem-leaf.

Branch leaf.

Branch.

Thuidium delicatulum.

Cross-section of leaf to show papillæ.

Spore-case with lid.

Secondary stems regularly feather-branched ; stem-leaves differing decidedly from the branch-leaves ; *vein* translucent; *spore-case* curved ; *lid* conic, beaked.

Brachythecium. — Plants often large, prostrate, irregularly divided, the branches erect; leaves usually smooth with folds

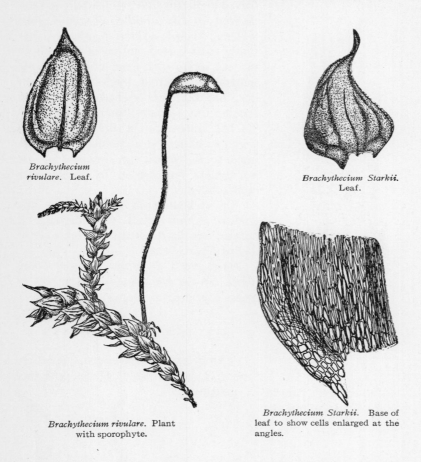

Brachythecium rivulare. Leaf.

Brachythecium Starkii. Leaf.

Brachythecium rivulare. Plant with sporophyte.

Brachythecium Starkii. Base of leaf to show cells enlarged at the angles.

extending lengthwise of the leaf and *veined* to the middle or above; *cells* loose, elongated, rhomboidal, enlarged at the base and angles ; *lid* conical, obtuse, or short-pointed.

Eurhynchium.—Plants somewhat feather-branched ; leaves heart-shaped, growing down the stem at the basal angles, serrate ; *cells* narrowly rhomboidal ; spore-case oval, nodding or horizontal, inflated and with long sharp beak.

Lid.

Leaf.

Eurhynchium: Hypnum Boscii.

Eurhynchium:
Hypnum Boscii.
Spore-case.

Plagiothecium.—Stems irregularly branching, not pinnate ; leaves usually flattened out in the same plane or all turned in one direction, ovate or oblong lanceolate, often somewhat oblique at base, two-veined or veinless. Leaf-cells elongated hexagonal to linear; seta smooth, spore-case oblong to cylindrical, curved. Lid from conical to short-beaked.

Spore-case.

Leaf-cells.
Plagiothecium Muellerianum.

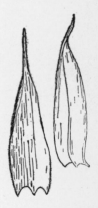

Leaves.

Amblystegium.—Plants usually small or medium size with numerous irregular entangled branches, often forming broad soft mats over the ground. Leaves mostly small, ovate acute, spreading regularly around the stem, straight or sometimes

276

HYPNUM CURVIFOLIUM. Hedw.

slightly curved. Leaf-cells comparatively broad, short six-sided, usually not abruptly enlarged in the angles. Pedicel tall and smooth. Spore-case more or less cylindrical and curved, with conical lid obtuse or acute.

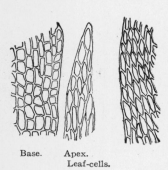

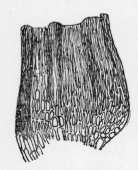

Base.   Apex.
Leaf-cells.

Leaves.

Amblystegium varium.

Harpidium. — Stems usually tall, more or less feather-branched ; leaves scythe-shaped and turned to one side, very acutely pointed ; *vein* simple, often reaching the apex; *cells*

Leaf.

Portion of leaf to show
enlarged alar cells.

Harpidium uncinatum.

narrow, linear, the alar much inflated. Plants often growing in water.

Ctenium.—Plants in compact tufts of a pale yellow-green, the branches and branchlets regularly and closely placed feather-like, giving the plant a beautiful plume-like appearance. Leaves hooked and turned to one side, with short double veins or

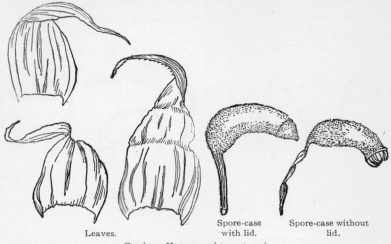

Leaves.   Spore-case   Spore-case without
             with lid.   lid.

Ctenium: Hypnum crista-castrensis.

none, somewhat serrate at apex. Spore-case large, curved horizontal.

Euhypnum.—Plants variously divided ; branches more or less densely feather-branched ; *leaves* obscurely two-veined,

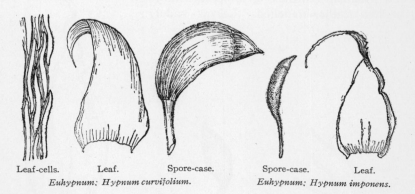

Leaf-cells.   Leaf.   Spore-case.   Spore-case.   Leaf.
Euhypnum: Hypnum curvifolium.   *Euhypnum: Hypnum imponens.*

membranous, shining, usually curved ; cells compact, narrowly linear, distinctly four-sided at the angles ; spore-case oblong cylindrical, curved, usually somewhat inclined or horizontal.

278

Calliergon.—Large plants with stem erect or inclined and with few cylindrical branches; leaves very concave, membranous, round to oblong or heart-shaped; *cells* very compact, narrow, alar cells inflated; spore-case oblong, horizontally curved.

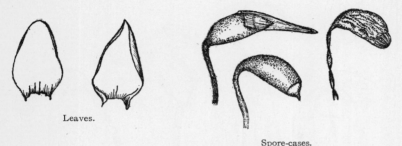

Leaves.

Spore-cases.

Calliergon: Hypnum Schreberi.

Pleurozium.—Plants feather-like, branches twice to three times divided; leaves membranous, shining; *veins* short, single or double; paraphyllia numerous; *cells* linear, uniform; spore-case short, egg-shaped; lid beaked.

Hylocomnium.—Plants of large size with few irregular branches, or sometimes more or less feather-branched. Leaves widely

Paraphyllia.

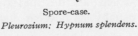

Spore-case.

Leaf.

Pleurozium: Hypnum splendens.

279

spreading or recurved ; *veins* two, and short ; *cells* long and narrow ; spore-case short, broadly ovate, horizontal.

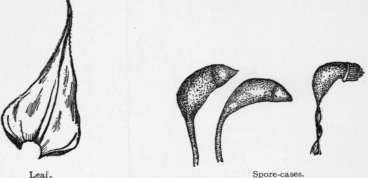

Leaf.   Spore-cases.

Hylocomnium: Hypnum triquetrum.

THE CEDAR MOSSES

HYPNUM: Sub-genus THUIDIUM, Schimp.

The species of this sub-genus are fern-like and grow in dense flat mats on decaying wood.

The generic name is derived from the Greek θύα, or θυία, an ancient name for some resinous-bearing evergreen. The moss was so called by Wm. Philipp Schimper, from its resemblance to a tiny cedar tree.

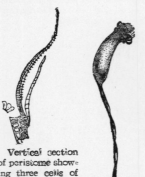

The primary stems are densely covered with rootlets, and the secondary are 1 to 3 times pinnately branching. The leaves on the stem are triangular heart-shaped with a strong vein, a more or less long-pointed apex, and a base extending downward on the stem ; papillæ are found on one or both faces ; leaf-like organs (*para-*

Vertical section of peristome showing three cells of the annulus and an inner and outer tooth.

Spore-case without lid.

Spore-cases with lids.

Thuidium delicatulum.

280

phyllia) on the stem between the true leaves are numerous and of many forms. The leaves on the branches are smaller, ovate, lance-shaped, concave and overlapping; the cells are small, round, six-sided, sometimes long, linear at the base and four-sided on the borders. The leaves at the base of the pedicel are long, and overlapping.

The spore-cases are narrowly ovate or cylindrical and arched, with conical or more or less long-beaked lids and long pedicels. The teeth are as in the genus *Hypnum*.

Two hundred and forty-four species are known at present, fifteen of them in North America.

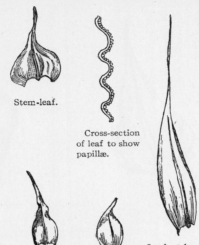

Stem-leaf.

Cross-section of leaf to show papillæ.

Branch-leaves.

Leaf at base of pedicel.

Thuidium delicatulum.

Inner tooth.
Outer tooth.
Annulus.
Spore-case wall.

Vertical section of peristome showing three cells of the annulus on the right and an outer and an inner tooth.

(*a*) and (*b*) Spore-cases with lids; (*c*) spore-case without lid; (*d*) spore case with lid.

Portion of peristome showing four outer teeth on the left with the inner membrane on the right, annulus at the base of the tooth on the extreme left.

Paraphyllia.

Thuidium minutulum.

281

Veil (*calyptra*).—Split up one side.

Spore-case.—Oblong-egg-shaped, nodding or horizontal, dark yellow-brown when old.

Pedicel (*seta*).—Smooth and ¾ to 1 inch long.

Lid (*operculum*).—With a long awl-shaped beak.

Annulus.—Large, of three rows of cells.

Teeth (*peristome*).—Double, as in genus *Hypnum*.

Spores.—Mature in autumn.

Distribution.—North America, Europe, Africa.

The Tiny Cedar Moss, *Hypnum* (*Thuidium*) *minutulum*, Hedw.

Habit and habitat.—Tiny fern-like mosses growing in woods on decaying trees and stumps.

Branch-leaves.

Name.—Hedwig, a great German botanist, gave this dainty moss its specific Latin name, *minutulum,* tiny, on account of its small size.

Plant (*gametophyte*).—Minute, twice pinnate; *stem* irregularly divided, densely covered with soft matted hairs; *branches* pinnately branching.

Stem-leaves.

Leaves.—Stem-leaves triangular, opaque; *apex* taper-pointed or with an abrupt short point; *margins* somewhat rolled back; *vein* stout, vanishing near the apex; *branch-leaves* oval, with taper point, concave; *vein* shorter; leaves covered with tiny protuberances.

Leaves at the base of the pedicel.—Thin, nearly smooth, the inner lance-shaped with a taper point.

Leaf-like organs (*paraphyllia*). — Numerous, and of various shapes covered with tiny projections.

Leaf at base of pedicel.

T. minutulum.

Habit of flowering. — Male and female flowers on the same plant; monoicous.

The Dainty Cedar Moss, *Hypnum* (*Thuidium*) *delicatulum*, Linn.—See Plate XXIII.

Habit and habitat.—Creeping fern-like plants on ground, roots of trees, and rocks. Common and exceedingly beautiful. The specimen photographed grew on a stone in a babbling brook.

Plate XXIII

THE DAINTY CEDAR-MOSS, *Thuidium delicatulum*, Linn.

Name.—The Dainty Cedar Moss is most attractive ; it was well known to the great Swedish botanist, Carolus Linnæus, who gave it the specific name *delicatulum,* dainty.

Plant (*gametophyte*). — Three times feather-branched, the primary stems densely rooting.

Leaves.—The stem-leaves densely crowded, enlarged at the base ; branch-leaves broadly oval ; *apex* long-pointed ; *base* concave ; *vein* strong ; *margin* serrate ; *cells* small, the apical truncate and crowned with 2 to 3 acute papillæ ; *paraphyllia* of varied forms.

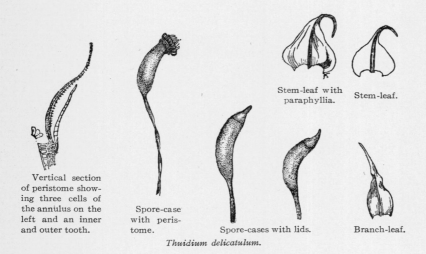

Vertical section of peristome showing three cells of the annulus on the left and an inner and outer tooth.

Spore-case with peristome.

Spore-cases with lids.

Stem-leaf with paraphyllia.

Stem-leaf.

Branch-leaf.

Thuidium delicatulum.

Leaves at the base of the pedicel.—Long-ciliate.

Habit of flowering.—Male and female flowers on separate plants (*dioicous*).

Veil (*calyptra*).—Split up one side.

Spore-case.—Cylindrical, arched.

Pedicel (*seta*).—One to one-and-a-half inches long.

Lid (*operculum*).—Conical.

Annulus.—Double.

Teeth (*peristome*).—Double as in *Hypnum.*

Spores.—Mature in winter.

Distribution.—Europe, North and South America.

HYPNUM: Sub-genus BRACHYTHECIUM, Schimp.

The plants of this sub-genus are generally large, prostrate or creeping, forming loosely matted tufts ; the stems branch irregularly, the branchlets somewhat regularly branching again, and covered densely with leaves.

The leaves are broadly oval and oblong-lance-shaped, usually with folds lengthwise; the apex is acutely pointed, either broadly or narrowly so ; the base is heart-shaped (*cordate*); the vein is single, continuous or vanishing half-way ; the cells are usually smooth and much elongated, the alar enlarged. There are no small leaf-like organs (*paraphyllia*).

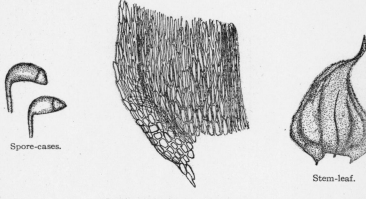

Spore-cases.

Stem-leaf.

Portion of the base of leaf to show
enlarged cells at the angle.
Brachythecium Starkii.

The spore-cases are oval or oblong, short, nodding, usually arched with a convex-conical, obtuse, or short-pointed lid ; they are borne on smooth or rough pedicels.

The generic name *Brachythecium* is derived from two Greek words, βραχύς, short, and θήκη, a case, relating to the short spore-case.

The peristome is double, the outer teeth being united at the base, slender, lance-shaped, closely and regularly cross-barred, with a distinct median line ; the inner teeth are lance-shaped with 2 to 3 well-developed cilia all attached to a wide basal membrane.

There are one hundred and sixty-three species known at present, about forty being found in North America.

Plate XXIV

BRACHYTHECIUM RIVULARE, Bruch. Ms.

Brachythecium rivulare, Bruch, Ms.—See Plate XXIV.

Habit and habitat.—Growing in dark or yellow-green mats on rocks and stones about springs and in swamps of mountainous woods.

Name.—The specific name *rivulare* refers to the habit of growing in wet places

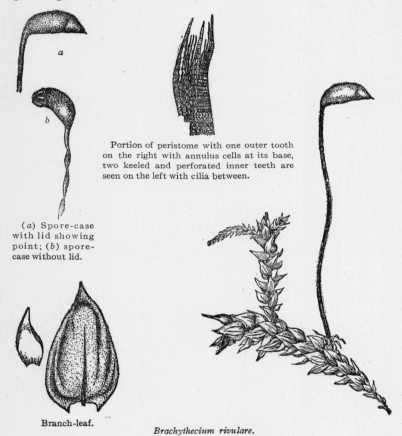

Portion of peristome with one outer tooth on the right with annulus cells at its base, two keeled and perforated inner teeth are seen on the left with cilia between.

(*a*) Spore-case with lid showing point; (*b*) spore-case without lid.

Branch-leaf.

Brachythecium rivulare.

Plants (gametophyte).—Woody, prostrate, naked, or with rooting filaments, secondary stems ascending from old stems, arched ½ to 3 inches long, nearly free from branches below, irregularly branching above.

Leaves.—Branch leaves erect spreading, oval to oval lance-

285

shape, concave or somewhat grooved; *apex* acute to short taper-pointed; *margin* with small sharp-pointed teeth above; *base* growing somewhat down the stem; *vein* extending ⅔ of the length of the leaf; *cells*, median, linear; basal, broader; alar, enlarged.

Habit of flowering.—Male and female flowers on different plants (*dioicous*).

Veil (*calyptra*).—Split up one side.

Spore-case.—Large, oblong or egg-shaped, horizontal or inclined.

Pedicel (*seta*).—Thick and rough, red-brown, 1 to 1½ inches long.

Lid (*operculum*).—Conical, with an abrupt slender point.

Teeth (*peristome*).—As in the genus.

Annulus.—Large.

Spores.—Chestnut colour, mature in autumn.

Distribution.—Universal in mountainous regions.

Brachythecium Starkii, (Brid.) Br. & Sc.

Habit and habitat.—In dark-green, loose mats on fallen logs and old tree-trunks in moist mountain regions.

Name.—The specific name was given in honour of Robert M. Starke.

Plant (*gametophyte*).—Prostrate, branching, the branches ascending, arched, ¼ to 1 inch long.

Leaves.—Branch-leaves distant, spreading, oval, lance-shaped, narrowly acute or taper-pointed; *apex* usually half twisted; *base* somewhat decurrent; *margin* serrate; *vein* extending beyond the middle; *cells*, the middle linear, the basal shorter and broader; the alar few, rhomboidal to quadrate; stem-leaves broadly oval and long taper-pointed, less strongly serrate, cells looser.

Brachythecium Starkii. Plant.

Leaves at the base of the pedicel (*perichætial leaves*).—Longer and narrower.

Habit of flowering.—Male and female flowers on one plant (*monoicous*).

Veil (calyptra).—Split up one side.

Spore-case.—Abruptly horizontal, short egg-shaped, dark red-brown, black when old.

Pedicel (seta).— Rough, red-brown, 1 to 1¼ inches high.

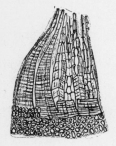

Portion of peristome showing two outer teeth on the left with annulus cells at the base, two keeled and perforated cells with cilia are seen at the right.

Spore-case with peristome.

Plant with female branch on the left and male branch on the right.

Leaf.

Brachythecium Starkii.

Lid (operculum).—Convex, conical, tipped with a short, sharp point.

Annulus.—Large, of about two rows of cells.

Teeth (peristome).—As in the genus.

Spores.—Chestnut, maturing in autumn and winter.

Distribution.—In the northern United States and Canada, across the continent, south to New Jersey; Europe.

Brachythecium Novæ-Angliæ, (Sull. & Lesq.) Jaeger & Sauer.—See Plate XXV.

Habit and habitat.—On earth and stones.

Name.—The specific name is the Latin for "New England."

Plant (gametophyte).—Forming loosely entangled mats; stem 1½ to 2 inches long, irregular; branches cylindrical, with rather short, overlapping, slightly spreading leaves.

Leaves.—Erect, spreading, sometimes very concave, not plaited, not glossy, incurved, broadly ovate,

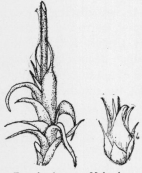

Female plant.   Male plant.

B. Novæ-Angliæ.

287

narrowly taper-pointed; *base* growing down the stem; decurrent; *vein* reaching the middle: *margin* finely saw-toothed all around; *cells* narrowly oblong-hexagonal, shorter and broader at the basilar angles.

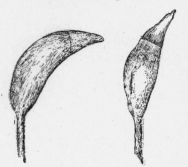

Leaves at the base of the pedicel.—Ovate, long, taper-pointed, recurved from the middle; vein not easily distinguishable.

Habit of flowering.—Male and female flowers on separate plants.

Perichætial leaves (dioicous).

Veil (calyptra).—Thin, split up one side.

B. Novæ-Angliæ. Spore-cases.

Spore-case.—Oblong, erect, slightly curved.

Pedicel (seta).—Rough, purple.

Lid (operculum).—Long, conical, taper-pointed.

Annulus.—Double, large.

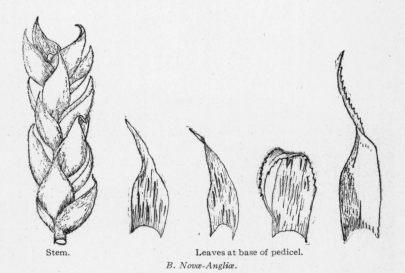

Stem.   Leaves at base of pedicel.

B. Novæ-Angliæ.

Teeth (peristome).—Teeth densely articulate, segments of the inner membrane as long as the teeth. *Cilia* well developed but without transverse spurs attached at intervals to the margin.

288

BRACHYTHECIUM NOVÆ-ANGLIÆ, (Sull. & Lesq.) Jaeger & Sauer

BRACHYTHECIUM STARKII, (Brid.) Br. & Sc.

Spores.—Mature in late fall and early spring.
Distribution.—Northeastern United States and Canada.

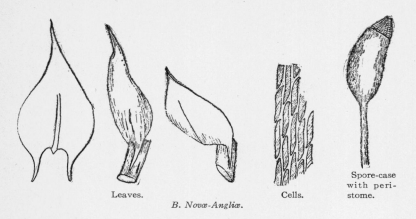

Leaves.

B. Novæ-Angliæ.

Cells.

Spore-case
with peri-
stome.

THE LONG-BEAKED HYPNUM

HYPNUM: Sub-genus EURHYNCHIUM, Schimp.

The species of this genus are robust, glossy plants, more or less feather-branched, prostrate or creeping.

The leaves are open, overlapping as shingles ; they resemble the bowl of a spoon, with the apex abruptly drawn out into a slender point and the margin serrate all around ; a vein extends to the middle or beyond ; the cells are smooth or slightly covered in a few species with tiny protuberances, they are narrowly rhomboidal, some- what worm-like and enlarged at the basal angles. The leaves at the base of the pedicel have root-like filaments.

Stem-leaf.

Stem.

H. Boscii.

The spore-cases are oval-oblong nodding or horizontal, on a smooth or rough pedicel, with lids more or less long-beaked. This character suggested the generic name from the Greek ἐν, well, and ῥύγχος, a beak. The annulus is compound or rarely none.

289

Seventy-four species are known in all, nineteen in North America.

Hypnum (Eurhynchium) Boscii, Schwaegr.—See Plate XXVI.

Habit and habitat.—A very beautiful and easily identified moss, growing in thick soft-golden cushions or in loose thin mats on the ground among grass or on the ground and on rocks in shady places and open fields.

Name. — The specific name Boscii was given by D. Fridericus Schwae- grichen, in honour of Louis Augustin Guillaume Bosc, a distinguished natur- alist.

Plants.—Stems prostrate, somewhat pinnately branching ; branches mostly simple, inflated, blunt, and cylindrical by the arrangement of the leaves.

Leaves.—Thin, dry and shining, closely overlapping, oblong-oval, very concave ; *apex* narrowed to a twisted slender point ; *base* clasping ; *margin* finely serrate to the base ; *cells* narrowly linear, those of the base shorter, thick and yellow-brown.

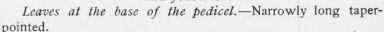

Lid.   Spore-cases.
H. Boscii.

Leaves at the base of the pedicel.—Narrowly long taper- pointed.

Habit of flowering.—Male and female flowers on the same plant (*monoicous*).

Veil (*calyptra*).—Split up one side.

Spore-case.—Brown, oblong, erect-incurved, gradually nar- rowed into the pedicel, strongly arched under the mouth when dry.

Pedicel (*seta*).—Smooth, red to red-brown, slightly twisted to the right.

Lid (*operculum*).—Conic, the beak about ½ the length of the urn.

Teeth (*peristome*).—As in the genus *Hypnum.*

Annulus.—Compound.

H. Boscii.
Breathing pore.

290

HYPNUM BOSCII, Schwaegr.

Spores.—Mature in autumn.

Distribution.—Vermont to Florida and Louisiana, west to Missouri and Illinois.

HYPNUM : Sub-genus PLAGIOTHECIUM, Schimp.

The species of this genus are partly prostrate, irregularly branching plants with rooting stems. They are soft and variable in size.

The leaves are thin, glossy and mostly entire; a vein is wanting or double; very short and thin; the cells are long and narrowly rhomboidal-hexagonal; larger at the base. Male and female flowers are usually found on the same plant.

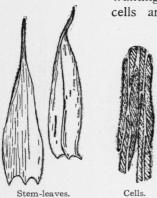

Stem-leaves.   Cells.

P. Muellerianum.

The veil is narrow and falls early. The spore-case is somewhat erect, oblique or almost horizontal, oval-oblong to cylindrical, somewhat arched, short-necked, thin, smooth or rarely wrinkled when dry.

The teeth are whitish.

The name is derived from the Greek πλάγιος, oblique, and θηκίον, a little chest, referring to the spore-case.

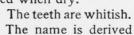

Spore-case
with lid.

Plagiothecium Muellerianum, Schimp.

Habit and habitat.—This moss is found in rocky ravines; it grows in loose, bright and shining green tufts.

Name.—The specific name, *Muellerianum*, was given by William Schimper in honour of Baron Ferdinand Mueller, Government botanist of Australia.

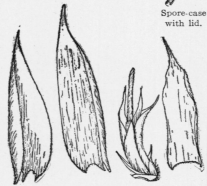

Leaves at base of pedicel.

P. Muellerianum.

291

Plant (*gametophyte*).—Very small ; stems with runners, creeping, with branches erect, rooting at the base and sometimes at the apex.

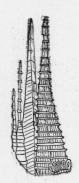

Leaves.—In two rows, spreading, concave, ovate-lance-shaped at the base, taper-pointed, with an abrupt, short, acute point ; *margin* entire ; *vein* wanting ; base not growing down the stem ; *cells* narrow, uniform.

Leaves at the base of the pedicel (*perichætial leaves*).—Half-clasping at the base, oblong-ovate, taper-pointed, entire.

Portion of peristome showing one outer tooth on the right with annulus cells at its base, one keeled inner tooth and two cilia on the left.

Spore-cases with peristome.   Dry spore-case.

P. Muellerianum.

Habit of flowering.—Male and female flowers on separate plants (*dioicous*).

Veil (*calyptra*).—Small.

Spore-case.—Somewhat nodding, tapering from the enlarged mouth toward the pedicel, long-necked, enlarged at the mouth and bell-shaped when dry.

Pedicel (*seta*).—Short, purple.

Lid (*operculum*).—Conical, short-beaked.

Teeth (*peristome*).—Distantly jointed, cilia short, robust, unequal.

Annulus.—Narrow, simple.

Spores.—The fruit is very rare.

Distribution.—Found in Europe and eastern North America.

HYPNUM: Sub-genus AMBLYSTEGIUM

The species of the **Sub-genus Amblystegium** vary in size from minute to large and robust and vary in colour from bright yellow-green to dark dull-green. The stems are prostrate, creeping, decumbent, ascending, or erect. The male and female flowers are usually on separate plants.

The stems are usually tender and soft, but are occasionally rigid. They are repeatedly branched, commonly irregularly so, with the branches more or less erect.

HYPNUM REPTILE Michx.

AMBLYSTEGIUM VARIUM, (Hedw.), Lindb.

The leaves spread in all directions. They are narrowly lance-shaped to broadly egg-shaped, concave, or flat, never eared at the b a s e and never with the cells narrowly l i n e a r. The base may or may not grow downward on the stem. Vein absent or prominent, margins entire or serrate.

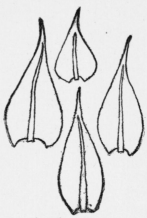

A. varium. Leaves.

The spore-cases are oval to cylindrical, symmetrical or unsymmetrical, erect to horizontal and usually constricted under the mouth when dry. The base tapers into a large or small collum. The colour varies from uniformly purple or brown through two shades to pale throughout. The peristome is normal, with usually 2 to 4 cilia, although in a few cases they are absent or rudimentary. The g e n e r i c name from the Greek ἀμβλὺς, blunt, and στέγος, a cover, refers to the character of the lid, which is convex or conic, usually bluntly pointed, rarely sharply pointed. The annulus consists of from 1 to 3 rows of cells. The calyptra is small and falls early. Sixteen species are known in North America, ten of them being found in both America and Europe.

Base.   Apex.

A. varium. Leaf-cells.

Amblystegium varium, (Hedw.) Lindb.—See Plate XXVII.

Habit and habitat.—This species is found growing in extensive loose or crowded tufts, bright green, dull dark-green or pale yellow-green, on ground, decayed wood, bases of trees and rocks in moist, wet or shady places.

Name.—The specific name, *varium,* refers to the variable character of the plant.

Plant (gametophyte).—The plants are of small or medium size, the stems obscurely angled, prostrate and branched, the branches slender, irregular, erect or ascending, never plume-like, straight or with tips incurved.

Leaves.—Leaf-cells spreading or appressed, flat or concave; variable in size and shape, lance-shaped to ovate-lance-shaped or broadly ovate; apex usually slender, straight or slightly curved; margin entire to toothed above; vein extending to the apex or well into the point; cells broad and applied end to end (*parenchymatous*) toward the base, and narrow, with the ends overlapping (*prosenchymatous*) toward the apex.

Habit of flowering.—Male and female flowers on separate plants.

Veil (calyptra).—Small and falling early, equal to or shorter than the spore-case, split half the length.

Spore-case.—Cylindrical, unsymmetrical, upright to horizontal, pale yellow-green when young, chestnut when mature; constricted under the mouth when dry; neck $\frac{1}{4}$ to $\frac{1}{2}$ the length of the spore-case.

Pedicel (seta).—One-half inch to 2 inches long, stout, reddish at the base, pale-yellow or dark throughout.

Lid (operculum).—Obliquely pointed from a high convex or conical base.

Annulus.—With two to three rows of cells.

Teeth (peristome).—Cinnamon brown or yellow, paler above, lance-shaped; cilia 2 to 4.

Spores.—Mature in late spring.

Distribution.—Common and widely distributed.

THE BOAT-HOOK MOSSES

HYPNUM: Sub-genus HARPIDIUM, Sulliv.

The species of the **Sub-genus Harpidium** are found usually in marshes. They have stems divided irregularly into long ascending rootless branches sometimes plume-like with short

branchlets which are all more or less curved at the apex like a boat-hook.

The leaves are firm and membranous with the apex prolonged into a slender point and turned to one side as a scythe-blade ; a single vein extends to above the middle or to the apex ; the cells are narrow, enlarged and inflated at the basal angles.

H. uncinatum. Leaf.

294

The name *Harpidium*, the Latin for "hook," describes the hooked leaves, the important character of the sub-genus.

The spore-cases are borne on long smooth pedicels, they are oblong-cylindrical, often arched, with short and conical lids. The teeth are as in the genus *Hypnum*.

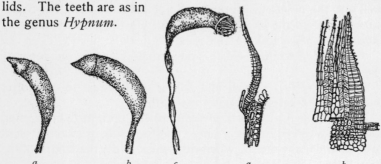

a   *b*   *c*   *a*   *b*

H. uncinatum. (*a*) and (*b*) Spore-cases with lids; (*c*) spore-case without lid.

H. uncinatum. (*a*) Vertical section of peristome showing three annulus cells on the right at the base of an outer tooth, inner tooth on the left; (*b*) portion of peristome showing on the right one outer tooth, on the left two keeled inner teeth and four cilia below three rows of annulus cells.

There are numerous species. In the "Kryptogamen Flora," of 1898, K. Gustav von Limpricht, a prominent bryologist, devotes about seven pages to a most intricate classification of the sub-genus *Harpidium*.

The Hooked Boat-hook Mosses, *Hypnum* (*Harpidium*) *uncinatum,* Hedw.—See Colour Plate III.

Habit and habitat.—In pale yellow-green tufts, erect or drooping, on stones bordering streams, or on shaded ground, rarely on decayed wood, common and variable in mountain regions.

Name.—The specific name, Latin *uncinatum,* hooked, refers to the character of the leaves.

Leaves.—Long, lance-shaped, grooved lengthwise, the taper-point spreading, scythe-shaped or hooked; *apex* minutely serrate; *vein* thin; *cells* narrow, more enlarged at the base, broader and rectangular at the angles, which are slightly hollow.

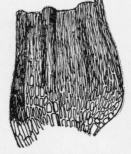

H. uncinatum. Right side from base of a leaf to show enlarged cells in the angle.

Leaves at the base of the pedicel (perichætial leaves).—Very long, the *outer* recurved from the middle, the *inner* soft, long, with a slender thread-like point; *apex* sharply serrate; *vein* present.

Habit of flowering.—Male and female flowers on the same plant (*monoicous*).

Veil (*calyptra*).—Split up one side.

Spore-case.—Nodding, cylindrical, incurved, constricted under the mouth when dry, brown-orange, darker when old.

Pedicel (*seta*).—Variable in length, smooth.

Lid (*operculum*).—Orange, highly convex, conical, acute.

Teeth.—Orange at the base, yellowish above; *segments* of the inner membrane slightly cleft; *cilia* two, as long as the outer teeth.

Annulus.—Broad, of three rows of cells.

Spores.—Mature in summer and autumn.

Distribution.—Universal.

COMB MOSSES

HYPNUM: Sub-genus CTENIUM

The species of the **Sub-genus Ctenium** are large and grow in loose tufts with stems erect or prostrate, rigid and compressed, simple and two-forked, closely

H. uncinatum. (*a*) Leaf from base of pedicel; (*b*) perigonial leaf; (*c*) an antheridium and a paraphysis.

C. crista-castrensis. Stem-leaves.

and regularly feather-branched; the branches are fern-like and the branchlets close, resembling the teeth of a comb, a characteristic which has suggested the generic name from the Greek, κτείς κτεν-), a comb.

The leaves have longitudinal folds with the apex turned to one side.

The spore-cases are raised on long pedicels; they are cylindrical-oblong, arched, and with broadly conical lids tipped with a point.

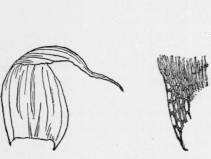

Stem-leaf.   Cells at base of leaf.   Female plant.

C. crista-castrensis.

The Knight's Plume Moss, *Hypnum* (*Ctenium*) *crista-castrensis*, L.—See Plate XXVIII.

Habit and habitat.—In loose, rigid, yellow-green tufts on decaying logs in mountainous regions.

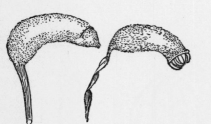

Spore-case with lid.   Spore-case without lid.   Leaf at base of pedicel.   Paraphyllia.

C. crista-castrensis.

Name.—The great Linnæus named this pretty moss *crista-castrensis* from its resemblance to a military plume or crest—Latin *crista*, a crest, and *castrensis*, military.

Plant (*gametophyte*).—The stems prostrate, 3 to 5 inches long, the tips upright; simple or twice-branched, closely and

297

regularly feather-branched, the branches resembling a fern frond; branchlets close, diverging horizontally and curved back at the apex like a plume.

Leaves.—Stem-leaves broad, gradually long lance-like and taper-pointed, thin, turned to one side as a scythe blade, with longitudinal folds ; *vein* double or none ; *margin* sharply serrate from the middle upward.

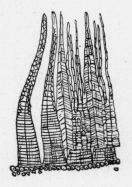

Leaf-like organs (paraphyllia).—Numerous, long, narrowly lance-shaped.

Leaves at the base of the pedicel (perichætial leaves).—Long, sheathing, white, veinless.

Habit of flowering.—Male and female flowers on separate plants (*dioicous*).

Veil (calyptra).—Thin, smooth, pointed and split up one side.

Spore-case.—Cylindrical-oblong, arched, green-brown when ripe, dirty-yellow when empty.

C. crista-castrensis. Portion of peristome showing on the left two outer teeth; on the right two keeled teeth of the inner membrane and six cilia.

Pedicel (seta).—One-and-a-half to two inches long.

Lid (operculum).—Broadly conical, sharp-pointed.

Teeth (peristome).—The outer teeth orange below, pale, serrate, and awl-pointed above ; the inner teeth long-pointed and cleft ; cilia three or four, thick and as long as the teeth.

Annulus.—Simple and narrow.

Spores.—Mature in summer and autumn.

Distribution.—North America, Europe, Asia.

HYPNUM: Sub-genus EUHYPNUM

The plants of this group generally have creeping stems which are more or less regularly feather-branched. The leaves are usually scythe-shaped and turned to one side, ovate lanceolate below and narrowly taper-pointed. The vein (*costa*) is short and double or none. The cells are linear and narrow, 4-sided

H. curvifolium. Branch-leaf.

H. imponens, Spore-cases with lids.

Plate XXVIII

THE KNIGHT'S-PLUME MOSS, *Hypnum crista-castrensis*, L.

at the angles; the inner leaves at the base of the pedicel are deeply folded; small leaf-like organs (*paraphyllia*) on the stem are few. The spore-cases are cylindrical-oblong on smooth

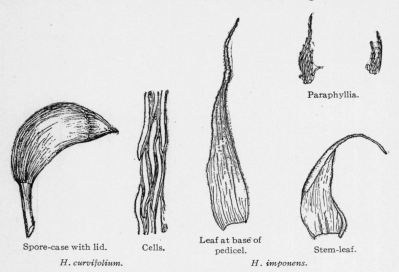

Paraphyllia.

Spore-case with lid.   Cells.   Leaf at base of pedicel.   Stem-leaf.

H. curvifolium.   *H. imponens.*

pedicels; the lids are large, from very acutely pointed to convex-conical. The prefix εὐ, proper, indicates that this sub-genus is the most typical among the different groups of *Hypnum*.

Hypnum (Euhypnum) reptile, Michx.—See Plate XXVII.

Habit and habitat.—Found in pale- or dusky-green, wide and loose tufts on the bark of living or decayed trees. Common and variable in sub-alpine regions, rare in the plains except northward.

Name.—From the Latin *reptilio,* creeping.

Plant (gametophyte). — Drooping, stems branching, the branches feather-branched, the branchlets erect and incurved.

Leaves.—Crowded, concave, long taper-pointed from an oblong base; *margin* sharply serrate above, flat or recurved below; *vein* double, short, yellowish; leaf-like organs (paraphyllia) on the stem, few and very small, lance-shaped or palm-like.

Leaves at the base of the pedicel (perichætial leaves).—The inner long, taper-pointed, longitudinally grooved with double vein and toothed apex.

299

Habit of flowering.—Male and female flowers on the same stems, (*monoicous*).

Veil (*calyptra*).—Thin, split up one side.

Spore-case.—Somewhat erect, cylindrical, yellowish, curved when dry.

H. reptile. Stem-leaves.

Pedicel.—Smooth.

Lid (*operculum*).—Large, yellow, shortly beaked from a highly convex base.

Teeth (*peristome*).—Long taper-pointed, orange at the base, segments of the inner membrane cleft between the cross bars; cilia shorter than the segments.

Annulus.—Large, compound.

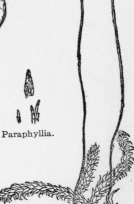

Paraphyllia.

H. reptile. Plant.

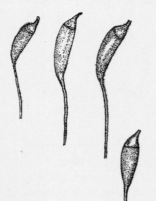

Spore-cases with lids.

Portion of the peristome showing on the left two outer teeth; on the right two inner teeth and four cilia.

H. reptile.

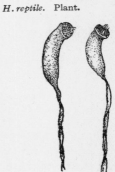

Spore-cases without lids.

300

Spores.—Mature in August.

Distribution.— North America and Europe.

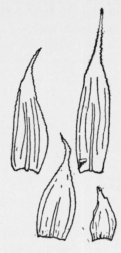

Perigonial leaves.

Male and female plant.

Leaves at base of pedicel.

H. reptile.

Hypnum imponens, Hedw.—See Plate XXIX.

Habit and habitat.—This moss is exceedingly handsome, growing in flat yellowish-green tufts on decayed trunks and about the bases of trees.

Paraphyllia.

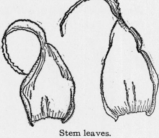

Stem leaves.

H. imponens.

Plant)gametophyte). — Prostrate, stems feather-branched.

Leaves.—The stem-leaves overlapping, lying in two rows on the lower side, base broadly ovate, orange, at the angles minutely ear-like ; *apex* thread-like, and turned to one side ; borders reflexed below, minutely toothed all around or almost entire ; *vein* double or none ; cells very narrow, linear, somewhat

301

worm-like, enlarged, and 4-sided at the basilar angles, the *branch-leaves* narrower, hooked, and rolled together at the apex of the branches ; the leaf-like appendages (*paraphyllia*) attached to the stem, large, palm-like or lance-like.

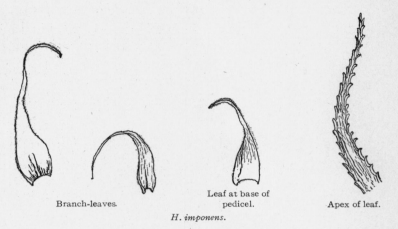

Branch-leaves.

Leaf at base of pedicel.

Apex of leaf.

H. imponens.

Leaves at the base of the pedicel (perichætial leaves).—Without a vein, gradually narrowed to a long thread-like flexuous and finely toothed point.

Habit of flowering. — Male and female flowers on separate plants (*dioicous*).

Veil (calyptra).—Thin, split up one side.

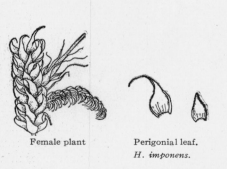

Female plant

Perigonial leaf.

Spore-cases with lids.

H. imponens.

Spore-case.—Cylindrical, pale-brown, somewhat erect or slightly incurved.

Pedicel (seta).—Long and slender.

Plate XXIX

HYPNUM IMPONENS, Hedw

Lid (operculum).—Convex, with an oblique point, orange at the apex.

Teeth (peristome).—Inner segments slightly cleft and as long as the cilia; outer, normal, cilia single, with small transverse spurs attached to the margin.

Annulus.—Large, compound, adherent to the mouth.

Spores.—Mature in the autumn.

Distribution.—Common in sub-alpine America, rare in Europe.

Portion of peristome showing on the left two outer teeth; on the right two inner teeth and two cilia.

Spore-case with peristome.

Spore-case with lid.

H. imponens.

Hypnum curvifolium, Hedw.—See Colour Plate XVI.

Habit and habitat.—This attractive moss grows in intricate tufts, yellowish-green and glossy. It is very common on decayed logs in shady woods.

Stem.

Branch-leaves.

Cells.

H. curvifolium.

303

Name.—The specific name, is from the Latin *curvum*, bent, and *folium*, a leaf.

Plant (*gametophyte*).—Large, stems, 3 to 4 inches long, prostrate with but few branches, these feather-branchlets compressed, unequal, and short

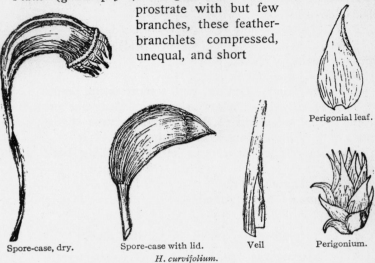

Spore-case, dry.   Spore-case with lid.   Veil   Perigonium.

Perigonial leaf.

H. curvifolium.

Leaves.—Crowded, in two rows, each leaf overlapping the one in front, scythe-shaped concave and turned to one side; *base*, eared; apex gradually long taper-pointed; margin slightly serrate; *vein* absent or slightly evident at the base, *cells* above pale, narrow, linear and worm-like; *cells* of the base and angles, shorter, broader, and golden-yellow.

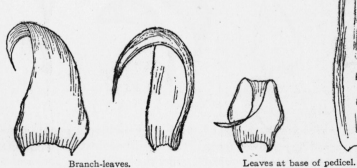

Branch-leaves.   Leaves at base of pedicel.

H. curvifolium

304

Leaves at the base of the pedicel (perichætial leaves).—Numerous, whitish, erect ; and close, the cells loose.

Habit of flowering.—Male and female flowers on separate plants (*dioicous*).

Veil (calyptra).—Thin and split up one side.

Spore-case.—Large, oblong, swollen, and arched, when young ; thin and distinctly ribbed, when dry.

Pedicel.—Long and slender.

Lid (operculum).—Conical, with a short abrupt point.

Teeth (peristome).—Yellow with small blade-like projections on the inside ; segments of the inner membrane slightly cleft ; cilia 2 to 3, nearly as long as the segments.

Annulus.—With three rows of cells, rolling back as the lid falls.

Spores.—Mature in fall.

Distribution.—North America.

THE EXQUISITE FEATHER-MOSS

HYPNUM, Sub-genus CALLIERGON

The species of the **Sub-genus Calliergon** are large, erect, or prostrate plants growing in wide mats on the ground, or on rocks; the branches are simple or compound and have but a few rooting filaments.

The sub-generic name is the Greek word καλλίεργον, beautifully made.

Stem-leaves. Spore-cases with lids. Spore-case without lid.

H. Schreberi.

The leaves are heart-shaped, oval or oval-oblong, deeply concave, spreading or overlapping, rarely turned to one side; the *apex* is obtuse, the *vein* variable, and the *cells* linear above and four-sided at the basal angles.

305

The spore-cases are borne on variable pedicels; they are oblong and incurved with convex-conical lids. An annulus is sometimes present, and the teeth are as in the genus *Hypnum*.

The Red-stemmed Feather-moss, *Hypnum (Calliergon) Schreberi,* Willd.—See Plate XXX.

Habit and habitat.—On shaded ground of hills and mountains. The specimen photographed grew on the dry knolls of a swamp in Lake Placid.

Spore-cases with lids
H. Schreberi.

Spore-case without lid.

Name.—The specific name was given by Karl Ludwig Willdenow in honour of D. J. C. Schreber.

Plant (gametophyte).—*Stems* rigid, dark-red, branching, the branches with somewhat regularly arranged branchlets; branches and branchlets obtuse at the apex.

Leaves.—Pale-green or yellow, loosely overlapping, broadly oval-oblong, slightly concave; *apex* obtuse or obtusely pointed, incurved; *base* recurved on the borders; *vein* double, short; *margin* entire; *base* extending down the stem; *cells* narrow, four-sided, orange at the base and the basal angles.

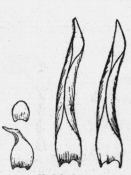

H. Schreberi.
Leaves at base of pedicel.

Leaves at the base of the pedicel (perichætial leaves).—The inner sheathing, erect, not plaited; *apex* short-pointed; *vein* none.

Leaf-like organs among the leaves (paraphyllia).—None.

Habit of flowering.—Male and female flowers on separate plants (*dioicous*).

Veil (calyptra).—Thin, split up one side.

Spore-case.—Oblong, dark-coloured, incurved.

Pedicel (seta).—Dark-red, long, twisted above.

Lid (operculum).—Red, conical, with a sharp point.

Annulus.—None.

Teeth (peristome).—Long, with lamellæ on the inside, inner

306

PLATE XXX

HYPNUM SCHREBERI, Willd.

segments split nearly the whole length; hair-like segments three, slightly shorter.

Spores.—Mature in autumn.

Distribution.—North and South America, Europe and Asia.

THE ARCHED FEATHER-MOSS

HYPNUM Sub-genus PLEUROZIUM

The species of this sub-genus increase yearly by arched branches or by rigid erect growths, the branches are short, unequal, and grow outward from the main stem, a character which suggested the name *Pleurozium*, a compound of the Greek πλευρὸν, a side, and ὄξος, a branch.

The leaves on the stem are larger than those on the branches, and are different in shape. Besides these leaves there are numerous large and many-parted leaf-like organs (*paraphyllia*).

The other characters of this sub-genus are similar to those of the genus *Hypnum*.

THE GLITTERING FEATHER-MOSS

HYPNUM (PLEUROZIUM) splendens, Hedw.
(See Plate XXXI.)

Habit and habitat.—The Glittering Feather-moss is one of the most beautiful species. It is common on rocks in deep woods, in swampy places, on stumps, and on fallen trees.

> "Glittering with yellow, red and green,
> As o'er the moss, with playful glide,
> The sunbeams dance from side to side."

Female plant.   Male plant.   Paraphyllia.
H. *splendens.*

307

Name.—J. G. Hedwig showed his appreciation of its beauty when he called it *splendens.*

Plant (gametophyte).—In loose tufts, rigid, pale olive-green; *stems* glittering, 4 to 8 inches high, increasing by annual arched branches, or by rigid, upright branches; *branches* once or twice feather-branched.

Leaves.—Stem-leaves, at the base, distant, small and scale-like; above, loosely overlapping, slightly concave, broadly oval-long, often narrowed into a long wavy point; *vein* (*costa*)

Stem-leaf. Apex. Perigonial leaf with paraphysis and antheridium. Branch-leaves.

H. splendens.

faintly double; *margin* finely toothed; branch-leaves smaller, oval-oblong, shorter pointed.

Leaves at the base of the pedicel (perichœtial leaves).—Narrowly pointed, sub-erect or recurved at the apex.

Leaf-like organs (paraphyllia).—Numerous, large, varied in form.

Habit of flowering.—Male and female flowers on different plants, (*dioicous*).

Veil (calyptra).—Thin, transparent, pointed, split on one side, large and persistent.

Spore-case.—Egg-shaped, horizontal by a curve of the pedicel under the base.

Pedicel (seta).—Curved under the spore-case, about one inch high, smooth.

Lid (operculum).—Large and beaked.

Teeth (peristome).—Double, as in the genus *Hypnum.*

PLATE XXXI

THE GLITTERING FEATHER-MOSS, *Hypnum splendens*, Hedw.

Annulus.—Single.

Spores.—Fruit not common, mature in spring.

Distribution.—Common in mountains or northward, America, Europe, northern Asia and Africa.

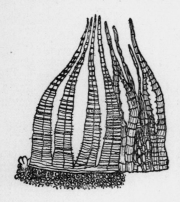

Portion of peristome showing on the left four outer teeth ; on the right two cilia, two inner teeth split along their length.

Spore-case with peristome.

Leaves at base of pedicel.

H. splendens.

THE WOOD REVELLERS

HYPNUM: Sub-genus HYLOCOMNIUM, Schimp.

The species of the **Sub-genus Hylocomnium** are large and robust, two or three times irregularly feather-branched. The stems grow from the apex only, or produce lateral branches.

The generic name *Hylocomnium* is derived from the Greek ὕλη, wood, and κόμος, a reveller; it was given to these mosses by William Philipp Schimper, to describe their habit of growing on wood.

The leaves spread abruptly from the base, or spread and turn to one side. There are no leaf-like organs (*paraphyllia*) among the leaves.

H. triquetrum. Spore-case without lid.

The spore-cases are red-brown, swollen egg-shaped or nearly globular, abruptly horizontal, inclined when dry on pedicels twisted to the right. The lids are convex, or conic, with no annulus, or a double one. The teeth are as the genus *Hypnum.*

309

Twenty-one species are known in all, five in America.

The Triangular Wood-reveller, *Hypnum* (*Hylocomnium*) *triquetrum,* Linn.—See plate XXXII.

Habit and habitat.—In large yellow or light-green mats 4 **to** 8 inches deep, on decayed wood in plains and mountains.

H. triquetrum. Female plant.

Name.—**The** specific name *triquetrum* was given **to** the moss by Linnæus to describe its habit of pointing its branches in three directions, the Latin *triquetrum* meaning "having three angles."

Plants (*gametophyte*).—*Stems* stout and rigid, erect, simple or slightly divided, branched unequally and irregularly or with feather branches not all in the same plane.

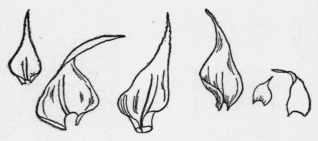

H. triquetrum. Branch leaves.

Leaves.—Very large, horizontally spreading both when wet or dry, stiff and membranous, glossy, triangular; *apex* acute; *vein*

Plate XXXII

THE TRIANGULAR WOOD-REVELER. *Hypnum triquetrum*, L.

double to the middle; *margin* closely toothed; *base* auriculate; *cells* of the basal angles wide, transparent, oblong six-sided. Branch-leaves narrower, and gradually smaller upward.

Habit of flowering.—Male and female flowers on separate plants (*dioicous*).

Veil (calyptra).—Split up one side.

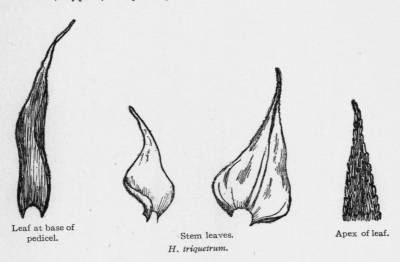

Leaf at base of pedicel.

Stem leaves.

Apex of leaf.

H. triquetrum.

Spore-case.—Oblong, horizontal or inclined by a curve of its pedicel under the base, narrowed at the mouth when dry.

Pedicel (seta).—Curved below the spore-case, 1 to 1½ inches high.

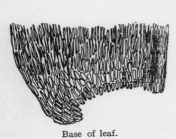

Base of leaf.

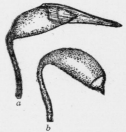

(*a*) Spore-case with veil;
(*b*) Spore-case with lid.

H. triquetrum.

311

Lid (operculum).—Convex with a tiny point in the centre.

Annulus.—Simple.

Teeth (peristome).—As in the genus *Hypnum.*

Spores.—Mature in autumn and winter.

Distribution.—Common in Europe; widely spread in America; common in the Adirondacks.

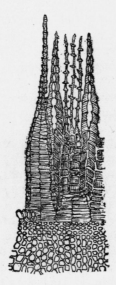

H. triquetrum. Portion of peristome showing on the left one outer tooth with annulus cells at its base; on the right two keeled and perforated inner teeth with three spurred cilia between.

AUTHORITIES CONSULTED

BRAITHWAITE. The Sphagnaceæ of Europe and North America. London, 1880.

BAUER. Mosses Collected in California, in Linnea. 1859.

BRIDEL. Bryologia Universa. Leipsic, 1826-1827.

BRITTON. How to Study the Mosses. *The Observer*, 1894-1897. Contributions to American Bryology. *Bull.* Torr. Bot. Club, 1889.

BRUCH AND SCHIMPER. Bryologia Europæa. Stuttgard, 1836-1855.

CHENEY. North American Species of Amblystegium. *Botanical Gazette*, 1897.

CORRENS. Unterauchungen über die Vermerung der Laubmoose. Jena, 1899.

CROMBIE. British Lichens. London, 1894.

ENGLER AND PRANTL. Die natürlichen Pflanzenfamilien. Leipzig, 1889.

EKHART. Synopsis Jungermaniarum. Coburg, 1832.

EVANS. Hepatics. Trans. of the Conn. Ac., Vol. III. 1892.

GOEBEL. (Dr. K., Professor in University of Rostock, Germany). Outlines of Classification and Special Morphology of Plants. Polytrichum commune. Translated by H. E. F. Garnsey, M. A., Revised by I. B. Balfour, M. A., Oxford, 1887.

GROUT. Revision of North American Isotheciacea and Brachythecia. *Memoirs* Torr. Bot. Club, 1897.

GROUT AND SMITH. The Bryologist. Brooklyn, 1898.

HAMPE. Mosses Collected in Southern United States by Beyrich, in Linnea. 1839.

HEDWIG. Species Muscorum Frondosorum. Edited by Schwaegrichen. Species Muscorum. Leipsic, 1801-1842. Musci Frondosi. Leipsic, 1787-1792.

HOOKER. WM. JACKSON. British Flora. London, 1830.

HOOKER AND TAYLOR. Muscologia Britannica. 1827.

HOWE. Hepaticæ and Anthocerotes of California. *Memoirs* Torr. Bot. Club, New York, 1899.

JÄGER AND SAUERBACH. Adumbratio Floræ Muscorum. 1870-1878.

KINDBERG. European and North American Bryineæ. 1897.

LESQUEREUX AND JAMES. Manual of the Mosses of North America. Boston, 1884.

LIMPRECHT. Die Laubmoose. 1895.

MICHAUX. Flora Boreali Americana.

MUELLER. Synopsis Muscorum Frondosorum.

PARIS. Index Bryologicus. 1894-1898.

PIERCE. The Nature of the Association of Algæ and Fungi in Lichens. Proceedings Calif. Acad. Sci. 1899.

SCHIMPER. Synopsis Muscorum Europæorum. Stuttgard, 1860.

SCHNEIDER. General Lichenology.

SULLIVANT AND LESQUEREUX. Icones Muscorum. Musci Alleghaniensis. Columbus, O., 1846.

SULLIVANT. Mosses and Hepatics of the United States. New York, 1856.

TUCKERMAN. North American Lichens. Boston, Part I, 1882; and New Bedford, Part II, 1888.

UNDERWOOD. North American Hepaticæ. 1883.

WILSON. Bryologia Britannica. London.

INDEX

Index

Index

Index

Index

Index